The Official
World Wildlife Fund Guide to
Endangered Species of North America

Volume 3

Species Listed
August 1989 to December 1991

BEACHAM PUBLISHING, INC.

WASHINGTON, D.C.

The Official World Wildlife Fund Guide to Endangered Species of North America

Originating Editor
John R. Matthews

Editor
Charles J. Moseley

Book, Cover, and Color Plate Design
Amanda Mott

Library of Congress
 Cataloging-in-Publication Data
The Official World Wildlife Fund Guide to Endangered Species
 of North America, Volume 3 / editor. Charles J. Moseley.
 Includes bibliographical references.
  Includes index and appendices.
  Describes 132 endangered or threatened species, listed between
August 1989 and December 1991, including their habitat, behavior,
and recovery.
   1. Nature conservation—North America. 2. Endangered
species—North America. 3. Rare animals—North America. 4.
Rare plants—North America. I. Moseley, Charles J., 1946- .
II. World Wildlife Fund.
QL84.2.035 1990   574.5'29'097—dc20   89-29757
ISBN 0-933833-29-6

Printed in the United States of America
First Printing, March 1992

Contents
Volume 3

About The Nature Conservancy

The mission of The Nature Conservancy is to preserve the plants, animals, and natural communities that represent the diversity of life on Earth. To achieve this goal, the Conservancy protects the lands and water that rare and endangered species need to survive. Since 1951, its efforts have helped save hundreds of species from possible extinction.

In the United States alone, the Conservancy has protected more then 5.5 million acres of high-quality wildlife habitat—a chain of barrier islands in Virginia, cypress sloughs in Illinois, tallgrass prairies in Oklahoma, and river valleys in California. The Conservancy manages more than 1,100 natural areas ranging from a one-acre bog in Connecticut to New Mexico's 500-square-mile Gray Ranch. These form the largest private nature preserve system in the world.

In addition to its work in the U.S., the Conservancy operates an extensive international program. Working in partnership with dozens of local organizations in Latin America, the Conservancy has helped boost conservation activities in 30 countries in Central and South America and the Caribbean. The Conservancy's Pacific program, meanwhile, is addressing environmental issues in Micronesia, Indonesia, and other parts of the Pacific region.

Both the domestic and international programs of the Conservancy adhere to three basic principles: sound science, partnerships, and innovative conservation tools. As a science-driven organization, the Conservancy has always sought to link its protection activities to high conservation priorities. (For example, the Conservancy seeks to acquire habitat that supports rare and endangered species.) Protection decisions are often based on information provided by the Natural Heritage network, the most complete inventory of the status and distribution of species in the country. The Conservancy coordinates and administers the network's central data bases.

The second key to the Conservancy's success is partnerships. Over the years, the Conservancy has built up mutually beneficial partnerships with government, business and industry, other conservation groups, and local communities and citizens. The Conservancy's non-confrontational approach and willingness to work with a broad variety of partners has greatly increased its effectiveness and credibility.

And finally, the Conservancy is renowned in environmental circles for its creative solutions and conservation techniques. For example, the Conservancy has pioneered the purchase of water rights in the West to restore shrinking wetland areas. The Conservancy has obtained hundreds of conservation easements and has encouraged private landowners to register ecologically valuable properties. It has worked with federal government agencies to perform biological inventories of public lands and engineered "debt-for-nature" swaps to provide long-term funding for conservation activities in Latin America. And often, of course, the Conservancy draws on its real-estate expertise to purchase natural areas outright.

The Nature Conservancy has offices in all fifty states. The international headquarters are located at 1815 North Lynn Street, Arlington, Virginia 22209. For more information call 703-841-5300.

Foreword

John C. Sawhill
President and Chief Executive Officer
The Nature Conservancy

Every year, a biologist named Steve Perlman dangles off the seacliff of a Nature Conservancy preserve on the island of Moloka'i in Hawaii to pollinate, by hand, one of the last surviving populations of the rare plant *Brighamia rockii*.*

Why the death-defying heroics? Because the unidentified insect that had pollinated *Brighamia rockii* for millennia is believed to have gone extinct. Without the assistance of someone like Perlman, this unique flowering plant would likely follow.

This *Brighamia*, which resembles a stalk with a cabbage on top, may not be a "keystone" species, one of the plants or animals upon which the health of the entire ecosystems depends. Life on Hawaii may continue just fine without it. But this example demonstrates, in a small way at least, the interrelatedness of nature. Nature is like an intricate tapestry, a marvelously complex fabric of which humans are an integral part. By driving so many species into extinction, we have in effect grasped a loose thread in that tapestry and begun to unravel it.

The consequences of this unraveling should deeply disturb anyone who cares about the future of life on earth. Like a tapestry that's frayed around the edges, the natural world has managed to retain its basic integrity despite the loss of thousands of species. But as species continue to vanish, the tapestry of nature will soon collapse.

Make no mistake: the world is experiencing an unparalleled epidemic of extinction. By some estimates, another species vanishes forever every hour of every day. This is some pretty grim arithmetic, especially when you consider that the so-called "background" rate of extinction—the rate at which species have gone extinct over the planet's history—has been about one species a year. In other words, today we're losing species perhaps 10,000 times faster than we have over the past 400 million years.

Yet despite this catastrophic blow to natural diversity, human beings and species remain on a collision course. In the United States and elsewhere the struggle is being drawn along economic lines, with the economic interests of people pitted against a particular species. For example, what's more important, logging jobs in the Pacific Northwest or saving the spotted owl? What's more important, saving the delta smelt or maintaining the flow of irrigation water for the farms of California's central valley?

Typically, these confrontations are posed as "either-or" propositions. We can either choose between the economic well-being of people, or the well-being of nature. But this is based on an inherently false assumption, because the welfare of mankind depends largely

---

*Brighamia rockii was proposed for listing as an Endangered species on September 20, 1991.

on the quality of the environment. Choosing between one or the other is a Hobson's choice—that is, no choice at all.

Even so, the arguments for saving species merit repeating. Many people instinctively understand the importance of reversing the tide of extinction, but lack the concrete examples to make a persuasive case. In my travels around the country on behalf of The Nature Conservancy, I try to frame the question as one of self-interest—to explain why biological diversity matters to our survival, our hopes, and our aspirations.

For one, it's almost impossible to measure the potential utility of diversity. Jim Buckley, the former senator from New York, puts this quite well. When someone asks him "What good is a snail darter?" he responds, "As practical men measure good, probably none. But we simply don't know. What value would we have placed on the cowpox virus before Jenner, or on a penicillin mold before Fleming, or on a wild rubber tree before Goodyear? Yet the life of every American, and of practically every citizen of the world, is different because of these species."

Like Jim Buckley, we can assert that species are valuable to mankind—for medicines, raw materials, crop strains, and so forth. But perhaps the most important argument for saving species gets back to the unraveling tapestry of life. All these extinctions should be telling us something, like the proverbial canary in the coal mine. In the old days, miners used to take canaries into the coal mines to warn them when the air wasn't safe to breathe. When the canary died, the miners knew that they had to get out. The current spate of extinctions is sounding a similar warning, for the whole planet. A world that can't support plants and animals can't long support us either.

Given this perilous state of affairs, it is incumbent upon us to do what we can to stop the slide toward extinction. This is the mission of The Nature Conservancy, and since 1951 our organization has been protecting the land, waters, and natural communities that endangered species need to survive.

Over that period, we've protected more than 6 million biologically significant acres in the United States. And this figure doesn't include the areas and species protected through our extensive international programs in Central and Latin America and the Pacific. We've used a broad array of conservation tools to achieve these results, from conservation easements to purchasing water rights to compiling the most complete database of endangered species in the country. And much of the time, we follow Mark Twain's advice. "Buy land," he said. "They don't make it anymore."

In these pages, you'll find many Conservancy success stories—places where the Conservancy's protection efforts have created viable habitats for the planet's rarest living things. But these pages tell another, more pessimistic story as well. Despite the efforts of The Nature Conservancy and other conservation groups like the World Wildlife Fund, wildlife habitat continues to be destroyed and species continue to go extinct.

Reversing these trends will require action on several fronts. For one, we need to raise public awareness about the plight—and importance—of endangered species. To be sure, the state of the environment commands greater attention now than ever before. But we still have a long way to go. Too many people still believe that nature is our servant, not our partner. In this regard, I agree with the writer Bill McKibben, who has said that greatest challenge facing environmentalists isn't acid rain or global warming; the greatest challenge facing environmentalist is to talk to people who *aren't* environmentalists.

On another level, we must protect the legislation that protects endangered species, in particular the Endangered Species Act. The Act, which is up for reauthorization this year, is coming under increasing political pressure as a result of confrontations over species like the spotted owl. It's critical that the conservation community block efforts to significantly weaken this statutory defender of biodiversity.

At the same time, however, we must employ more effectively the protection mechanisms already found in the Act. For example, the "habitat conservation plan" concept provides a creative way to circumvent disputes in a manner that benefits both species and the economy. The Nature Conservancy has had the opportunity to participate in two extremely successful HCPs, one in California's Coachella Valley and the other in Clark County, Nevada. In both these cases, the presence of an endangered species had halted large development projects. But through extensive negotiations, compromises were reached that satisfied both developers and environmentalists. There's no reason the HCP-type solutions can't be pursued in other areas of contention.

But perhaps most important, society as a whole needs to adopt a more sensitive approach to questions of land use in and around natural areas. Experience has shown us that activities like clearcutting of forests, overgrazing of pastureland, poorly planned real-estate development, and poor mining practices can all degrade neighboring lands and waters. We need look not farther than a place like the Everglades, where the park's natural wonders are threatened by the demand for water to the south and agricultural run-off to the north.

Consequently, to save species we will increasingly have to focus on saving large-scale ecological systems—entire watersheds and landscapes. It's no longer enough to set aside small, isolated tracts of habitat and assume that extinction will stop. Successful conservation efforts in the future must be carried out on a regional, not local scale. Such an approach would welcome environmentally compatible economic activity, because economic development and environmental protection need not be mutually exclusive. We can have both. But for this to work, industry and environmentalists must be willing to transcend the narrow confines of self-interest and seek broader-based solutions.

The Nature Conservancy's new "Last Great Places" initiative is exploring the potential for this type of large-scale ecosystem protection. Through this program, the Conservancy hopes to demonstrate that the combination of good science, solid partnerships, and sustainable resource management can enable people and endangered species to live together in harmony.

If our society can adopt such an approach to living—if we can learn to see ourselves as part of the natural tapestry—we will be able to blunt the extinction crisis. We will avoid the divisive political debates that currently cloud the conservation horizon. And biologists like Steve Perlman won't have to spend their time hand-pollinating plants.

The choice is ours. We can save the diverse splendor of the natural world, or allow it to disappear. What will future generations think of us if we permit the latter? Teddy Roosevelt eloquently argued this point more than 80 years ago, when he said that "Nothing short of defending the country in war compares with the central task of leaving this land a better land for our descendants than it was for us."

This book, with its descriptions of our rarest living things, reminds us of what we need to save. Roosevelt reminds us of why we need to save them.

Endangered Species Act at the Crossroads

Michael J. Bean
Environmental Defense Fund

The Endangered Species Act of 1973 embodies Congress' most straightforward and ex-plicit commitment to the conservation of biological diversity. For nearly two decades, it has served as a leading example to the world of a governmental commitment with far-reaching implications. Among other things, the Act requires all federal government agencies to en-sure that none of their actions jeopardizes the continued existence of any species. Private landowners and others also face significant restrictions on their proposed activities as a re-sult of the Act's broad prohibition against the "taking" of protected wildlife.

For most of the Act's history, it has functioned without major controversy. The most prominent exception, and a watershed in the Act's evolution, was the late-1970s contro-versy over construction of the Tellico Dam and its impact upon the snail darter. Recently, however, several significant controversies arising under the Endangered Species Act have created greater pressure within Congress and the Executive Branch to weaken the Act than at any time since the snail darter/Tellico Dam controversy.

The most prominent and immediate of the controversies stems from the listing in June 1990 of the northern spotted owl as a threatened species. Exactly what measures will be required to protect the owl are uncertain, but a significant reduction in "old growth" timber harvesting on almost 7 million acres of federal forest lands in Washington, Oregon, and California is very likely. Estimates of expected job losses over the next decade as a result range from over 100,000, according to the industry, to about 30,000, according to the Bush administration, or only 7,000, according to the Wilderness Society.

Last October, Oregon Senator Bob Packwood offered an amendment to the Interior Ap-propriations bill that would have forced a speedy resolution of the owl issue by directing that federal timber harvesting plans be quickly considered for an exemption from the En-dangered Species Act. A mechanism for exempting federal activities from the require-ments of the Act has been in place since the 1978 amendments that followed in the wake of the snail darter. Senator Packwood apparently worried that without his amendment, the exemption mechanism would never be invoked, because the Forest Service was trying to scale back logging plans to accommodate the needs of the owl rather than clinging firmly to the more ambitious desires of the timber industry. Thus, he wanted to force a showdown quickly. Environmentalists, portraying the Packwood measure as an assault upon the Endangered Species Act, engineered its defeat by a wide margin. While support for the Act was shown to be widespread, it was far from clear how deep that support was, or how easily it might be eroded if other industries join forces with the timber industry in an assault upon the Act.

One industry that appears ready to join the fray is the homebuilding industry. Its views are reflected in a recently issued report of the Advisory Commission on Regulatory Barriers to Affordable Housing, a special commission established by Secretary Jack Kemp of the Department of Housing and Urban Development. The Commission's report, entitled "Not in My Back Yard," singles out the costs of complying with the Endangered Species Act and Section 404 of the Clear Water Act (providing for federal regulation of development in wetlands) as contributing significantly to the cost of housing. These added costs stem not just from higher lumber costs allegedly caused by restrictions on federal timber sales, but also from endangered species mitigation measures required when endangered species are "incidentally taken" in the course of developing their habitat. The homebuilders' favorite example is a system of "rat preserves" for which developers in Riverside County, California have been made to contribute in return for being allowed to develop within the habitat of the Stephens' kangaroo rat. Ironically, these mitigation requirements have been imposed under the authority of a 1982 amendment that land developers sponsored; before then all taking of endangered species was simply prohibited.

Another industry that may ally itself with opponents of the Act is the commercial fishing industry. Although a once very volatile controversy over the required use of "turtle excluder devices" by shrimp fishermen to reduce the drowning of sea turtles in shrimp nets has subsided, there is deep lingering resentment against the Act by some within the shrimp industry and their representative in Congress. The possibility of restrictions on the very lucrative groundfish fishery off Alaska stemming from the recent listing of the Steller sea lion as a threatened species has added to the commercial fishing industry's anxieties, as has the potential listing of the Atlantic bluefin tuna.

Perhaps the greatest current anxieties, however, stem from recent Fish and Wildlife Service proposals to list several runs of native salmon in the Pacific Northwest as endangered. While no final listing decision has yet been made with respect to most of these runs, and the actions that would be required as a result of their listing are conjectural, organized opposition to the Act has already begun on the basis of claims that hydroelectric dams will have to be operated less efficiently (or even dismantled), fishing restricted, timber harvest curtailed, and land use generally restricted. This may only be fear-mongering, but it is effective fear-mongering.

The chorus of industries with a legitimate or perceived complaint against the Act has been joined by a number of ideological opponents of environmental regulation. The most eye-opening evidence of that came last summer with a nationally syndicated column by Ed Meese and conservative legal scholar Bruce Fein advocated changes to the Act. As Attorney General, Meese had never shown the slightest interest in the Endangered Species Act. Suddenly, however, he was nearly passionate about it. His conversion followed close on the heels of widely publicized remarks by Secretary Lujan in which Lujan revealed his view that the Act was too strong and needed more "balance." More recently, Lujan's Director of the Bureau of Mines, T. S. Ary, told an audience that he didn't believe in endangered species and thought environmentalists a "bunch of nuts." He later apologized for the remark about environmentalists, but it still isn't clear whether he believed in endangered species. The Bush Administration's views on what should be done with the Endangered Species Act are no clearer.

Various changes in the Act have been proposed by its opponents. One would require consideration of economic impacts at the time of listing. Currently, the law requires that listing decisions be based solely upon the actual biological status of a species. Opponents of the Act want the Secretary of the Interior to be able to take into account the possible economic impact of a proposed listing and, if those impacts are "too great," to abandon or limit the listing. Former Secretary Watt tried employed this exact strategy, with the result that few new species were being listed. Congress' response was a 1982 amendment that required listing decisions to be based solely upon biology. A variation on this theme, recently suggested by Senator Packwood, is an idea to authorize exemptions from the requirements of the Act at the time of, and as part of, the listing. The exemption process added to the Act in 1978 (establishing the Endangered Species Committee, or "God Committee") was intended to be a measure of last resort, undertaken only when all other efforts to reconcile conflicting interests under the Act had failed. Senator Packwood's idea would make the exemption process a matter of first resort.

Other critics have suggested eliminating protection below the species level. At present, the Act allows the protection of not only species, but also subspecies and, for vertebrates only, distinct populations. Many recent controversies concern such "lesser" taxa, e.g., the northern spotted owl (a subspecies), the various salmon runs currently under petition (populations), and the Mojave desert tortoise (a population). If only full species could be protected, the universe of potentially listed entitles would be dramatically smaller and many of these controversies would disappear. The cost of running the endangered species program would also shrink markedly, a point made in a recent assessment of the program by the Interior Department Inspector General. On the other hand, many of the better known and more popular "species" protected by the Act would lose their protection, e.g., the bald eagle, the brown pelican, the wolf, the grizzly bear, the California sea otter, the peregrine falcon, and others. There are also some strong scientific arguments against this proposal in that populations are the"units" of evolution and ecology and the preservation of a species may ultimately require preservation of its genetically distinct populations.

Clearly, the potential exists for a serious and well-funded effort to weaken the Endangered Species Act. Several different industries in several different regions could collaborate to exploit problems with the Act, joined by various ideological critics of endangered species protection. Support for the Endangered Species Act in Congress is a mile wide, but its depth is hard to gauge. Thus, the situation is highly fluid and uncertain.

In the last great endangered species upheaval, the snail darter/Tellico Dam controversy of the 1970s, legislative damage to the Endangered Species Act was held to a minimum. This was due in large measure to the fact that the conflict between the darter and the dam had been something of an aberration, an apparently irreconcilable conflict between the conservation needs of a species and a major economic development. In all but a tiny minority of instances, it had been possible to accommodate the competing interests of conservation and development without unacceptable impacts upon either. Because of that fact, most members of Congress were persuaded that only modest refinements, and not fundamental changes, were needed. In addition, defense of the Act was aided by the fact that Tellico Dam was a project of dubious economic merit. There were many in Congress willing to ridicule a three-inch fish, but very few who passionately defended the merits of the dam.

Today the situation is markedly different. Rather than there being one aberrational conflict, conflicts are now sufficiently numerous and substantial that the perception of the Act as source of recurrent problems is growing. In addition, in today's conflicts, it is not a single pork barrel project of dubious economic merit at stake, but major industries with importance throughout sizeable regions. These differences make the task of defending the Act more challenging than ever before.

The challenge to environmental interests in defending the Act will be to show that irreconcilable conflicts are still the rare exception and that at least some of the seemingly intractable problems are in fact capable of resolution. Of the controversies currently getting attention, one for which this may be possible is the prospective listing of several native runs of salmon in the Columbia and Snake River basins. Popularly, this impending controversy has been characterized as "bigger than the spotted owl," with all manner of dire predictions made about the impact of these listings upon the region's economy. Should some of the more apocalyptic scenarios actually occur, defending the Act will be exceedingly difficult. The task for supporters of the Act, therefore, is to help identify and design solutions that allow for improvement in the status of the affected salmon stocks without serious adverse economic impacts. Building on earlier work in both the energy and water fields, the Enviromnental Defense Fund is urging attention to the possibility of using market incentives and inter-regional markets to shift both the timing of hydroelectric power production and irrigated agricultural use patterns to produce benefits to salmon and economic interests alike. Preliminary discussions of these ideas have been held with the Bonneville Power Administration, Pacific Gas and Electric, Southern California Edison, the Los Angeles Department of Water and Power, and others. There appears to be a reasonable chance that these ideas may be embraced as a solution to the salmon problem that averts the calamities forecast by others.

It is likely, however, that a major political fight is brewing over endangered species. Since the current authorization for the Act expires September 30, 1992, Congress must take action to keep the law in effect. This has galvanized both opponents and supporters and brought forth a number of proposed amendments that would weaken the legislation. However, despite the current controversies, there are persuasive argruments for maintaining the provisions of the Act and resolving controversial cases through established procedures.

Editor's Introduction

This new volume of *The Official World Wildlife Guide to Endangered Species of North America* appears as controversies involving the Endangered Species Act have multiplied and are attracting wide national media attention. Efforts to protect the northern spotted owl have curtailed federal timber sales on almost 7 million acres of old-growth forest in the Pacific Northwest. The listing of the Snake River sockeye salmon and proposals to list Columbia and Snake River runs of chinook and coho salmon raise the possibility of changes in the operation of a number of hydroelectric dams, which would affect a large number of people and industries in Washington and Oregon. In his introductory essay Michael J. Bean of the Environmental Defense Fund discusses these controversies and what they may portend for the future of the Endangered Species Act. But beyond the relatively few species whose listing generates national headlines lie the stories of hundreds of species of plants and animals that face the possibility of extinction. The main purpose of the *Guide* is to present accurate, detailed, and objective information on the entire array of these vulnerable species.

Volume three of the *Guide* contains species accounts of the 92 plant and 40 animal species that have been listed as Threatened or Endangered since August 1989. Over the last two years (and for the coming two or three) the listing process has been heavily influenced by the legal process. A number of species, including the northern spotted owl and the silver rice rat, have been listed as the result of court decisions. Other legal actions have produced settlements that have had an even greater effect on the number and types of species listed. In settling a lawsuit brought by the Sierra Club Legal Defense Fund on behalf of a Hawaii conservation group, the Fish and Wildlife Service (FWS) agreed to propose for listing all 186 Category 1 Hawaiian candidate plant species by September 30, 1992. Of the 92 new plant listings in this volume, 44 are Hawaiian species. The settlement of a similar lawsuit in California will result in the proposed listing of over 100 Category 1 California plant species by the mid-1990s.

In assembling this volume we have changed only slightly our species account format. In most cases the name and address of the FWS contact at the field office level has been added. These botanists and biologists have worked closely on the species during the listing process and are most likely to have the most detailed and current information. Their cooperation has been invaluable in compiling the *Guide*, in providing information and photographs, and in directing us to experts at universities and other federal agencies. Generally the accounts in this volume have less to say about recovery efforts, mainly because FWS only begins the time-consuming tasks of drafting and implementing a recovery plan after a listing decision has been made.

As in the previous volumes the species accounts are arranged alphabetically by scientific name within the classifications of plants, mammals, birds, etc. The Ready Reference Index, which indexes the species by common name, precedes the accounts and is limited to the species treated in this volume. The index is cumulative for all three volumes and has entries for families, scientific names, and a variety of common name combinations. A state-by-state listing of the newly listed species appears as Appendix I and supplements the list in previous volumes.

Several new appendixes have been added to provide an update on species treated in the earlier volumes as well as to give an indication of future listings. Appendix IV gives FWS's evaluation of recovery status of listed species. It is drawn from a December 1990 report to Congress, *Endangered and Threatened Species Recovery Program*, in which FWS characterized the status of listed species under its jurisdiction as "Improving," "Stable," "Declining," "Extinct," or "Unknown." Those species under the jurisdiction of the Commerce Department's National Marine Fisheries Service, such as whales, sea lions, and ocean fishes, are not included. The 406-page report, which also contains very brief descriptions of recent recovery activities for each species, is available through the Government Printing Office in Washington, D.C.

To provide some indication of future listings we have included appendixes listing proposed species and Category 1 candidate species. Specific information on proposed species can be found in the *Federal Register* published on the date the species was proposed. Category 1 species are those FWS acknowledges as qualifying for proposal as Threatened or Endangered but which are temporarily "on hold" because of staff or budget shortages. Since the legal settlements mentioned above require FWS to propose all Category 1 plant species found in Hawaii and California over the next few years, they are virtually certain to be listed. It should be noted, however, that Category 1 status is not an entirely reliable guide to the most vulnerable species. In the case of some species not enough is currently known about their range or population for FWS to classify them as Category 1. Other lower category candidate species may suddenly be gravely threatened by specific projects such as dam or highway construction.

A major addition to the *Guide* is Appendix V, the Endangered Species Photo Locator. This directory was originally published separately in 1990 and has been expanded and updated for inclusion in this volume. It's purpose is to provide editors, researchers, conservationists, and others with sources for photographs of federally listed plants and animals. The sources suggested were contacted during the extensive photo search undertaken to illustrate the three volumes of the *Guide*. We were fortunate to locate photos and illustrations of almost all of these rare and seldom photographed species. Publishing the directory is one way we have chosen to thank the photographers and other photo sources for their cooperation in what initially seemed a near-impossible task. Instructions on using the directory can be found on page 1528.

The large number of newly listed Hawaiian plants has presented a challenging photo research task. Because many of these species are extremely rare (many are located in remote areas and some have not been seen in years) we have used a greater number of line drawings to illustrate the accounts than in the previous volumes. Most of these have been reproduced from the *Manual of the Flowering Plants of Hawai'i* by S. H. Sohmer, Derral Herbst, and Warren Wagner, recently published by the University of Hawaii Press and the

Editor's Introduction

Bishop Museum Press. We wish to thank the authors and their publishers for readily granting us permission to reproduce some of Yevonn Wilson-Ramsey's excellent illustrations. Additional thanks must also go to Dr. Herbst for his generous assistance in locating photographs of Hawaiian plants and his guidance on the use of illustrations of closely related species when neither photo nor illustration was available for the listed species.

Finally, no work on endangered species should fail to note the enormous role played by The Nature Conservancy in protecting rare species and their habitats. Besides owning and managing preserves, the Conservancy has been instrumental in establishing and supporting state Natural Heritage Programs, undertaking important field research, and negotiating conservation agreements with private landowners. We are pleased to have John C. Sawhill, president and chief executive officer of The Nature Conservancy, introduce this volume of the *Guide* and elaborate on the role of the Conservancy in the continuing struggle to protect the diversity of species on the planet.

Charles J. Moseley
January 1992

Color Photo Credits — Volume 3

Cover Photos
American Peregrine Falcon
Little Kern Golden Trout
San Joaquin KIt Fox
San Francisco Garter Snake
— Susan Middleton with David Liittschwager

Page C-1
Michigan Monkey-Flower — Michigan Natural
    Features Inventory
Roan Mountain Bluet — Paul Somers
Walker's Manioc — Paul M. Montgomery
Fringed Campion — Jessie M. Harris

Page C-2
Western Prairie Fringed Orchid — Welby Smith
Leafy Prairie Clover — Jessie M. Harris
Barneby Ridge-Cress — Ben Franklin

Page C-3
Northeastern Bulrush — Bruce A. Sorrie
Gentian Pinkroot — George Rogers/Missouri
    Botanical Garden
Dudley Bluffs Bladderpod — Robert L. Powell
Garett's Mint — Jonathan A. Shaw
Sebastopol Meadowfoam —
    Marianne Austin-McDermon
Baker's Sticky Seed — Marianne Austin-McDermon

Page C-4
Terlinga Creek Cat's Eye — Paul M. Montgomery
Sacramento Prickly-Poppy — Peggy Olwell
San Joaquin Wooly-Threads — B. "Moose" Peterson
Texas Trailing Phlox — Paul M. Montgomery
Dudley Bluffs Twinpod — Robert L. Powell

Page C-5
California Jewelflower — Marianne
    Austin-McDermon
Kern Mallow — Marianne Austin-McDermon
Chamaesyce celastroides var. *kaenana* —
    Robert Gustafson
Diella falcata — Robert Gustafson
Alsinidendron trinerve — Robert Gustafson
Bakersfield Cactus — Susan Middleton and
    David Liittschwager

Page C-6
Lower Keys Rabbit — Alan S. Maltz
Silver Rice Rat — Numi Goodyear
Northern Spotted Owl — B. "Moose" Peterson
Florida Salt Marsh Vole — Charles A. Woods

Page C-7
Golden-Cheeked Warbler — G. Lasley/VIREO
Yellow-Blotched Map Turtle —
    Terry L. Vandeventer
Shenendoah Salamander — David Liebman
Cheat Mountain Salamander — Ray E. Ashton, Jr.
Roanoke Logperch — Noel Burkhead and
    Robert Jenkins

Page C-8
Gulf Sturgeon — John Moran
Tulotoma Snail — Malcolm Pierson
Puritan Tiger Beetle — T. Schultz
Cracking Pearly Mussel —
    A. E. Spreitzer/OSU Museum of Zoology
Northeastern Beach Tiger Beetle — T. Schultz
Winged Mapleleaf Mussel—
    A. E. Spreitzer/OSU Museum of Zoology
Mitchell's Satyr Butterfly — Larry West

Ready Reference Index for Volume 3
(Refer to Volume 3 Index for listing by Scientific Names)

NOTE: Most Hawaiian plant species included in this volume do not have common names.

PLANTS

MAMMALS

BIRDS

REPTILES AND AMBHIBIANS

FISHES

MUSSELS

SNAILS AND CRUSTACEANS

INSECTS

The Official
World Wildlife Fund Guide to
Endangered Species of North America

Abutilon eremitopetalum
No Common Name

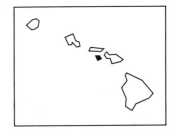

Robert Gustafson

Status . . . . Endangered
Listed . . . . September 20, 1991
Family . . . . Malvaceae (Mallow)
Description . . . . . . Shrub with heart-shaped
leaves and green flowers,
hidden by long, green
sepals.
Habitat . . . . Lowland dry shrubland.
Threats . . . . Alien plant species, low
numbers.
Region 1 . . . . Hawaii (Lanai)

Description

Abutilon eremitopetalum is a shrub in the mallow family with grayish green, hairy, heart-shaped, toothed leaves, about 7 to 12 centimeters (2.7 to 4.6 in) long, alternately arranged on the stem. One or two flowers are borne at the leaf axils. The petals, which are green on the upper surface and reddish below, are hidden by long green sepals. The fruit is a hairy brown capsule. This species has also been known as *Abutilon cryptopetalum* and *Abortopetalum eremitopetalum*.

Habitat

This species grows on the island of Lanai, Hawaii, on the dry, leeward slopes of the Lanaihale Ridge. This broad ridge runs northwest to southeast across this small island and is commonly known by the name of its highest peak, Lanaihale, which is 1,027 meters (3,370 ft) high. A lowland dry shubland plant community is found on the leeward slopes and valleys. This stony, eroded land has an annual rainfall of only 25 to 64 centimeters (10 to 25 in), mostly occurring between November and April. Dominant members of this plant community are lama (*Diospyros sandwicensis*), wiliwili (*Erythrina sandwicensis*), 'a'ali'i (*Dodonaea viscosa*), and nehe (*Lipochaeta* ssp.). Another Endangered plant species, *Tetramolopium remyi*, is found in this habitat. A lowland wet forest community occurs on the summit and narrow valleys of

Lanaihale. This community supports four plant species federally listed as Endangered: *Cyanea macrostegia* var. *gibsonii*, *Gahnia lanaiensis*, *Phyllostegia glabra* var. *lanaiensis*, and *Viola lanaiensis*. All of these Endangered plant species are endemic to Lanaihale.

Historic Range

Abutilon eremitopetalum was first collected in 1930 from Maunalei Valley, Lanai. It has been found in widely scattered colonies at elevations between 215 to 305 meters (700 to 1,000 ft) in the areas of Kalulu, Mahana, Maunalei, Mamaki, and Paawili on the northern, northeastern, and eastern portions of Lanai.

Current Distribution

This species is now known from a single population of about 30 plants in Kahea Gulch on the northeastern part of the island.

Conservation and Recovery

The main threat to *Abutilon eremitopetalum* is competition from invasive alien plant species, such as lantana (*Lantana camara*), koa haole (*Leucaena leucocephala*), and sourbush (*Pluchea carolinensis*). These aggressive species are more successful than native species in competing for water, space, and light.

Additional threats are the degradation of the habitat through the browsing of axis deer and the species' low numbers and limited distribution. Although *Abutilon eremitopetalum* is not a preferred food of the deer, their activities promote erosion and open up areas for invasive species. With only a single known population, the species is extremely vulnerable to extinction brought about by an unpredictable human or natural event. Because this area is dry much of the year, wildfires are a special concern.

Additional Sources

Bates, D. M. 1990. "Malvaceae." In *Manual of the Flowering Plants of Hawaii*, by W. L. Wagner, D. R. Herbst, and S. H. Sohmer. University of Hawaii Press and Bishop Museum Press, Honolulu.

Cuddihy, L. W., and C. P. Stone. 1990. *Alteration of Native Hawaiian Vegetation: Effects of Humans, Their Activities and Introductions*. University of Hawaii Cooperative National Park Resources Study Unit, Honolulu.

Culliney, J. L. 1988. *Islands in a Far Sea: Nature and Man in Hawaii*. Sierra Club Books, San Francisco.

Contacts

Regional Office of Endangered Species
U.S. Fish and Wildlife Service
Eastside Federal Complex
911 N.S. 11th Avenue
Portland, Oregon 97232-4181

Derral R. Herbst
U.S. Fish and Wildlife Service
300 Ala Moana Boulevard, Room 6307
P.O. Box 50167
Honolulu, Hawaii 96850

Abutilon sandwicense
No Common Name

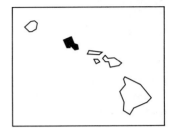

John Obata

Status . . . . Endangered
Listed . . . . October 29, 1991
Family . . . . Malvaceae (Mallow)
Description . . . . . . Shrub with heart-shaped leaves and single, drooping flowers with green petals often tipped with reddish brown.
Habitat . . . . Steep slopes in dry to moist forest.
Threats . . . . Invasive alien plant species, fire, cattle.
Region 1 . . . . Hawaii (Oahu)

Description

Abutilon sandwicense is a shrub of the mallow family that grows to 3 meters (10 ft) and is covered with short glandular hairs. The heart-shaped leaves are 8 to 22 centimeters (3 to 9 in) long. Single drooping flowers are borne on long stems at the leaf axils. The flowers have bright green petals, often tipped with reddish brown. A greenish yellow stamenal column with about 350 stamens protrudes from the flower. The species has also been known by the name *Abortopetalum sandwicense*.

Habitat

This species is endemic to the Waianae Mountain Range on the western side of the island of Oahu, Hawaii. This island is dominated by the remnants of two ancient volcanoes that have eroded into two "mountain ranges," which consist of long, narrow ridges. The Waianae Range lies on the western side of the island, while the Koolau Range traverses the eastern side. The Waianae Range, which runs northwest to southeast for about 40 miles, lies in the rain shadow of the Koolau Range, and, except for the summit of Mt. Kaala, the highest point on the island, receives much less rainfall.

A number of plant communities occur in the Waianae Mountains, ranging from coastal dry shrubland to lowland dry forest to lowland wet forest. *Abutilon sandwicense* is found on steep slopes in dry to moist lowland forest at elevations between 300 and 600 meters (1,000 to 2,000 ft). It occurs in association with kukui or candlenut (*Aleurites moluccana*), uhiuhi (*Caesalpinia kavaiensis*), lama or persimmon (*Diospyros*), aulu or soapberry (*Sapindus oahuensis*), and Christmasberry (*Schinus terebinthifolius*).

The diverse habitats of the Waianae Mountains contain a large number of vulnerable native Hawaiian plant species. In October 1991 the Fish and Wildlife Service (FWS) listed *Abutilon sandwicense* and 25 other plant species from Oahu's Waianae Mountains as Endangered. This group listing was the result of the settlement of a 1989 lawsuit against the FWS brought by the Sierra Club Legal Defense Fund on behalf of a Hawaii conservation group. The terms of the settlement called for the proposed listing before October 1992 of 186 Hawaiian candidate plant species.

Historic Range

Abutilon sandwicense was first collected in 1932. It has been found in the Waianae Mountains between Makaleha Valley in the north and Nanakuli Valley in the south.

Current Distribution

The species is now known from Kaawa Gulch, Kaimuhole Gulch, Makaha Valley, Makaha-Waianae Kai Ridge, Makaleha Valley, Manuwai Gulch, and Nanakuli Valley. These seven populations lie within a 12.5 square-mile area of state land and comprise an estimated 300 to 400 individual plants.

Conservation and Recovery

The major threats to *Abutilon sandwicense* are competition from aggressive alien species, trampling and browsing by cattle, and fire. Christmasberry (*Schinus terebinthifolius*), an aggressive tree introduced to Hawaii early in this century, forms dense thickets and may also release chemicals that inhibit the growth of other species. Koster's curse (*Clidemia hirta*) is a cultivated shrub that spread to the Koolau Mountains in the 1960s and the Waianae Mountains at the beginning of the 1970s. It forms a dense understory that replaces native species. Molasses grass (*Melinus minutiflora*), which ranges from the dry lowlands to the lower wet forests of the leeward ridges, grows in dense mats that smother native vegetation. It is also fire adapted and provides fuel for spreading wildfires. Huehue haole (*Passiflora suberosa*) is a vine that covers the subcanopy of dryland habitats. All of these alien species are a threat to *Abutilon sandwicense*.

Most feral cattle were eliminated from the island by the mid-1900s. They have, however, had a major affect on the native vegetation. Much of the low- to mid-elevation forest between 210 and 550 meters (700 and 1,800 ft) was destroyed by cattle and goats. Ranching continues in the Mokuleia area on the west side of the Waianae Mountains, and some cattle move into the upland forest where they consume native vegetation, threatening *Abutilon sandwicense*.

Fire is an additional threat to *Abutilon sandwicense* populations which lie near the Makua Military Reservation and Schofield Barracks because weapons practice there has ignited wildfires. Within a 14-month period from 1989 to 1990, 10 fires resulted from exercises on the reservation. In order to minimize fire damage, the army has constructed firebreaks between the target areas and the surrounding forest.

Additional Sources

Cuddihy, L. W., and C. P. Stone. 1990. *Alteration of Native Hawaiian Vegetation: Effects of Humans, Their Activities and Introductions.* Cooperative National Park Resources Study Unit, University of Hawaii Press, Honolulu.

Culliney, J. L. 1988. *Islands in a Far Sea: Nature and Man in Hawaii.* Sierra Club Books, San Francisco.

Stone, C. P., and J. M. Scott, eds. 1985. *Hawai'i's Terrestrial Ecosystems: Preservation and Management.* Cooperative National Park Resources Study Unit, University of Hawaii Press, Honolulu.

Wagner, W. L., D. R. Herbst, and S. H. Sohmer. 1990. *Manual of the Flowering Plants of Hawaii.* University of Hawaii Press and Bishop Museum Press, Honolulu.

Contacts

Regional Office of Endangered Species
U.S. Fish and Wildlife Service
Eastside Federal Complex
911 N.S. 11th Avenue
Portland, Oregon 97232-4181

Derral R. Herbst
U.S. Fish and Wildlife Service
300 Ala Moana Boulevard, Room 6307
P.O. Box 50167
Honolulu, Hawaii 96850

Alsinidendron obovatum
No Common Name

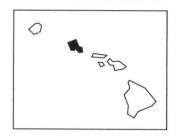

Yevonn Wilson-Ramsey from *Manual of the Flowering Plants of Hawai'i*

Status . . . . Endangered
Listed . . . . October 29, 1991
Family . . . . Caryophyllaceae (Pink)
Description . . . . . . Small shrub with thick, elliptic leaves and dense clusters of flowers, lacking petals but having five white and green sepals.
Habitat . . . . Ridges and slopes in lowland moist forest.
Threats . . . . Alien plant species, feral pigs, low numbers.
Region 1 . . . . Hawaii (Oahu)

Description

Alsinidendron obovatum is a small, branching shrub of the pink family that grows to 1 meter (3 ft). The thick, somewhat fleshy leaves are elliptic, 4 to 11 centimeters (1.6 to 4.3 in) long, with three or five large veins. The flowers lack petals, but have five sepals, which are white on the inside and green or green-veined on the outside. They are borne in dense clusters of 7 to 12. In fruit, the sepals turn purple and become fleshy, forming a stucture resembling a berry.

Alsinidendron obovata differs from *Alsinidendron trinerve*, a closely related Endangered plant from Oahu, in having more closed flower clusters, shorter flower stalks, sepals with a rounded rather than an acute tip, and a different habitat.

Habitat

This species is endemic to the Waianae Mountain Range on the western side of the island of Oahu, Hawaii. This island is dominated by the remnants of two ancient volcanoes that have eroded into two "mountain ranges," which consist of long, narrow ridges. The Waianae Range lies on the western side of the island, while the Koolau Range traverses the eastern side. The Waianae Range, which runs northwest to southeast for about 40 miles, lies in the rain shadow of the Koolau Range, and, except for the summit of Mt. Kaala, the highest point on the island, receives much less rainfall.

A variety of plant habitats are found in the Waianae Mountains, ranging from coastal dry shrubland to lowland dry forest to lowland wet forest. *Alsinidendron obovatum* grows on ridges and slopes in lowland moist forest dominated by koa (*Acacia koa*) and ohia (*Metrosideros polymorpha*) at elevations between 560 and 760 meters (1,850 and 2,500 ft). Associated plant species include ko'oko'olau (*Bidens*), and Java plum (*Syzgium comini*).

The diverse habitats of the Waianae Mountains contain a large number of vulnerable native Hawaiian plant species. In October 1991 the Fish and Wildlife Service (FWS) listed *Alsinidendron obovatum* and 25 other plant species from Oahu's Waianae Mountains as Endangered. This group listing was the result of the settlement of a 1989 lawsuit brought against the FWS by the Sierra Club Legal Defense Fund on behalf of a Hawaii conservation group. The terms of the settlement called for the proposed listing before October 1992 of 186 Hawaiian candidate plant species.

Historic Range

Alsinidendron obovatum was first collected in 1911. It has been known only from the northern and southern ends of the Waianae Mountains.

Current Distribution

The species survives in Kapuna and Pahole gulches on state land. The two known populations, which are about a half a mile apart, contain a total of about 100 plants.

Conservation and Recovery

The major threats to *Alsinidendron obovatum* are competition from molasses grass (*Melinus minutiflora*), an aggressive nonnative species, and habitat degradation by feral pigs. Molasses grass, which ranges from the dry lowlands to the lower wet forests of the leeward ridges, grows in dense mats that smother native vegetation.

Feral pigs, which are managed by the state as game animals, have been in the Waianae Mountains for about 150 years and have had a major effect on the native flora. Their rooting destroys plants and opens the habitat to invasive species. They also help spread these alien species by carrying seed on their bodies and in their feces.

The low number of known plants and their limited distribution makes the species vulnerable to extinction through unpredictible human or natural events. Some plants are located near hiking trails and are exposed to being trampled.

Additional Sources

Culliney, J. L. 1988. *Islands in a Far Sea: Nature and Man in Hawaii*. Sierra Club Books, San Francisco.

Stone, C. P., and J. M. Scott, eds. 1985. *Hawai'i's Terrestrial Ecosystems: Preservation and Management*. Cooperative National Park Resources Study Unit, University of Hawaii Press, Honolulu.

Contact

Derral R. Herbst
U.S. Fish and Wildlife Service
300 Ala Moana Boulevard, Room 6307
P.O. Box 50167
Honolulu, Hawaii 96850

Alsinidendron trinerve
No Common Name

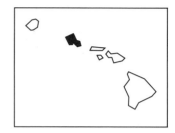

Robert Gustafson   *Color Plate C-5*

Status . . . . Endangered
Listed . . . . October 29, 1991
Family . . . . Caryophyllaceae (Pink)
Description . . . . . . Small, branching shrub
                       with thick, fleshy leaves
                       and clusters of green and
                       white flowers.
Habitat . . . . Slopes in wet forest.
Threats . . . . Feral pigs, alien plant
                       species, low numbers.
Region 1 . . . . Hawaii (Oahu)

Description

Alsinidendron trinerve is a small, branching shrub of the pink family that grows to 1 meter (3 ft). The thick, somewhat fleshy leaves are elliptic, 4 to 11 centimeters (1.6 to 4.3 in) long, with three or five large veins. The flowers, which are borne in open clusters of 7 to 12, lack petals, but have five sepals, white on the inside and green or green-veined on the outside. In fruit, these sepals turn purple and become fleshy, forming a stucture resembling a berry.

Alsinidendron trinerve differs from *Alsinidendron obovatum,* a closely related Endangered plant also from Oahu, in having more open flower clusters, longer flower stalks, sepals with an acute rather than a rounded tip, and a different habitat.

Habitat

Alsinidendron trinerve is endemic to the Waianae Mountain Range on the western side of the island of Oahu, Hawaii. This island is dominated by the remnants of two ancient volcanoes that have eroded into two "mountain ranges," which consist of long, narrow ridges. The Waianae Range lies on the western side of the island, while the Koolau Range traverses the eastern side. The Waianae Range, which runs northwest to southeast for about 40 miles, lies in the rain shadow of the Koolau

Range, and, except for the summit of Mt. Kaala, the highest point on the island, receives much less rainfall.

A variety of plant habitats are found in the Waianae Mountains, ranging from coastal dry shrubland to lowland dry forest to lowland wet forest. *Alsinidendron trinerve* grows on slopes in wet forest dominated by ohia (*Metrosideros polymorpha*) and kawau (*Ilex anomala*) at elevations between 900 and 1,000 meters (3,000 and 4,000 ft). Associated plant species include pilo (*Coprosma ochracea*), 'ape'ape (*Gunnera*), and alani (*Melicope sandwicensis*).

The diverse habitats of the Waianae Mountains contain a large number of vulnerable native Hawaiian plant species. In October 1991 the Fish and Wildlife Service (FWS) listed *Alsinidendron trinerve* and 25 other plant species from Oahu's Waianae Mountains as Endangered. This group listing was the result of the settlement of a 1989 lawsuit brought against the FWS by the Sierra Club Legal Defense Fund on behalf of a Hawaii conservation group. The terms of the settlement called for the proposed listing before October 1992 of 186 Hawaiian candidate plant species.

Historic Range

Alsinidendron trinerve was first collected in 1816 or 1823. It has been known from the north-central and southern Waianae Mountains and has not been found on any other island.

Current Distribution

The species survives on Mt. Kaala and Mt. Kalena on federal land. The two known populations, which are about a mile apart, consist of about 13 plants.

Conservation and Recovery

The major threats to *Alsinidendron trinerve* are competition from an alien plant species and habitat degradation by feral pigs. *Alsinidendron trinerve* is directly threatened by blackberry (*Rubus argutus*), which has been recognized as a noxious weed by the Hawaii State Department of Agriculture. This non-native species occurs in the Waianae Mountains between 1,000 and 2,300 meters (3,300 and 7,500 ft) and forms impenetrable thickets.

Feral pigs, which are managed by the state as game animals, have been in the Waianae Mountains for about 150 years and have had a major effect on the native flora. Their rooting destroys plants and opens the habitat to invasive species. They also help spread alien species by carrying seed on their bodies and in their feces.

The extremely low number of surviving plants and their limited distribution make *Alsinidendron trinerve* vulnerable to extinction through unpredictible human or natural events. Some plants are located near hiking trails and could be trampled.

Additional Source

Cuddihy, L. W., and C. P. Stone. 1990. *Alteration of Native Hawaiian Vegetation: Effects of Humans, Their Activities and Introductions.* Cooperative National Park Resources Study Unit, University of Hawaii Press, Honolulu.

Contact

Derral R. Herbst
U.S. Fish and Wildlife Service
300 Ala Moana Boulevard, Room 6307
P.O. Box 50167
Honolulu, Hawaii 96850

Price's Potato-Bean
Apios priceana

Paul Somers

Status	Threatened
Listed	January 5, 1990
Family	Fabaceae (Pea)
Description	Vine with compound leaves and clusters of greenish white flowers.
Habitat	Forest openings, disturbed areas.
Threats	Cattle grazing and trampling, herbicides, clearcutting, natural succession.
Region 4	Alabama, Kentucky, Mississippi, Tennessee

Description

Price's potato-bean is a perennial twining vine that grows from a large tuber to a height of 5 meters (15 ft). The alternate leaves are pinnately compound and consist of 5 to 7 leaflets, which are ovate-lanceolate to ovate in shape. The flowers, which are borne in clusters at the leaf axils, are greenish white, tinged with purplish pink. Individual flowers are about 2 centimeters (0.8 in) long. Plants flower from mid-June through August and bear fruits, which are cylindrical beans up to 20 centimeters (8 in.) long, through September.

This species can be most easily distinguished from the more common ground-nut (*Apios americana*) by its flower. The uppermost petal of the Price's potato-bean flower has a fleshy appendage at its tip and is yellow-green. The Ground-nut flower is purplish maroon and lacks the fleshy tip.

Habitat

Price's potato-bean grows in forest openings and along wood edges in well-drained soils. It is often found where bluffs descend to streams. Some populations also occur in disturbed areas such as roadside rights-of-way or powerline cuts.

Plants associated with Price's potato-bean include *Quercus muhlenbergii, Lindera benzoin,* tall bellflower (*Campanula ameri-*

cana), cane (*Arundinaria gigantea*), bass-wood (*Tilia americana*), white ash (*Fraxinus americana*), sugar maple (*Acer saccharum*), slippery elm (*Ulmus rubra*), redbud (*Cercis canadenisis*), and Virginia creeper (*Parthenocissus quinquefolius*).

Historic Range

This species was first collected in 1896 from Warren County, Kentucky. It has been documented from twenty-one sites in five states: Illinois, Kentucky, Tennessee, Alabama, and Mississippi.

Current Distribution

Of the 21 historic populations only 13 exist today. The species is no longer found at the Illinois site, which is in a national forest, or in Warren County, Kentucky, where it was first collected. Currently there are four populations in Mississippi and three each in Tennessee, Kentucky, and Alabama. Only five populations consist of more than 50 plants.

The Mississippi populations occur in the northeastern part of the state in Oktibbeha, Clay, and Lee counties. In Oktibbeha County there are two populations of between 50 and 80 plants each. In Clay County there is a single population of between 15 and 20 plants. The Lee County population is the largest in the state with several hundred plants on an acre of privately owned land.

In Tennessee, Price's potato-bean is known from sites in three counties. The largest population is in Marion County, where hundreds of plants are scattered on a bluff near a road. A population of between 20 and 30 plants occurs along a creek in Montgomery County. The third site, in Williamson County, supports only two plants.

Populations in Kentucky are found in the western counties of Livingston, Trigg, and Lyon. The Livingston County population, which in 1984 consisted of between 50 and 65 plants, has recently been severely reduced by cattle grazing and trampling. The Lyon County site supports a population of between 25 and 30 plants, while the Trigg County site supports only a few plants.

In Alabama there are three known sites of Price's potato-bean. Populations of between 15 and 30 plants occur in Madison and Autauga counties. A site in Marshall County supports less than five plants.

Conservation and Recovery

Price's potato-bean has undergone a major decline in recent years as almost half of the known populations have disappeared. The species was never common and the loss of plants is attributed to cattle grazing and trampling, clear-cutting, natural succession, and the application of herbicides to maintain rights-of-way.

Most of the remaining populations occur on privately owned land and lack adequate protection. Only two sites are on federal land. The Trigg County, Kentucky, site, which contains only a few plants, is on Tennessee Valley Authority land in an area designated as a Conservation Education Center. The Autauga County, Alabama, site, which has 15 to 30 plants, is on land administered by the Army Corps of Engineers. The Nature Conservancy owns and protects the Montgomery County, Tennessee, site, which supports 20 to 30 plants.

The voluntary cooperation of landowners is necessary to prevent destruction of remaining populations through clear-cutting or the introduction of cattle. Where Price's potato-bean occurs along powerline cuts and roadside rights-of-way, the Fish and Wildlife Service is working with the responsible agencies to plan maintenance and construction activities. Since Price's potato-bean is native to forest openings, it is also threatened by natural succession. Four populations are declining because of the closing of the forest canopy and competition from plants that are adapted to such conditions. Selective cutting at some sites might be necessary to save populations.

Additional Sources

Kentucky Nature Preserves Commission. 1982. "Summary Status Report on *Apios priceana* in Kentucky." Unpublished report.

Kral, R. 1983. *A Report on Some Rare, Threatened, or Endangered Forest-related Vascular Plants of the South.* USDA, Forest Service, Technical Publication R8-TP2.

Medley, M. E. 1980. "Status Report of *Apios priceana.*" U.S. Fish and Wildlife Service, Atlanta, Georgia.

Seabrook, J. A., and L. A. Dionne. 1976. "Studies in the Genus *Apios.* I. Chromosome Number and Distribution of *Apios americana* and *A. priceana.*" *Canadian Journal of Botany* 54:2567-2572.

Woods, M. 1988. "A Revision of *Apios* and *Cochlianthus* (Leguminosae)." Ph.D diss. Southern Illinois University, Carbondale.

Contacts

Regional Office of Endangered Species
U. S. Fish and Wildlife Service
Richard B. Russell Federal Building
75 Spring Street, S.W.
Atlanta, Georgia 30303

Cary Norquist
U.S. Fish and Wildlife Service
6578 Dogwood View Parkway, Suite A
Jackson, Mississippi 39213

Sacramento Prickly Poppy

Argemone pleiacantha ssp. *pinnatisecta*

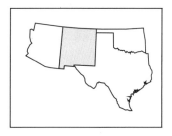

Peggy Olwell/USFWS   *Color Plate C-4*

Status . . . . Endangered
Listed . . . . August 24, 1989
Family . . . . Papaveraceae (Poppy)
Description . . . . . . Perennial with prickly branches; long, narrow leaves; pale yellow latex; white flowers.
Habitat . . . . Canyon slopes and bottoms, disturbed areas.
Threats . . . . Livestock grazing, flash floods, water diversion, road maintenance.
Region 2 . . . . New Mexico

Description

Sacramento prickly poppy is a perennial with 3 to 12 prickly stems that branch from the base and grow to a height of 50 to 150 centimeters (20 to 60 in). The attractive flowers have white petals that are 3 to 4 centimeters (1.2 to 1.6 in) in length and width and have numerous yellow stamens. The long, narrow leaves have box-shaped sinuses between their spine-tipped lobes. Like many members of the poppy family, Sacramento prickly poppy has a latex, or sap. The pale yellow to milky white color of the latex distinguishes it from *Argemone pleicantha* ssp. *pleicantha* which has yellow-orange latex. It was first collected in 1953 and described in 1958.

Habitat

This species is found only in canyons in the Sacramento Mountains in south-central New Mexico (Otero County). It grows at elevations of 1,300 to 2,000 meters (4,200 to 7,100 ft) in limestone canyons, fields, slopes, floodplain and channel deposits, and on roadsides. It prefers relatively moist, but not wet, locations and is most often found on north-facing slopes, canyon bottoms, roadsides, and near leaks in water pipelines.

Historic Range

Sacramento prickly poppy was first collected on the western slopes of the Sacramento Mountains. It is known from nowhere else.

Current Distribution

The species is currently found in about 10 canyons in the Sacramento Mountains. Populations occur in the Lincoln National Forest, Oliver Lee State Park, on land administered by the Bureau of Land Management (BLM), on New Mexico and Otero County highway rights-of-way, and on private land. Surveys in 1987 and 1988 recorded about 1,300 plants, three-quarters of which were found in the Alamo Canyon System of the Lincoln National Forest. Only two other canyons contained more than 100 plants. The San Andreas Canyon on BLM land supports only 12 plants.

Conservation and Recovery

The main threats to the species are livestock grazing, flash flooding, and the diversion of water supplies. Livestock grazing has a double effect on the Sacramento prickly poppy. Younger plants are eaten or trampled and the ability of mature plants to reproduce is diminished. Overgrazing also disturbs the topsoil and reduces the overall plant cover; this, in turn, increases the probability of flash flooding. In 1978 a flash flood almost completely destroyed one canyon population of a hundred plants.

Another threat is pipeline diversion of spring outflow for human and livestock use. This produces artificially dry conditions that will not support the species. The construction of a pipeline in one canyon was probably responsible for the largest reduction in Sacramento prickly poppy numbers. Plants that occur on highway rights-of-way are also vulnerable to mowing and the application of herbicides.

Additional Sources

Hutchens, C. R. 1974. *A Flora of the White Mountain Area, Southern Lincoln and Northern Otero Counties.* University of New Mexico Press, Albuquerque.

Malaby, S. 1987. "*Argemone pleiacantha* ssp. *pinnatisecta* Survey." U.S. Forest Service, Albuquerque.

_____. 1988. "Report on *Argemone pleiacantha* ssp. *pinnatisecta*." U.S. Forest Service, Albuquerque.

Soreng, R. J. 1982. "Status Report on *Argemone pleiacantha* ssp. *pinnatisecta*." U.S. Fish and Wildlife Service, Albuquerque.

_____. 1986. "Fresnal Canyon Preserve for *Argemone pleiacantha* ssp. *pinnatisecta*." The Nature Conservancy, Albuquerque.

Contacts

Regional Office of Endangered Species
U.S. Fish and Wildlife Service
P.O. Box 1306
Albuquerque, New Mexico 87103

Charlie McDonald
U.S. Fish and Wildlife Service
3530 Pan American Highway NE, Suite D
Albuquerque, New Mexico 87107

Pelos del Diablo
Aristida portoricensis

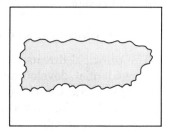

Karen A. Westphal and Elizabeth M. Harris

Status . . . . Endangered
Listed . . . . August 8, 1990
Family . . . . Poaceae (Grass)
Description . . . . . . Tufted grass, growing in bunches.
Habitat . . . . Serpentine slopes and red clay soils.
Threats . . . . Residential development, mining.
Region 4 . . . . Puerto Rico

Description

Pelos del diablo is a tufted grass that grows to a height of 30 to 50 centimeters (12 to 20 in). The stems occur in bunches and are slender, erect or spreading at the base. The blades are from 5 to 10 centimeters long (2 to 4 in) with margins rolled over the upper surface.

Habitat

This grass species grows only on serpentine slopes and red clay soils in southwestern Puerto Rico.

Historic Range

Pelos del diablo was first collected in 1903 from Cerro Las Mesas, Mayaguez, in southwestern Puerto Rico. It was later found in the nearby Guanajibo area and at Hormigueros. Once more common on the southwest part of the island, it was largely eliminated by residential and agricultural development. Its actual historic range will probably never be precisely determined.

Current Distribution

Today pelos del diablo occurs in two locations: the original Cerro Las Mesas site and in the Sierra Bermeja. Very few plants remain at Cerro Las Mesas. The Sierra Bermeja is a small range of coastal hills at the southwestern tip of the island. The grass grows in exposed rock crevices along the upper slopes.

Conservation and Recovery

The principal threats to pelos del diablo are residential development and mining. Portions of the Cerro Las Mesas population have been lost to recent housing construction. Both sites are threatened by habitat alteration for housing or agriculture. In addition, the Sierra Bermeja has been proposed as a site for gold and copper mining. Some land has also been cleared for cattle grazing, destroying habitat formerly occupied by the species.

Additional Sources

Department of Natural Resources. 1989. "Natural Heritage Program Status Information on *Aristida portoricensis*." San Juan, Puerto Rico.

Liogier, H. A., and L. F. Martorell. 1982. *Flora of Puerto Rico and Adjacent Islands: A Systematic Synopsis*. University of Puerto Rico, Río Piedras, Puerto Rico.

Contacts

Regional Office of Endangered Species
U. S. Fish and Wildlife Service
Richard B. Russell Federal Building
75 Spring Street, S.W.
Atlanta, Georgia 30303

Susan Silander
U.S. Fish and Wildlife Service
P.O. Box 491
Boquerón, Puerto Rico 00622

Guthrie's Ground-Plum
Astragalus bibullatus

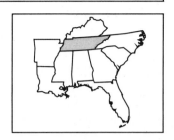

Paul Somers

Status	Endangered
Listed	September 26, 1991
Family	Fabaceae (Pea)
Description	Perennial with pinnate leaves and a cluster of purple pea flowers.
Habitat	Cedar glades.
Threats	Residential and commercial development.
Region 4	Tennessee

Description

Guthrie's ground-plum is a perennial member of the pea family with short stems (5 to 15 cm; 2 to 6 in) arising from a tap root. The pinnate leaves are 5 to 10 centimeters (2 to 4 in) long and are composed of about 24 leaflets. During April and May an upward curving spike bears 10 to 16 purple pea flowers. After flowering the spike begins curving downward. The fruits are fleshy pods, red above and yellow beneath, which mature in May and June.

The more common *Astragalus tennesseensis* can be distinguished from Guthrie's ground-plum by its yellow flowers, reddish brown topped fruits, and overall hairiness.

Habitat

Guthrie's ground-plum is found only in the unique cedar glade habitat in the central basin of Tennessee. It grows on thin, fossiliferous Lebanon limestone outcroppings at glade margins and areas within glades that are only partially shaded. This habitat is usually wet in the winter and spring, and hot and dry in the summer and fall.

Historic Range

Herbarium specimens indicate that Guthrie's ground-plum was first collected around 1880 in Tennessee, but incorrectly identified as *A. crassicarpus*. The species was rediscovered in Rutherford County, Tennessee, in 1980 and described as a new species in 1987. It is extremely limited in range and has seldom been collected. Records indicate that it was found in 1901 at La Vergne in Rutherford County and in 1948 in Davidson County. Neither of these populations survive.

Current Distribution

Today Guthrie's ground-plum is known from only three sites in Rutherford County, all on private land. The first site contains two colonies about a quarter of a mile apart. One is on a 1.5-acre cedar glade and contained 171 plants in 1988. The other colony is on a residential lot and contained about 50 plants in 1990. A group of about 100 plants that a wildflower enthusiast grew from seed collected at the first site is growing on private land about a mile to the northwest.

The second Guthrie's ground-plum site is located about 12 miles from the first and contains a dwindling population that in 1988 numbered only five plants. Several dozen plants had been recorded there in 1984 and it is likely that drought conditions during those years caused the decline.

The third site, discovered in 1990, is about a mile from the first site. It contains a small colony of about 40 plants and a large colony of about 200 plants. The plants occur in an unspoiled cedar glade and constitute the largest known population.

Conservation and Recovery

The greatest threat to this rare species is destruction of plants in the course of residential or industrial development. All three populations are located near the expanding metropolitan area of Murfreesboro. They occur on privately owned land that can readily be developed. The landowners have been notified by the Fish and Wildlife Service about the presence and importance of the species.

Secondary threats to Guthrie's ground plum include competition from woody plants, such as cedar, and livestock grazing. Active management of these sites would eventually be required to ensure the survival of the species.

Additional Sources

Barneby, R. C., and E. L. Bridges. 1987. "A New Species of *Astragalus* (Fabaceae) from Tennessee's Central Basin." *Brittonia* 39(3): 358-363.

Quarterman, E. 1986. "Biota, Ecology, and Ecological History of Cedar Glades: Introduction." *ASB Bulletin* 33(4):124-127.

Somers, P., and S. Gunn. 1990. "Status Report: *Astragalus bibullatus* Barneby and Bridges." U.S Fish and Wildlife Service, Atlanta.

Contacts

Regional Office of Endangered Species
U. S. Fish and Wildlife Service
Richard B. Russell Federal Building
75 Spring Street, S.W.
Atlanta, Georgia 30303

Robert R. Currie
U.S. Fish and Wildlife Service
330 Ridgefield Court
Asheville, North Carolina 28806

Sentry Milk-Vetch
Astragalus cremnophylax var. *cremnoplylax*

Susan Rutman

Status	Endangered
Listed	December 5, 1990
Family	Fabaceae (Pea)
Description	Low, mat-forming perennial with short, compound leaves and small, white or pale purple flowers.
Habitat	Limestone crevices.
Threats	Trampling by humans.
Region 2	Arizona

Description

Sentry milk-vetch is a small, mat-forming perennial in the pea family. Plants grow from a thick tap root to a height of about 2.5 centimeters (1 in) and form mats up to 25 centimeters (10 in) across. The short stems have compound leaves, less than 1.3 centimeters (0.5 in) long, composed of from five to nine tiny leaflets. Minute white or pale purple flowers (0.5 cm; 0.2 in) bloom in late April or early May. The fruit is egg-shaped and densely hairy; seeds set in late May and June.

Habitat

This species is restricted to a single site on the south rim of Grand Canyon National Park. It grows in shallow soils in crevices and depressions on Kaibab limestone, preferring sunny, well-drained soils or limestone surfaces. Sentry milk-vetch and rock-mat (*Petrophytum caespitosum*) are the dominant species in the dwarf plant community there.

Historic Range

Sentry milk-vetch was discovered in 1903 but misidentified at the time. It was rediscovered in 1947, west of El Tovar, Grand Canyon National Park, and described as a new species the following year. In 1979 a closely related form was described from specimens collected on Buckskin Mountain in Arizona. It was given the name *Astragalus cremnophylax* var. *myrior-*

raphis. Sentry milk-vetch then became known as *Astragalus cremnophylax* var. *cremnophylax.* The species has not been found at any other location.

Current Distribution

Sentry milk-vetch is known only from the single population on the south rim of the Grand Canyon. Extensive searches of nearby areas have failed to find other populations. An inventory of plants in 1988 counted 489 plants; in 1989 the number had declined to about 440.

Conservation and Recovery

The main threat to sentry milk-vetch is the trampling of plants by visitors to Grand Canyon National Park. The site is near the rim and accessible by car or on foot. In the past sentry milk-vetch mats have endured considerable foot traffic. The 1988 survey determined that 65 percent of all plants had suffered trampling and that more than half had been severely damaged. Between May 1989 and May 1990, plants in the most heavily visited area suffered a 63 percent decline. Trampling not only destroys seedlings, but reduces the vigor of mature plants, leading to decreased flower and seed production. Monitoring of the site will continue in order to establish whether the sole remaining population is self-sustaining. The National Park Service has rerouted pedestrian traffic, which has lessened, but not altogether eliminated, damage to the plants.

Additional Sources

McDougall, W. B. 1964. *Grand Canyon Wildflowers.* The Museum of Northern Arizona, Flagstaff.

O'Brien, S. 1984. "Status of *Astragalus cremnophylax* and Recommendations to Protect It." Unpublished report to Grand Canyon National Park.

Phillips, A. M., III, et al. "Status Report, *Astragalus cremnophylax* Barneby." U. S. Fish and Wildlife Service, Albuquerque.

Contacts

Regional Office of Endangered Species
U.S. Fish and Wildlife Service
P.O. Box 1306
Albuquerque, New Mexico 87103

Sue Rutman
Ecological Services Field Office
3616 West Thomas Road, Suite 6
Phoenix, Arizona 85019

Baker's Sticky Seed
Blennosperma bakeri

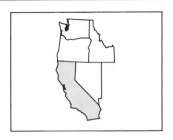

Marianne Austin-McDermon   *Color Plate C-3*

Status	Endangered
Listed	December 2, 1991
Family	Asteraceae (Aster)
Description	Annual with narrow, alternate leaves and yellow flower heads.
Habitat	Vernal pools and swales.
Threats	Residential and agricultural development.
Region 1	California

Description

Baker's sticky seed is an annual in the aster family that grows to a height of about 30 centimeters (12 in). The stems and leaves are mostly hairless; the leaves are alternate and narrow. Flower heads, with yellow disk and ray flowers, bloom in March and April. It is distinguished from similar members of its genus by the presence of red stigmas in the ray flowers. It is also known by the common name, Sonoma sunshine.

Habitat

Baker's sticky seed is found only in vernal pools and other seasonal wetlands in California's Cotati and Sonoma valleys, which lie north of San Francisco. These wetlands occur where a non-porus layer, such as clay, hardpan, or volcanic stone, lies beneath surface depressions. In these places winter rains form pools which gradually dry out during the spring and summer. This unique habitat will not support plant species that are intolerant of inundation or aquatic species that require permanent standing water. In the Cotati Valley, vernal pools form on Huichica loam and Clear Lake clay soil types where there is an impervious layer 2 to 3 feet below the surface.

Baker's sticky seed is sometimes found together with two other federally Endangered plants: Burke's goldfields (*Lasthenia burkei*) and Sebastopol meadowfoam (*Limnanthes vinculans*). The portion of the valley where these three species occur is about 16 miles long and from 5 to 11 miles wide. It is bounded on the north by the town of Windsor; on the south by the town of Hessel; on the west by the Laguna de Santa Rosa, a tributary of the Russian River; and on the east by the foothills of the Sonoma and Mayacmas mountains.

Other plants associated with these vernal pools include fringed downingia (*Downingia concolor*), *Navarretia* spp., smooth lasthenia (*Lasthenia glaberrima*), and Lobb's buttercup (*Ranunculus lobii*).

Historic Range

Baker's sticky seed was first collected in 1946. It is endemic to Sonoma County and has been found nowhere else.

Current Distribution

At present there are 30 known populations of Baker's sticky seed in vernal pools in the southern portion of the Cotati Valley and four populations in Sonoma Valley. These scattered sites stretch from the vicinity of Santa Rosa south to the town of Hessel. Most of the vernal pools are on private land. One site, the Todd Road Reserve, is owned by the California Department of Fish and Game. It contains populations of Baker's sticky seed and Sebastopol meadowfoam (*Limnanthes vinculans*). Four other sites are owned by county or city agencies.

Conservation and Recovery

The overwhelming threat to Baker's sticky seed and other vernal pool species is the destruction of their unique habitats for residential and agricultural development. So far about 90 percent of the Cotati Valley has been developed. The pressing need for affordable housing within commuting distance of San Francisco has increased development throughout the valley.

The construction of housing developments near Santa Rosa is destroying populations of Baker's sticky seed and Sebastopol meadowfoam. Recently more than a dozen pools have been filled without the landowners obtaining permits from the Army Corps of Engineers as required by the federal Clean Water Act. In part because most of the pools are relatively small, the Corps of Engineers has been reluctant to involve itself in examining the ecological effects of destroying these seasonal wetlands. Now that Baker's sticky seed and other vernal pool species have been listed under the Endangered Species Act, the Corps is required to consult with the Fish and Wildlife Service whenever an activity might affect the species, regardless of the size of the wetland.

Baker's sticky seed faces an additional threat related to development. Because the area's population has increased, Santa Rosa is planning to expand its wastewater treatment facility. Currently, treated wastewater is used to irrigate about 4,500 acres of cropland. Expansion plans call for the construction of a series of terraces planted with water-tolerant grasses and flooded with wastewater for treatment. The water would then be recycled for irrigation. The current plan calls for the wastewater capacity to be increased to irrigate 7,500 acres. Even if vernal pools were not directly flooded, the increase in residential and agricultural development, as well as the probable spread of the semi-aquatic grasses, would further threaten Baker's sticky seed and other vernal pool species.

A lesser threat to Baker's sticky seed is

livestock grazing, which has reduced populations of vernal pool annuals at many of their historic sites.

Additional Sources

Holland, R. F. 1976. "The Vegetation of Vernal Pools: a Survey." In *Vernal Pools: their Ecology and Conservation*, a symposium sponsored by the Institute of Ecology, University of California, Davis, May 1 and 2, 1976. Institute of Ecology Publication No. 9.

Ornduff, R. 1977. "Rare Plant Status Report for *Blennosperma bakeri*." California Native Plant Society, Sacramento.

Waaland, M. 1989. "Santa Rosa Plains Endangered Plant Protection Program Report, Section A." Sonoma County Planning Department and California Department of Fish and Game.

Contacts

Regional Office of Endangered Species
U.S. Fish and Wildlife Service
Eastside Federal Complex
911 N.S. 11th Avenue
Portland, Oregon 97232-4181

Jim A. Bartel
U.S. Fish and Wildlife Service
Sacramento Field Office
2899 Cottage Way, Room E-1823
Sacramento, California 95825

Palma de Manaca
Calyptronoma rivalis

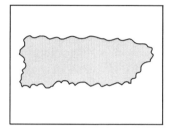

Willaim M. Houghton/Fairchild Tropical Garden

Status	Threatened
Listed	February 6, 1990
Family	Arecaceae (Palm)
Description	Palm, with pinnate fronds clustered at the crown.
Habitat	Stream banks in subtropical moist and wet forests.
Threats	Deforestation, flash floods.
Region 4	Puerto Rico

Description

Palma de manaca is a short-trunked palm tree that can reach 9 to 12 meters (30 to 40 feet) in height and 15 to 25 centimeters (6 to 10 in) in diameter. The pinnate leaves or fronds are clustered at the crown and may reach 3.6 meters (12 ft) in length. Triads of flowers (two males and one female), are borne in a drooping cluster about 1 meter (3 ft) long. The small, spherical, reddish fruits are only 6 millimeters (0.25 in) long.

Habitat

This species is found in semievergreen, subtropical, moist and wet forests of the karst region of northwestern Puerto Rico. Populations occur on level ground along stream banks.

Historic Range

Palma de manaca is found only on the island of Puerto Rico. It was first collected in 1901 at San Sebastian in western Puerto Rico. Until recently the species was known only from that location. It was described as *Caliptrogyne occidentalis* in 1923, but in 1938 was placed in a separate genus, *Calyptronoma*. In 1981 additional populations were discovered along the Camuy River, and since then more trees have been found along the Guajataca River.

Current Distribution

About 275 palma de manaca trees are believed to exist. The San Sebastian location contains 44 trees and the recently discovered river populations consist of about 220 individuals. In addition to these three natural populations, a small number of cultivated seedlings have been introduced into the Rio Abajo Commonwealth Forest and Camp Guajataca, which is owned by the Boy Scouts.

Conservation and Recovery

The principal threats to palma de manaca are deforestation and flash flooding. Timber cutting for road construction in the Camuy area destroyed a large portion of that population. Deforestation of areas surrounding palm locations also increases the likelihood of flash flooding. Such flooding increases the erosion of the palm's stream bank habitat, washes away seeds, and destroys seedlings.

Long-term prospects for palma de manaca are brighter than for many other rare Puerto Rican plants since the species produces large quantities of viable seed. Seedlings have been cultivated and the introduction efforts have so far been successful.

Additional Sources

Vivaldi, J. L., and R. O. Woodbury. "Status Report on *Calyptronoma rivalis* [O. F. Cook] L. H. Bailey." U.S. Fish and Wildlife Service, Atlanta.

Contacts

Regional Office of Endangered Species
U. S. Fish and Wildlife Service
Richard B. Russell Federal Building
75 Spring Street, S.W.
Atlanta, Georgia 30303

Susan Silander
U.S. Fish and Wildlife Service
P.O. Box 491
Boquerón, Puerto Rico 00622

Small-Anthered Bittercress
Cardamine micranthera

Nora Murdock

Status	Endangered
Listed	September 21, 1989
Family	Brassicaceae (Mustard)
Description	Erect perennial, with short, alternate leaves and four-petaled, white flowers.
Habitat	Seepages, stream banks.
Threats	Low numbers, habitat alteration, flooding, alien plant species.
Region 4	North Carolina

Description

Small-anthered bittercress is a perennial mustard with an erect stem growing to a height of 20 to 40 centimeters (7.8 to 15.6 in). The short basal leaves have small rounded teeth and lateral lobes; the stem leaves are about half an inch long, alternate, mostly unlobed, and have rounded teeth. The four-petaled, white flowers bloom in April; the fruit is a silque (seed pod) about 1 centimeter long (0.4 in).

Cardamine micranthera is distinguished from the closely related species, *C. rotundifolia*, by the size and shape of its anthers (nearly round), its erect growth form, and the smaller size of its silques.

Habitat

This species only grows in seepages, on stream banks, and in moist woods along a few streams in Stokes County, North Carolina, north of Winston-Salem.

Historic Range

Small-anthered bittercress was first described in 1940. In the 1960s the only known population in Forsyth County was lost when the site was converted to a cattle pasture. Attempts to locate the known sites in Stokes County were unsuccessful, and the species was believed to be extinct.

Current Distribution

In 1985 the species was rediscovered in Stokes County, and subsequent searches found three more populations. Three plants constitute the smallest population, while in the largest, about 200 plants, occurs along a stream bank. All four sites are located on private land.

Conservation and Recovery

The low number of existing small-anthered bittercress populations and the fact that the only sites are on private land puts the species at risk of extinction caused by logging or the conversion of its habitat to pasture. In addition, the species faces natural threats. One site is a midstream sandbar, which is vulnerable to flooding. At other sites the invasive Japanese honeysuckle (*Lonicera japonica*) may eliminate the species.

Additional Sources

Cooper, J., S. Robinson, and J. Funderburg. 1977. *Endangered and Threatened Plants and Animals of North Carolina: Proceedings of the Symposium on Endangered and Threatened Biota of North Carolina*. State Museum of Natural History, Raleigh, North Carolina.

Leonard, S. 1986. "Pursuing the Small-Anthered Bittercress." North Carolina Wildflower Preservation Society, Spring Newsletter.

Radford, A., H. Ahles, and C. Bell. 1964. *Manual of the Vascular Flora of the Carolinas*. University of North Carolina Press, Chapel Hill.

Contacts

Regional Office of Endangered Species
U.S. Fish and Wildlife Service
Richard B. Russell Federal Building
75 Spring Street, S.W.
Atlanta, Georgia 30303

Nora Murdock
U.S. Fish and Wildlife Service
330 Ridgefield Court
Asheville, North Carolina 28806

Cassia mirabilis
No Common Name

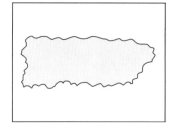

Susan Silander

Status	Endangered
Listed	April 5, 1990
Family	Caesalpiniaceae (Cassia)
Description	Shrub with simple pinnate leaves and solitary, yellow flowers.
Habitat	Silica sands.
Threats	Sand extraction, development.
Region 4	Puerto Rico

Description

Cassia mirabilis is a prostrate, ascending or erect shrub that grows to a height of about 1 meter (3 ft). The leaves are simple pinnate, alternate, and only 3 to 5 millimeters (0.1 to 0.2 in) long, with scattered white hairs. The solitary, yellow flowers are about 2 centimeters (1 in) wide, with one petal much larger than the others. The smooth, bean-like fruits are about 2.5 to 3.8 centimeters (1 to 1.5 in) long and contain 12 to 15 seeds. This species has also been known as *Chamaecrista mirabilis,* and *Chamaecrista glandulosa* var. *mirabilis.*

Habitat

Cassia mirabilis is endemic to the silica sands of northern Puerto Rico, which are fine, white, highly acidic, and extremely porus. Impermeable hardpan lies about a foot below the surface.

Historic Range

Herbarium collections indicate that *Cassia mirabilis* was once common throughout the silica sands of northern Puerto Rico. Urbanization and agricultural development have all but eliminated the species.

Current Distribution

Cassia mirabilis survives at only three sites on the island: two areas in Dorado and along the southern shore of the Tortuguero Lagoon. Together, these three sites support a population of 150 to 200 plants.

Conservation and Recovery

All three *Cassia mirabilis* sites are threatened with alteration that could eliminate the species. One small Dorado population was discovered during a survey for a local highway project. These plants will have to be transplanted to avoid their complete destruction. The other Dorado site has been proposed as the location of a large office building. The population along the Tortuguero Lagoon is on land designated by the commonwealth as a natural reserve. It is the largest population and is threatened by sand extraction, squatters, and trash dumping.

Additional Sources

Liogier, H. A., and L. F. Martorell. 1982. *Flora of Puerto Rico and Adjacent Islands: A Systematic Synopsis.* University of Puerto Rico, Río Piedras, Puerto Rico.

Vivaldi, J. L., and R. O. Woodbury. 1981. "Status Report on *Chamaecrista glandulosa* var. *mirabilis* (Pollard) Irwin & Barneby." U.S. Fish and Wildlife Service, Atlanta.

Contacts

Regional Office of Endangered Species
U. S. Fish and Wildlife Service
Richard B. Russell Federal Building
75 Spring Street, S.W.
Atlanta, Georgia 30303

Susan Silander
U.S. Fish and Wildlife Service
P.O. Box 491
Boquerón, Puerto Rico 00622

California Jewelflower
Caulanthus californicus

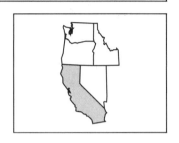

Marianne Austin-McDermon   *Color Plate C-5*

Status	Endangered
Listed	July 19, 1990
Family	Brassicaceae (Mustard)
Description	Branching annual, bearing white flowers with purple to green tips.
Habitat	Valley saltbush scrub and juniper woodland.
Threats	Conversion of habitat to cropland, urbanization, livestock grazing.
Region 1	California

Description

California jewelflower is an annual mustard that grows to a height of 30 centimeters (12 in) and produces several flowering branches. The plant has a basal rosette of leaves as well as clasping stem leaves with wavy margins. The flowers are white with purple to green tips. The narrow seedpods are sword-shaped and are about 2.5 centimeters (1 in) long. The shape and size of the seedpods is one of the characteristics that distinguishes the species from closely related *Caulanthus* species.

Habitat

California jewelflower is found only in grasslands and adjacent plant communities of the southern San Joaquin Valley between Fresno and Los Angeles. Alien grasses, introduced during the time of the Franciscan missionaries, outcompeted native plant species and now dominate these grasslands. California jewelflower occupies sites with reduced grass cover, such as valley sink scrub, valley saltbush scrub, and juniper woodland. Valley sink scrub is dominated by alkali-tolerant species of the Chenopodiaceae (goosefoot) family, such as iodinebush (*Allenrolfea occidentalis*) and sea-blight (*Suaeda* spp.). Valley saltbush scrub, dominated by the same plants, occurs on the gently rolling hills and supports a denser understory of annual herbs. Juniper woodlands, dominated by the California juniper (*Juniperus californica*), often border grassland sites above the valley floor on sloping terraces. Three other San Joaquin Valley herbs are also listed as Threatened or Endangered and are limited to the same habitats: Kern mallow (*Eremalche kernensis*), San Joaquin wooly-threads (*Lembertia congdonii*), and Hoover's wooly-star (*Eriastrum hooveri*).

Historic Range

California jewelflower was known from 47 sites in six counties in and around the San Joaquin Valley: Fresno, Kern, Kings, San Luis Obispo, Santa Barbara, and Tulare. In the late nineteenth century it was described as abundant south of Tulare.

Current Distribution

This species has been extirpated from Fresno, Kings, and Tulare counties. It is now found at only 10 sites in Santa Barbara, Kern, and San Luis Obispo counties. Drought conditions in recent years have caused plant populations to fluctuate greatly from year to year. The Santa Barbara County population occurs on private land in Santa Barbara Canyon and in 1988 consisted of several thousand plants. The landowners have entered into a voluntary agreement with The Nature Conservancy to protect the species. In Kern County a single introduced population occurs on the Paul Paine Preserve, owned by The Nature Conservancy. Only four of the 24 plants flowered in 1988. The eight sites in San Luis Obispo County contained a few thousand plants in 1988, but only 400 to 600 were observed in 1989. Two of these eight sites are on Bureau of Land Management (BLM) land and receive some degree of protection from overgrazing.

Conservation and Recovery

Conversion of land to agriculture and urbanization are responsible for claiming 96 percent of native plant habitat on the valley floor. Livestock grazing is the likely cause of the further loss of species populations in recent decades. The Nature Conservancy is preserving one introduced population and helping to protect another on private property. BLM is expected to review the grazing practices it allows on the two California jewelflower sites that it manages.

Additional Sources

Heady, H. F. 1977. "Valley Grassland." In *Terrestrial Vegetation of California*, edited by M. G. Barbour and J. Major. John Wiley and Sons, New York.

Hoover, R. F. 1970. *The Vascular Plants of San Luis Obispo County, California*. University of California Press, Berkeley.

Taylor, D. W., and W. B. Davilla. 1986. "Status Survey of Three Plants Endemic to the San Joaquin Valley." U.S. Fish and Wildlife Service, Sacramento.

Contacts

Regional Office of Endangered Species
U.S. Fish and Wildlife Service
Eastside Federal Complex
911 N.S. 11th Avenue
Portland, Oregon 97232-4181

Jim A. Bartel
U.S. Fish and Wildlife Service
2800 Cottage Way, Room E-1823
Sacramento, California 95825

Centaurium sebaeoides
No Common Name

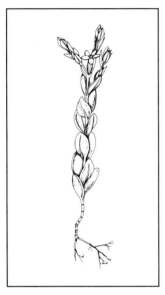

Yevonn Wilson-Ramsey from *Manual of the Flowering Plants of Hawai'i*

Status . . . . Endangered
Listed . . . . October 29, 1991
Family . . . . Gentianaceae (Gentian)
Description . . . . . . Annual with clasping, fleshy leaves and tubular white or pale pink flowers.
Habitat . . . . Volcanic or clay soils in arid coastal areas.
Threats . . . . Feral goats and cattle, alien plant species.
Region 1 . . . . Hawaii (Kauai, Oahu, Maui, Molokai)

Description

Centaurium sebaeoides is an annual of the gentian family that grows to 20 centimeters (8 in). The fleshy leaves are obovate or elliptic, 0.7 to 3.2 centimeters (0.3 to 1.3 in) long, and somewhat clasp the stem. The white or pale pink, tubular, lobed flowers are arranged along the ends of the stems. Cylindrical capsules contain numerous small brown seeds.

This species has also been known as *Schenkia sebaeoides* and *Erythraea sebaeoides*. It is the only member of the gentian family native to Hawaii.

Habitat

Centaurium sebaeoides grows on volcanic or clay soils in dry, rocky coastal sites on a number of the Hawaiian Islands. Associated species include ko'oko'olau (*Bidens*) and nehe (*Lipochaeta*).

Historic Range

Centaurium sebaeoides was first described in 1853. It has been found at scattered sites on Kauai, Oahu, Molokai, and Maui.

Current Distribution

Today this species is known from populations on state land in the Awaawapuhi Valley on Kauai, at Kaena on Oahu, near Hoolehua on Molokai, and on West Maui. Two populations exist on Kauai; the other three islands support one population each.

The total species population is estimated at fewer than 1,000 plants.

Conservation and Recovery

The main threats to *Centaurium sebaeoides* are degradation of its habitat by cattle and feral goats, and competition from invasive non-native plant species.

Cattle have had a major affect on native Hawaiian vegetation. Much of the low- to mid-elevation forest between 210 and 550 meters (700 and 1,800 ft) was destroyed by cattle. Most feral cattle were eliminated from the islands by the mid-1900s. However, ranching operations continue, and some cattle move into unfenced areas where they consume native vegetation, threatening *Centaurium sebaeoides* and other rare species. Feral goats, which are managed as game animals by the state, have been on the islands for over 150 years. Because of their agility they were able to reach areas inaccessible to cattle. Although a major control effort greatly reduced the goat population in the early years of this century, remaining animals still pose a threat to rare species.

Alien plant species also threaten most native species. *Centaurium sebaeoides* faces direct competiton from koa haole (*Leucaena leucocephala*), an alien tree that colonizes disturbed, lowland areas.

Additional Sources

Cuddihy, L. W., and C. P. Stone. 1990. *Alteration of Native Hawaiian Vegetation: Effects of Humans, Their Activities and Introductions.* Cooperative National Park Resources Study Unit, University of Hawaii Press, Honolulu.

Culliney, J. L. 1988. *Islands in a Far Sea: Nature and Man in Hawaii.* Sierra Club Books, San Francisco.

Stone, C. P., and J. M. Scott, eds. 1985. *Hawai'i's Terrestrial Ecosystems: Preservation and Management.* Cooperative National Park Resources Study Unit, University of Hawaii Press, Honolulu.

Wagner, W. L., D. R. Herbst, and S. H. Sohmer. 1990. *Manual of the Flowering Plants of Hawai'i.* University of Hawaii Press and Bishop Museum Press, Honolulu.

Contacts

Regional Office of Endangered Species
U.S. Fish and Wildlife Service
Eastside Federal Complex
911 N.S. 11th Avenue
Portland, Oregon 97232-4181

Derral R. Herbst
U.S. Fish and Wildlife Service
300 Ala Moana Boulevard, Room 6307
P.O. Box 50167
Honolulu, Hawaii 96850

Chamaesyce celastroides var. kaenana
No Common Name

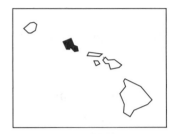

Robert Gustafson   Color Plate C-5

Status . . . .   Endangered
Listed . . . .   October 29, 1991
Family . . . .   Euphorbiaceae (Spurge)
Description . . . . . .   Low-growing shrub with
                          leaves in opposite rows
                          and flower clusters on
                          small side branches.
Habitat . . . .   Talus slopes in coastal dry
                          shrubland.
Threats . . . .   Alien plant species,
                          recreational activities.
Region 1 . . . . Hawaii (Oahu)

Description

Chamaesyce celastroides var. *kaenana* is a low-growing shrub of the spurge family up to 1.5 meters (5 ft) tall. The opposite, hairless leaves, up to 6.5 centimeters (2.6 in) long, are arranged in rows along the stem. The flower clusters appear on small side branches. The seed capsules contain small gray or white seeds.

This species has also been known as *Euphorbia celastroides* var. *kaenana, E. celastroides* var. *niuensis,* and is currently considered the same species as *Chamaesyce celastroides* var. *niuensis.*

Habitat

Chamaesyce celastroides var. *kaenana* is endemic to the Waianae Mountain Range on the western side of the island of Oahu, Hawaii. This island is dominated by the remnants of two ancient volcanoes that have eroded into two "mountain ranges," which consist of long, narrow ridges. The Waianae Range lies on the western side of the island, while the Koolau Range traverses the eastern side. The Waianae Range, which runs northwest to southeast for about 40 miles, lies in the rain shadow of the Koolau Range, and, except for the summit of Mt. Kaala, the highest point on the island, receives much less rainfall.

A variety of plant habitats are found in the Waianae Mountains, ranging from coastal dry shrubland to lowland dry forest to lowland wet forest. *Chamaesyce celastroides* var. *kaenana* is found on coastal dry shrubland on windward talus slopes between elevations of 9 and 640 meters (30 and 700 ft). Associated vegetation includes mao (*Gossypium tomentosum*), pauohiiaka (*Jacquemontia ovalifolia* ssp. *sandwicensis*), sandalwood (*Santalum freycinetianum*), and ilima (*Sida fallax*).

The diverse habitats of the Waianae Mountains contain a large number of vulnerable native Hawaiian plant species. In October 1991 the Fish and Wildlife Service (FWS) listed this and 25 other plant species from Oahu's Waianae Mountains as Endangered. This group listing was the result of the settlement of a 1989 lawsuit against the FWS brought by the Sierra Club Legal Defense Fund on behalf of a Hawaii conservation group. The terms of the settlement called for the proposed listing before October 1992 of 186 Hawaiian candidate plant species.

Historic Range

Chamaesyce celastroides var. *kaenana* was first collected in 1911. It has been found in the northwestern Waianae Mountains and the southeastern Koolau Mountains. It is not known to occur on any other Hawaiian island.

Current Distribution

Today *Chamaesyce celastroides* var. *kaenana* is found only in the area around Kaena Point at the northwest tip of Oahu. Five known populations, containing fewer than 300 plants, occur over three square miles of federal and state land.

Conservation and Recovery

The main threats to *Chamaesyce celastroides* var. *kaenana* are competition from aggressive alien plant species, fire, and the effects of recreational activity.

Koa haole (*Leucaena leucocephala*), an agressive tree which colonizes disturbed lowland shrub areas, directly threatens some populations. All dry shrubland species are at risk from fires which may be accidentally set in nearby reactional areas. In addition hikers may trample plants inadvertently.

Additional Sources

Cuddihy, L. W., and C. P. Stone. 1990. *Alteration of Native Hawaiian Vegetation: Effects of Humans, Their Activities and Introductions.* Cooperative National Park Resources Study Unit, University of Hawaii Press, Honolulu.

Culliney, J. L. 1988. *Islands in a Far Sea: Nature and Man in Hawaii.* Sierra Club Books, San Francisco.

Stone, C. P., and J. M. Scott, eds. 1985. *Hawai'i's Terrestrial Ecosystems: Preservation and Management.* Cooperative National Park Resources Study Unit, University of Hawaii Press, Honolulu.

Wagner, W. L., D. R. Herbst, and S. H. Sohmer. 1990. *Manual of the Flowering Plants of Hawai'i.* University of Hawaii Press and Bishop Museum Press, Honolulu.

Contacts

Regional Office of Endangered Species
U.S. Fish and Wildlife Service
Eastside Federal Complex
911 N.S. 11th Avenue
Portland, Oregon 97232-4181

Derral R. Herbst
U.S. Fish and Wildlife Service
300 Ala Moana Boulevard, Room 6307
P.O. Box 50167
Honolulu, Hawaii 96850

Chamaesyce kuwaleana
No Common Name

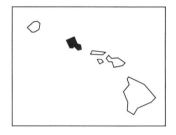

Steve Perlman/National Tropical Botanical Garden

Status	Endangered
Listed	October 29, 1991
Family	Euphorbiaceae (Spurge)
Description	Shrub with reddish brown young bark; untoothed, oval leaves; and flower clusters in leaf axils.
Habitat	Arid volcanic cliffs.
Threats	Alien plant species, low numbers.
Region 1	Hawaii (Oahu)

Description

Chamaesyce kuwaleana is an erect shrub of the spurge family that grows to a height of 90 centimeters (36 in). Young bark is reddish brown; older bark is dark gray. The untoothed leaves, which have a whitish waxy coating on the upper surface, are oval to circular and are arranged in two rows along the stem. Flower clusters appear at the leaf axils. This species has also been known as *Euphorbia kuwaleana.*

Habitat

Chamaesyce kuwaleana is endemic to the Waianae Mountain Range on the western side of the island of Oahu, Hawaii. This island is dominated by the remnants of two ancient volcanoes that have eroded into two "mountain ranges," which consist of long, narrow ridges. The Waianae Range lies on the western side of the island, while the Koolau Range traverses the eastern side. The Waianae Range, which runs northwest to southeast for about 40 miles, lies in the rain shadow of the Koolau Range, and, except for the summit of Mt. Kaala, the highest point on the island, receives much less rainfall.

A variety of plant habitats are found in the Waianae Mountains, ranging from coastal dry shrubland to lowland dry forest to lowland wet forest. *Chamaesyce kuwaleana* is found on arid, volcanic cliffs at an elevation of 320 meters (1,050 ft). Associated vegetation includes ilima (*Sida fallax*) and 'a'ali'i (*Dodonaea viscosa*).

The diverse habitats of the Waianae Mountains contain a large number of vulnerable native Hawaiian plant species. In October 1991 the Fish and Wildlife Service (FWS) listed *Chamaesyce kuwaleana* and 25 other plant species from Oahu's Waianae Mountains as Endangered. This group listing was the result of the settlement of a 1989 lawsuit brought against the FWS by the Sierra Club Legal Defense Fund on behalf of a Hawaii conservation group. The terms of the settlement called for the proposed listing before October 1992 of 186 Hawaiian candidate plant species.

Historic Range

Chamaesyce kuwaleana was first described in 1949. It has been found in the central Waianae Mountains and on Moku Manu Island off the eastern coast of Oahu. It is not known from any other Hawaiian island.

Current Distribution

Today *Chamaesyce kuwaleana* is found only at Kauaopuu Peak in the Waianae Mountains. While most of the several hundred known plants occur on federal land, some are on state land.

Conservation and Recovery

As with other rare native Hawaiian plant species, the major threat to *Chamaesyce kuwaleana* is competition from alien plant species. It is directly threatened by koa haole (*Leucaena leucocephala*), an aggressive tree that colonizes disturbed lowland shrubland.

The low number of known plants and their limited distribution make the species vulnerable to extinction through unpredictable human or natural events. Plants such as *Chamaesyce kuwaleana* that inhabit dry habitats are especially susceptible to wildfires.

Additional Sources

Cuddihy, L. W., and C. P. Stone. 1990. *Alteration of Native Hawaiian Vegetation: Effects of Humans, Their Activities and Introductions*. Cooperative National Park Resources Study Unit, University of Hawaii Press, Honolulu.

Culliney, J. L. 1988. *Islands in a Far Sea: Nature and Man in Hawaii*. Sierra Club Books, San Francisco.

Stone, C. P., and J. M. Scott, eds. 1985. *Hawai'i's Terrestrial Ecosystems: Preservation and Management*. Cooperative National Park Resources Study Unit, University of Hawaii Press, Honolulu.

Wagner, W. L., D. R. Herbst, and S. H. Sohmer. 1990. *Manual of the Flowering Plants of Hawai'i*. University of Hawaii Press and Bishop Museum Press, Honolulu.

Contacts

Regional Office of Endangered Species
U.S. Fish and Wildlife Service
Eastside Federal Complex
911 N.S. 11th Avenue
Portland, Oregon 97232-4181

Derral R. Herbst
U.S. Fish and Wildlife Service
300 Ala Moana Boulevard, Room 6307
P.O. Box 50167
Honolulu, Hawaii 96850

Cumberland Rosemary
Conradina verticillata

Paul Somers

Status	Threatened
Listed	November 29, 1991
Family	Lamiaceae (Mint)
Description	Shrub with narrow, bunched leaves and clusters of lavender, purple, or white flowers.
Habitat	Sandy gravel in river floodplains.
Threats	Habitat destruction by recreational users, decline in water quality.
Region 4	Kentucky, Tennessee

Description

Cumberland rosemary is a shrub in the mint family that grows up to 45.7 centimeters (1.5 ft) high. The reclining branches have tight bunches of very narrow leaves about 2.5 centimeters (1 in) long. The purple, lavender, or occasionally white flowers are about 1.8 centimeters long (0.5 in) and appear in clusters at the stem ends. Plants flower from mid-May to early June.

From its discovery in 1894 until its recognition as a separate species in 1933, Cumberland rosemary was considered a separate population of *Conradina canescens*, a coastal plain species. It has also been known by the scientific name *Conradina montana*.

Habitat

Cumberland rosemary grows in the sandy gravel of river floodplains on the Cumberland Plateau in north-central Tennessee and south-central Kentucky. It requires a well drained substrate free of organic matter and specific topographic features, such as narrow channels or depressions, that enhance sand and gravel deposition. Periodic flooding of its habitat keeps successional vegetation from becoming established.

Associated plants include grasses, such as big bluestem (*Andropogon gerardii*), wild rye grass (*Elymus virginicus*), and Indian grass (*Sorghasturm nutans*), as wells as a variety of herbs, including goat's rue (*Teph-*

rosia virginiana), Aster linarifolius, Coreopsis pubescens, American lovage (Lygusticum canadense), and a rare goldenrod, Solidago spathulata). Also occuring in the same habitat are two plant species that are candidates for federal listing: Calamovilfa arcuata and Marshallia grandiflora.

Historic Range

This species was first collected in 1894 from the banks of the Clear Fork River near Rugby, Tennessee. Botanists believe that in the past it occurred over a wider area of the plateau, but its range has been reduced by deterioration of its sand/gravel habitat brought about by siltation associated with coal mining, erosion, and waste discharges.

Current Distribution

There are three distinct populations of Cumberland rosemary in Tennessee: along the South Fork Cumberland River and its tributaries in Morgan, Scott, and Fentress counties; along the Caney Fork River in Cumberland and White counties; and along the Obed River system in Morgan and Cumberland counties. Each of these populations consist of a number of scattered colonies. The four colonies that are found in Kentucky along the South Fork Cumberland River (McCreary County) are considered part of the Tennessee population on that river. In all, 48 scattered colonies are known to survive.

A great deal of Cumberland rosemary habitat is managed by the Park Service. Colonies along the South Fork Cumberland River are within a national recreation area, and much of the Obed River has been designated a National Wild and Scenic River. However habitat along portions of

the Obed and along the Caney Fork River is privately owned.

Conservation and Recovery

The main threat to Cumberland rosemary is habitat destruction brought about by recreational activities. Populations within the Big South Fork National River and Recreation Area are exposed to the impact of an increasing number of hikers, campers, rafters, and off-road vehicles. Visitation to the recreation area has increased from 120,000 in 1986 to 730,000 in 1989.

Dam construction has probably had a destructive impact on historic populations. However, development of new hydropower sites within the plant's range has for the most part been precluded by inclusion of these rivers in the National Wild and Scenic River System.

Additional Sources

Jennison, H. M. 1933. "A New Species of Conradina from Tennessee." Journal of the Elisha Mitchell Scientific Society 48: 268-269.

Patrick, T. S., and B. E. Wofford. 1981. "Status Report: Conradina verticillata Jennison." U.S. Fish and Wildlife Service, Southeast Region.

Contacts

Regional Office of Endangered Species
U. S. Fish and Wildlife Service
Richard B. Russell Federal Building
75 Spring Street, S.W.
Atlanta, Georgia 30303

Robert R. Currie
U.S. Fish and Wildlife Service
330 Ridgefield Court
Asheville, North Carolina 28806

Cranichis ricartii
No Common Name

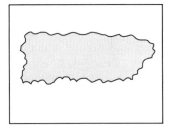

James D. Ackerman

Status . . . . Endangered
Listed . . . . November 29, 1991
Family . . . . Orchidaeae (Orchid)
Description . . . . . . Terrestrial orchid with spike of green flowers.
Habitat . . . . Moist serpentine scrub forest.
Threats . . . . Collectors, forest management practices, low numbers.
Region 4 . . . . Puerto Rico

Description

Cranichis ricartii is a small, terrestrial orchid that reaches a height of 27 centimeters (10.5 in). The cylindrical roots are fleshy and covered with shaggy hairs. The erect basal leaves are 2 to 3 centimeters (0.8 to 1.2 in) long. Small green flowers, which have lip petals with white margins, are borne on a leafless spike. The fruits are elliptical capsules.

Habitat

This orchid grows in rich organic soil in moist serpentine scrub forest at elevations above 680 meters (2,250 ft) in the western mountains of Puerto Rico. It is often found in association with the orchid *Cranichis tenuis*.

Historic Range

Cranichis ricartii was discovered in 1979 in the Maricao Commonwealth Forest in western Puerto Rico. It has not been found elsewhere.

Current Distribution

This orchid species is limited to three locations in the Maricao Commonwealth Forest. Only about 30 plants have been found, not all of them appearing every year.

Conservation and Recovery

Although *Cranichis ricartii* is found in a protected commonwealth forest, its continued existence is threatened by collectors, maintenance activities, and the low number of known plants. Orchids are highly sought by collectors and laws against collection are difficult to enforce. Forest management practices such as the establishment of tree plantations and selective cutting have been proposed for the Maricao Commonwealth Forest. These practices, as well as trail cutting and shelter construction, could affect *Cranichis ricartii*.

Additional Sources

Ackerman, J. D. 1989. *"Prescotia* and *Cranichis* of Puerto Rico and the Virgin Islands." *Lindleyana* 1:42-47.

Contacts

Regional Office of Endangered Species
U. S. Fish and Wildlife Service
Richard B. Russell Federal Building
75 Spring Street, S.W.
Atlanta, Georgia 30303

Susan Silander
Caribbean Field Office
U.S. Fish and Wildlife Service
P.O. Box 491
Boquerón, Puerto Rico 00622

Terlingua Creek Cat's Eye
Cryptantha crassipes

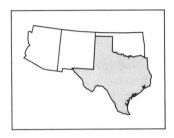

Paul M. Montgomery   *Color Plate C-4*

Status	Endangered
Listed	September 30, 1991
Family	Boraginaceae (Borage)
Description	Hairy, whitish perennial with narrow leaves and a terminal cluster of white and yellow flowers.
Habitat	Arid savannah over gypsiferous, chalky shale.
Threats	Residential development, off-road vehicles.
Region 2	Texas

Description

Terlingua Creek cat's eye is a perennial of the borage family that grows to a height of 60 centimeters (24 in). It has an overall silvery appearance with a terminal cluster of white and yellow flowers. Slender, erect, hairy stems arise from a mound of leaves at the base. The narrow leaves are whitish and hairy. The flowers have yellow knobs rising above laid-back petals. Fruits are egg-shaped, hairy nutlets. Flowering occurs from late March to early June; fruiting continues through July.

Habitat

This species is found only on rounded hills and gentle slopes over gypsiferous, chalky shale in the Trans-Pecos scrub savannah in Brewster County, Texas. It grows in full sun in an arid climate at elevations between 960 and 1,010 meters (3,150 and 3,320 ft).

Associated vegetation includes Havard's buckwheat (*Eriogonum havardii*), perennial spurge (*Euphorbia perennans*), Schott acacia (*Acacia schottii*), Mormon tea (*Ephedra* spp.), and creosote (*Larrea tridentata*).

Historic Range

Terlingua Creek cat's eye was first discovered in the late 1930s in Brewster County and described as a new species in 1939. Since then it has been collected only infrequently and no other locations have been found.

Current Distribution

Today only six populations of Terlingua Creek cat's eye are known, all on private land in Brewster County, near Big Bend National Park in southwest Texas. According to a 1987 status survey, these populations range in size from less than a hundred to a few thousand plants. The total species population was about 3,750. All populations appeared to be healthy, but only mature plants were observed; no juvenile or seedling plants were in evidence.

Conservation and Recovery

Because Terlingua Creek cat's eye occurs only on private land, none of the sites are protected. Small tracts of land in Brewster County, including some with populations of Terlingua Creek cat's eye, have been sold by a resort, and development of these tracts may eliminate some populations. It is likely that plants have already been destroyed by a network of roads constructed by the resort owners. The Fish and Wildlife Service has had difficulty contacting the many owners of Terlingua Creek cat's eye sites because most of the small tracts have been sold to out-of-state buyers.

In addition to development, the species is threatened by uncontrolled off-road vehicle use. Several of the hills near the closest town are rutted, and a few sites show evidence of vehicle tracks.

Additional Sources

Poole, J. M. 1987. "Status Report on *Cryptantha crassipes*." U.S. Fish and Wildlife Service, Albuquerque.

Contacts

Regional Office of Endangered Species
U.S. Fish and Wildlife Service
P.O. Box 1306
Albuquerque, New Mexico 87103

Phillip Clayton
U.S. Fish and Wildlife Service
c/o Corpus Christi State University
Campus Box 338
6300 Ocean Drive
Corpus Christi, Texas 78412

Cyanea macrostegia
var. gibsonii
No Common Name

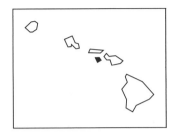

Joel Lau

Status	Endangered
Listed	September 20, 1991
Family	Campanulaceae (Bellflower)
Description	Palm-like tree with elliptic to oblong leaves and clusters of blackish purple flowers.
Habitat	Lowland wet forest.
Threats	Alien plant species, low numbers.
Region 1	Hawaii (Lanai)

Description

Cyanea macrostegia var. *gibsonii* is a palm-like tree in the bellflower family that grows to 1 to 7 meters (3.2 to 23 ft). The elliptic to oblong leaves are 20 to 80 centimeters (8 to 31 in) long, smooth on the upper surface, and hairy beneath. The leaf stem is often covered with prickles. Clusters of 5 to 15 flowers appear among the leaves. These are blackish purple on the outside, white or pale lilac within. The fruits are yellowish-orange berries.

This species has also been known as *Cyanea gibsonii*. In 1988 it was classified as a subspecies of *Cyanea macrostegia*, a similar tree which is common on Maui.

Habitat

This species grows on the summit of the Lanaihale Ridge and the upper valley slopes on the island of Lanai, Hawaii. A broad ridge runs northwest to southeast across the island and is commonly known by the name of its highest peak, Lanaihale, which is 1,027 meters (3,370 ft) high. A lowland wet forest community is found on the Lanaihale summit and narrow valleys. Although annual rainfall is only about 94 centimeters (37 in), the area is usually cloud-covered in the afternoon and shrouded in fog at night. Dominant members of the plant community are ohia (*Metrosideros polymorpha*) and uluhe fern (*Dicranopteris linearis*). Three other Endangered plant species, *Gahnia lanaiensis, Phyllostegia glabra* var. *lanaiensis,* and *Viola lanaiensis,* are found in this plant community. A lowland dry shrubland plant community occurs on the leeward slopes and valleys of Lanaihale. This community supports two plant species federally listed as Endangered: *Abutilon eremitopetalum* and *Tetramolopium remyi.* All of these Endangered plant species are endemic to Lanaihale.

Historic Range

Cyanea macrostegia var. *gibsonii* was first collected in 1879 from the summit of Lanaihale. It has also been found on the upper slopes of Mahana, Kaiholena, and Maunalei valleys.

Current Distribution

This tree is presently known from two gulches in the upper Kaiholena Valley and a feeder gulch into Maunalei Valley. The Maunalei population was last documented in the late 1980s, and at the time was the healthiest of the three. In 1989 only one tree was found at one of the Kaiholena sites.

Conservation and Recovery

The main threats to *Cyanea macrostegia* var. *gibsonii* are competition from invasive species and the browsing of seedlings by axis deer. The sole tree located in 1989 was almost covered by kahili ginger (*Hedychium gardnerianum*). This and other aggressive alien species are often more successful than native species in competing for water, space, and light.

Besides destroying plants directly, browsing by deer promotes erosion and opens up ground for the invasive plant species. With only a very few individual trees in existence *Cyanea macrostegia* var. *gibsonii* is extremely vulnerable to extinction through an unpredictable human or natural event.

Additional Sources

Cuddihy, L. W., and C. P. Stone. 1990. *Alteration of Native Hawaiian Vegetation: Effects of Humans, Their Activities and Introductions.* University of Hawaii Cooperative National Park Resources Study Unit, Honolulu.

Culliney, J. L. 1988. *Islands in a Far Sea: Nature and Man in Hawaii.* Sierra Club Books, San Francisco.

Lammers, T. G. 1988. "New Taxa, New Names, and New Combinations in the Hawaiian Lobelioideae (Campanulaceae)." *Systematic Botany* 13(4): 496-508.

_____. 1990. "Campanulaceae." In *Manual of the Flowering Plants of Hawai'i,* by W. L. Wagner, D. R. Herbst, and S. H. Sohmer. University of Hawaii Press and Bishop Museum Press, Honolulu.

Tomich, P. Q. 1986. *Mammals in Hawai'i.* 2d ed. Bishop Museum Special Publication 76. Bishop Museum Press, Honolulu.

Contacts

Regional Office of Endangered Species
U.S. Fish and Wildlife Service
Eastside Federal Complex
911 N.S. 11th Avenue
Portland, Oregon 97232-4181

Derral R. Herbst
U.S. Fish and Wildlife Service
300 Ala Moana Boulevard, Room 6307
P.O. Box 50167
Honolulu, Hawaii 96850

Cyanea pinnatifida
No Common Name

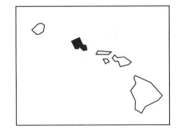

Yevonn Wilson-Ramsey from *Manual of the Flowering Plants of Hawai'i*

Status . . . . Endangered
Listed . . . . October 29, 1991
Family . . . . Campanulaceae (Bellflower)
Description . . . . . . Unbranched shrub with large, lobed leaves and clusters of purple-striped, greenish white flowers.
Habitat . . . . Steep, rocky slopes in moist forest.
Threats . . . . Feral pigs, alien plant species, low numbers.
Region 1 . . . . Hawaii (Oahu)

Description

Cyanea pinnatifida is an unbranched shrub of the bellflower family that grows 0.8 to 3 meters (2.6 to 10 ft) tall. The deeply lobed leaves are 25 to 60 centimeters (10 to 24 in) long and 16 to 50 centimeters (6 to 20 in) wide. Greenish white, purple-striped flowers appear in clusters of 8 to 15 at the leaf axils. The fruits have not been described. This species has also been known by the names *Lobelia pinnatifida*, *Rollandia pinnatifida*, *Delissea pinnatifida*, and *Cyanea selachicauda*.

Habitat

Cyanea pinnatifida is endemic to the Waianae Mountain Range on the western side of the island of Oahu, Hawaii. This island is dominated by the remnants of two ancient volcanoes that have eroded into two "mountain ranges," which consist of long, narrow ridges. The Waianae Range lies on the western side of the island, while the Koolau Range traverses the eastern side. The Waianae Range, which runs northwest to southeast for about 40 miles, lies in the rain shadow of the Koolau Range, and, except for the summit of Mt. Kaala, the highest point on the island, receives much less rainfall.

A number of plant communities are found in the Waianae Mountains, ranging from coastal dry shrubland to lowland dry forest to lowland wet forest. *Cyanea pinnatifida* is found in diverse moist forest on steep, rocky slopes at an elevation between 490 and 520 meters (1,500 and 1,600 ft). Associated species are mamaki (*Pipturus albidus*) and a variety of ferns.

The diverse habitats of the Waianae Mountains contain a large number of vulnerable native Hawaiian plant species. In October 1991 the Fish and Wildlife Service (FWS) listed *Cyanea pinnatifida* and 25 other plant species from Oahu's Waianae Mountains as Endangered. This group listing was the result of the settlement of a 1989 lawsuit brought against the FWS by the Sierra Club Legal Defense Fund on behalf of a Hawaii conservation group. The terms of the settlement called for the proposed listing before October 1992 of 186 Hawaiian candidate plant species.

Historic Range

Cyanea pinnatifida was first collected in 1817 from the central Waianae Mountains. It has not been found anywhere else.

Current Distribution

At present there is a single known population of *Cyanea pinnatifida*, consisting of three plants on private land in Kaluaa Gulch.

Conservation and Recovery

The main threats to *Cyanea pinnatifida* are habitat degradation by feral pigs, competition from invasive alien plant species, and the low numbers and limited distribution of the species.

Feral pigs, which are managed by the state as game animals, have inhabited the Waianae Mountains for about 150 years and have had a major effect on the native flora. Their rooting behavior destroys plants and opens the habitat to invasive species. They also help spread these alien plants by carrying seed on their bodies and in their feces.

One of these alien species is a direct threat to *Cyanea pinnatifida*. Koster's curse (*Clidemia hirta*) is a cultivated shrub that spread to the Koolau Mountains in the 1960s and the Waianae Mountains at the beginning of the 1970s. It forms a dense understory that replaces native species.

With only three individual plants surviving, *Cyanea pinnatifida* is extremely vulnerable to extinction through an unpredictable human or natural event. In addition, the species is found near trails and there is a danger that plants might be collected or trampled.

Additional Sources

Cuddihy, L. W., and C. P. Stone. 1990. *Alteration of Native Hawaiian Vegetation: Effects of Humans, Their Activities and Introductions.* Cooperative National Park Resources Study Unit, University of Hawaii Press, Honolulu.

Stone, C. P., and J. M. Scott, eds. 1985. *Hawai'i's Terrestrial Ecosystems: Preservation and Management.* Cooperative National Park Resources Study Unit, University of Hawaii Press, Honolulu.

Contacts

Regional Office of Endangered Species
U.S. Fish and Wildlife Service
Eastside Federal Complex
911 N.S. 11th Avenue
Portland, Oregon 97232-4181

Derral R. Herbst
U.S. Fish and Wildlife Service
300 Ala Moana Boulevard, Room 6307
P.O. Box 50167
Honolulu, Hawaii 96850

Cyanea superba
No Common Name

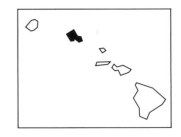

Yevonn Wilson-Ramsey from *Manual of the Flowering Plants of Hawai'i*

Status	Endangered
Listed	September 11, 1991
Family	Campanulaceae (Bellflower)
Description	Unbranched palm-like tree with a crown of large leaves and clusters of curved, white, tubular flowers.
Habitat	Moist forest understory.
Threats	Low numbers, feral pigs, alien plant species.
Region 1	Hawaii (Oahu)

Description

Cyanea superba is a palm-like tree of the bellflower family that grows to a height of 6 meters (20 ft). It is unbranched and crowned with a rosette of large oblanceolate leaves, 50 to 100 centimeters (20 to 40 in) long. Curved white tubular flowers hang in pendant clusters below the leaves.

This species has been known by a variety of scientific names, including *Lobelia superba*, *Cyanea regina*, *Delissea regina*, *D. superba*, and *Macrochilus superbus*.

Habitat

This species grows in the understory of moist forests on western Oahu, Hawaii. It occurs on well-drained, rocky soil at elevations between 535 and 700 meters (1,760 and 2,200 ft). Canopy species such as kukui or candlenut (*Aleurites moluccana*) and *Pisonia brunoniana* keep the open understory in shade. *Cyanea superba* will not grow in direct sunlight.

Historic Range

Cyanea superba was first collected on Oahu in 1817. It was collected again in 1870 from the gulches of Makaleha on Mt. Kaala in the Waianae Mountains. It was not seen again until it was rediscovered in the Waianae Mountains in 1971. Because of the small number of collections, the precise historic range is not known with certainty. It was apparently always rare and has been found nowhere else in Hawaii.

Current Distribution

The species is presently known from two small populations that total fewer than 20 plants. One population grows on state land in Pahole Gulch. It is found in an area of 167 square meters (1,800 sq ft) and in April 1990 consisted of twelve plants. The second population occurs on federal land administered by the Department of Defense in Kahanahaiki Valley, in the Waianae Mountains. At this site seven plants occur in an area of 56 square meters (600 sq ft).

Conservation and Recovery

Cyanea superba faces a number of threats. The extremely low number of known plants and their limited distribution makes the species vulnerable to extinction through unpredictible human or natural events. In addition the species faces habitat degradation from the activities of feral pigs and competition from invasive non-native species. When surveyed in 1990, scientists observed feral pigs and noted the effects of rooting around plants in both populations. Invasive alien species such as strawberry guava (*Psidium cattleianum*) and Christmasberry or wililaiki (*Schinus terebinthifolius*) threaten to crowd out surviving plants.

Additional Sources

Hawaii Natural Area Reserves System. 1988. "Plant Survey of the Pahole Natural Area Reserve." Report No. 2. May 1988. Division of Forestry and Wildlife, Department of Land and Natural Resources, Honolulu, Hawaii.

Lammers, T. G. 1990. "Campanulaceae." In *Manual of the Flowering Plants of Hawai'i,* by W. L. Wagner, D. R. Herbst, and S. H. Sohmer. University of Hawaii Press and Bishop Museum Press, Honolulu.

Contacts

Regional Office of Endangered Species
U.S. Fish and Wildlife Service
Eastside Federal Complex
911 N.S. 11th Avenue
Portland, Oregon 97232-4181

Derral R. Herbst
U.S. Fish and Wildlife Service
300 Ala Moana Boulevard, Room 6307
P.O. Box 50167
Honolulu, Hawaii 96850

Cyanea undulata
No Common Name

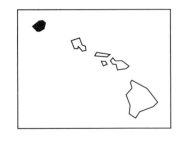

David Lorence/National Tropical Botanical Garden

Status	Endangered
Listed	September 20, 1991
Family	Campanulaceae (Bellflower)
Description	Unbranched shrub with narrowly elliptic leaves and a cluster of curved yellowish flowers.
Habitat	Stream bank.
Threats	Low numbers, alien plant species.
Region 1	Hawaii (Kauai)

Description

Cyanea undulata is an unbranched shrub in the bellflower family that grows to a height of from 1.8 to 3.6 meters (6 to 12 ft). The narrowly elliptic leaves are 28 to 36 centimeters (11 to 14 in) long and have wavy margins. The leaf stems are winged. While the upper leaf surface is smooth, the lower surface is covered with fine, reddish brown hairs. Five or six curved, hairy, yellowish flowers are borne in a cluster; the fruits are orange berries.

Habitat

This species grows along a stream bank in the Wahiawa drainage basin in the southern part of the island of Kauai, Hawaii. Of all the islands, Kauai has the largest number of endemic plants, and the Wahiawa Mountain area is one of the oldest and most diverse montane wet forests in Hawaii. This area, which covers about 1,200 acres, is roughly triangular in shape, with Kapalaoa, Mt. Kahili, and Puuauuka forming the corners. Elevations range from 610 meters (2,000 ft) to 1,000 meters (3,300 ft).

In addition to *Cyanea undulata*, four other plant species endemic to the Wahiawa drainage basin are listed as Endangered: *Dubautia pauciflorula*, *Hesperomannia lydgatei*, kamakahala (*Labordia lydgatei*), and

Viola helenae. Another 18 extremely rare plant species occur in the area.

Historic Range

Cyanea undulata was first collected in 1908 and again the following year from woods surrounding the Wahiawa Swamp. Since then it was believed extinct until rediscovered in 1988 along the bank of a tributary of the Wahiawa Stream. The species is not known from any other locale.

Current Distribution

This recently discovered population consists of three or four plants—the only known surviving members of the species. The land is owned by a corporation which manages it to preserve the quality of water for agricultural irrigation.

Conservation and Recovery

The main threats to *Cyanea undulata* are the species' extreme low numbers and competition from introduced alien plant species. With only three or four plants constituting the entire species population, *Cyanea undulata* is highly vulnerable to extinction. An unpredictable human or natural event could easily destroy these plants. Although the Wahiawa drainage has been largely undisturbed, alien plant species are now spreading upstream. Strawberry guava (*Psidium cattleianum*) and melastoma (*Melastoma candidum*) are aggressive species that outcompete native species. They gained a foothold in the basin in 1982 when Typhoon Iwa opened sections of the forest canopy. This invasion is assisted by the actions of feral pigs which transport seed and open additional ground through their rooting. Although there are only slight indications of pig activity in the basin, any increase could quickly help spread invading plants.

Additional Sources

Cuddihy, L. W., and C. P. Stone. 1990. *Alteration of Native Hawaiian Vegetation: Effects of Humans, Their Activities and Introductions*. Cooperative National Park Resources Study Unit, University of Hawaii Press, Honolulu.

Culliney, J. L. 1988. *Islands in a Far Sea: Nature and Man in Hawaii*. Sierra Club Books, San Francisco.

Stone, C. P., and J. M. Scott, eds. 1985. *Hawai'i's Terrestrial Ecosystems: Preservation and Management*. Cooperative National Park Resources Study Unit, University of Hawaii Press, Honolulu.

Lammers, T. G. 1990. "Campanulaceae." In *Manual of the Flowering Plants of Hawai'i*, by W. L. Wagner, D. R. Herbst, and S. H. Sohmer. University of Hawaii Press and Bishop Museum Press, Honolulu.

Contacts

Regional Office of Endangered Species
U.S. Fish and Wildlife Service
Eastside Federal Complex
911 N.S. 11th Avenue
Portland, Oregon 97232-4181

Derral R. Herbst
U.S. Fish and Wildlife Service
300 Ala Moana Boulevard, Room 6307
P.O. Box 50167
Honolulu, Hawaii 96850

Leafy Prairie-Clover
Dalea foliosa

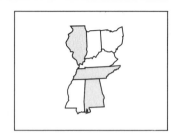

Jessie M. Harris   *Color Plate C-2*

Status . . . . Endangered
Listed . . . . May 1, 1991
Family . . . . Fabacae (Pea)
Description . . . . . . Perennial with pinnately
                        compound, alternate leaves
                        and a dense spike of
                        purple, pea-like flowers.
Habitat . . . . Edges of cedar glades,
                        riparian prairie remnants.
Threats . . . . Development, dam
                        construction.
Region 3 . . . . Illinois
Region 4 . . . . Alabama, Tennessee

Description

Leafy prairie-clover is a perennial of the pea family with tall, erect stems, which grow to a height of 50 centimeters (18 in). The pinnately compound, alternate leaves are 3.5 to 4.5 centimeters (1.4 to 1.8 in) long and are composed of 20 to 30 leaflets. Small, purple flowers bloom in dense spikes at the end of the stems in late July and continue through August. In the fall the stems die but remain standing and disperse seed throughout the winter. This species has also been known as *Petalostemum foliosum*.

Habitat

Leafy prairie-clover grows in the prairie-like areas on the edges of cedar glades in Tennessee and Alabama. In Illinois it grows on prairie remnants along the Des Plains River in thin soils over a limestone substrate.

Historic Range

This species was first described in 1868. It has been found only in Tennessee, Alabama, and Illinois. In Tennessee it occured in Bedford, Davidson, Marshall, Maury, Rutherford, Williamson, and Wilson counties in the central portion of the state. In Illinois it was known from six counties in the northeastern part of the state: Boone, Kane, Kankakee, La Salle, Ogle, and Will counties. In the late 1960s the first Alabama populations were discovered in Franklin, Jefferson, and Morgan counties.

New populations were found in 1984 in Jefferson County and in 1989 in Lawrence County.

Current Distribution

Today leafy prairie-clover survives at only 14 sites: two in Alabama, three in Illinois, and nine in Tennessee. The Alabama populations consist of a healthy, reproducing population of about 50 plants in Morgan County and a small population on a powerline right-of-way owned by the Tennessee Valley Authority (TVA). In Illinois, three populations are known along the Des Plains River in Will County. Two of these are protected by the Will County Forest Preserve District; the third site adjoins a right-of-way for a proposed highway. In Tennessee the species survives in Bedford, Davidson, Maury, Rutherford, Williamson, and Wilson counties. In Rutherford County a population of 25 to 30 plants occurs in a state park. Two other sites in the county support populations of two plants each, neither of which is expected to survive. A single Davidson County population is on land slated for development and will probably be lost. In Williamson County, a small population occurs on land owned by The Nature Conservancy, although a portion of the population grows on adjacent private land. Two populations of 20 to 30 plants occur in Wilson County on land managed by the Tennessee Department of Conservation. In Bedford County a healthy population of about 250 plants was discovered during 1990 field surveys. The largest and healthiest population in the state, consisting of about 650 plants, is in Maury County on land owned by the TVA. Another population of about 50 plants is also found in the county.

From 1987 through 1990 the Tennessee Department of Conservation made extensive field surveys in search of new leafy prairie-clover populations. Over 200 potential sites were examined and only two new populations were discovered.

Conservation and Recovery

Most of the known populations are threatened by destruction or alteration of their habitat. The most significant threats are from commercial, residential, and industrial development, intensive right-of-way maintenance, and possible dam construction.

The Morgan County, Alabama, population is vulnerable to residential development or conversion to pasture. In Illinois, two populations are protected, but the third is threatened by proposed highway construction. The Illinois Department of Conservation and the Will County Forest Preserve District are working with the state transportation agency to ensure that construction will not destroy the leafy prairie-clover population. In the spring of 1988, the Department of Conservation attempted to reestablish the Kankakee County population by replanting 105 leafy prairie-clover plants. Unfortunately an extremely dry summer destroyed all but six.

In Tennessee, most of the Williamson County site is owned by The Nature Conservancy. The large Maury County population, which is owned by TVA, will be damaged if the Columbia Dam on the Duck River is completed according to the original proposal. TVA is currently evaluating the impact of the dam on federally Endangered mussels in the area. If the proposal is modified to allow for a lower floodpool level, the leafy prairie-clover population would not be affected by the dam. The higher floodpool level, however, would destroy about half of the population.

Additional Sources

Baskin, J. M., and C. Baskin. 1973. "The Past and Present Geographical Distribution of *Petalostemon foliosus* and Notes on Its Ecology." *Rhodora* 756:132-140.

Kral, R. 1983. *A Report on Some Rare, Threatened, or Endangered Forest-related Vascular Plants of the South.* USDA, Forest Service, Technical Publication R8-TP2.

Kurz, D. R., and M. L. Bowles. 1981. "Report on the Status of Illinois Vascular Plants Potentially Endangered or Threatened in the United States." Natural Land Institute, Rockford, Illinois.

Smith, D. K., and B. E. Wofford. 1980 "Status Report—*Petalostemum foliosum* Gray (*Dalea foliosa* [Gray] Barneby)." U.S. Fish and Wildlife Service, Atlanta.

Tennessee Valley Authority. 1988. "Biological Asessment of Columbia Dam Alternatives, Duck River, Tennessee." Knoxville, Tennesee.

Contacts

Regional Office of Endangered Species
U. S. Fish and Wildlife Service
Richard B. Russell Federal Building
75 Spring Street, S.W.
Atlanta, Georgia 30303

Robert R. Currie
U.S. Fish and Wildlife Service
330 Ridgefield Court
Asheville, North Carolina 28806

Garrett's Mint
Dicerandra christmanii

Jonathan A. Shaw   *Color Plate C-3*

Status . . . . Endangered
Listed . . . . September 21, 1989
Family . . . . Lamiaceae (Mint)
Description . . . . . . Aromatic shrub with pro-
                            fuse, white or pale pink
                            flowers.
Habitat . . . . Well-drained fine sand soils.
Threats . . . . Agricultural and residential
                            development.
Region 4 . . . . Florida

Description

Garrett's mint is a strongly aromatic mint that grows to a height of 50 centimeters (19.5 in). Clusters of erect, supple stems arise from a woody root. The narrowly oblong, opposite leaves, about 2.5 centimeters (1 in) long, have untoothed margins, blunt tips, and are covered with conspicuous, sunken glands. Leaves at the base of the plant are larger than those that occur with flower buds at each stem node.

Flowers are borne on short stalks in pairs at intervals along the stems. The lipped, tubular corolla of the flower is about 1.5 centimeters (0.6 in) long. Flower color is white or pale pink with purplish rose dots. Four large stamens protrude from the corolla.

Each half of the anther (the pollen-bearing structure) is tipped by a horn or spur.

Until 1989, plants of this species were considered to be scrub mint (*Dicerandra frutescens*), which was listed as Endangered in 1985. Taxonomic analysis has shown it to be a separate species. The factors which distinguish the two species are the anther and corolla color, the oils produced, average leaf length, and anther connective glandularity. These differences are more apparent on live plants than on herbarium specimens.

Habitat

Garrett's mint grows on well-drained, fine sand soils along the margins of sand pine forests. It favors bare, sandy areas in full sunlight.

Historic Range

Since Garrett's mint (*D. christmanii*) has only recently been recognized as a separate species from scrub mint (*D. frutescens*), little is known of its specific historic range. Both species are found only in Highlands County, Florida, in the Southern Central Florida Ridge Sandhill geographical province.

Current Distribution

Before its division into two species, four populations of scrub mint (*D. frutescens*) were known in Highlands County. The two populations in the northern part of the range have been determined to be Garrett's mint.

Conservation and Recovery

The scrub/sandhill habitat favored by Garrett's mint has been reduced by over 75 percent in Highlands County, mainly by agricultural and residential development. The Fish and Wildlife Service has developed a recovery plan for scrub mint which applies to the newly designated Garrett's mint. For further details on recovery efforts see the species account for *D. frutescens* on page 133 in volume one of the *Guide to Endangered Species*.

Additional Sources

Huck, R. B, et al. 1989. "A New *Dicerandra* (Labiatae) from the Lake Wales Ridge of Florida, with a Cladistic Analysis and Discussion of Endemism." *Systematic Botany* 14(2):197-213.

Contacts

Regional Office of Endangered Species
U. S. Fish and Wildlife Service
Richard B. Russell Federal Building
75 Spring Street, S.W.
Atlanta, Georgia 30303

David J. Wesley
U.S. Fish and Wildlife Service
3100 University Boulevard South, Suite 120
Jacksonville, Florida 32216

Diellia falcata
No Common Name

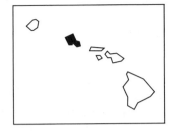

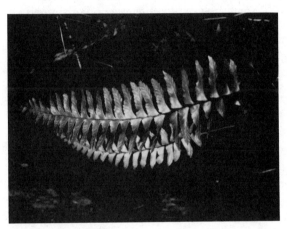

Robert Gustafson   Color Plate C-5

Status . . . . Endangered
Listed . . . . October 29, 1991
Family . . . . Polypodiaceae (Fern)
Description . . . . . . Terrestrial fern with sickle-shaped or triangular leaflets.
Habitat . . . . Dry lowland forest.
Threats . . . . Feral animals, alien plant species, wildfires.
Region 1 . . . . Hawaii (Oahu)

Description

Diellia falcata is a terrestrial fern that grows from an underground stem (rhizome) 1 to 5 centimeters (0.4 to 2 in) long. The fronds are 20 to 100 centimeters (8 to 40 in) tall and have dark brown to pale tan stalks. There are 12 to 45 undivided leaflets (pinnae) on each side of the stem axis. The lower leaflets are rounded; farther up the frond they become larger and are sickle-shaped or triangular. The fruitdots or sori, which are the fern's spore-bearing bodies, appear as short lines on the underside of the leaflet margins. This species has also been known as *Schizoloma fal-cata, Lindsaea falcata,* and *Diellia erecta* var. *falcata.*

Habitat

Diellia falcata is endemic to the Waianae Mountain Range on the western side of the island of Oahu, Hawaii. This island is dominated by the remnants of two ancient volcanoes that have eroded into two "mountain ranges," which consist of long, narrow ridges. The Waianae Range lies on the western side of the island, while the Koolau Range traverses the eastern side. The Waianae Range, which runs northwest to southeast for about 40 miles, lies in the rain shadow of the Koolau Range, and, except for the summit of Mt. Kaala, the highest point on the island, receives much less rainfall.

A variety of plant habitats are found in the Waianae Mountains, ranging from coastal dry shrubland to lowland dry forest to lowland wet forest. *Diellia falcata* is found in the shaded understory of lowland dry forest at elevations between 390 and 820 meters (1,280 and 2,700 ft). It is found in association with aulu or soapberry (*Sapindus oahuensis*), lama or persimmon (*Diospyros sandwicensis*), and 'ala'a (*Pouteria sandwicensis*).

The diverse habitats of the Waianae Mountains contain a large number of vulnerable native Hawaiian plant species. In October 1991 the Fish and Wildlife Service (FWS) listed *Diellia falcata* and 25 other plant species from Oahu's Waianae Mountains as Endangered. This group listing was the result of the settlement of a 1989 lawsuit brought against the FWS by the Sierra Club Legal Defense Fund on behalf of a Hawaii conservation group. The terms of the settlement called for the proposed listing before October 1992 of 186 Hawaiian candidate plant species.

Historic Range

This fern, discovered between 1838 and 1842, is endemic to the island of Oahu. It has been found throughout most of the Waianae Mountains, from Manini Gulch to Palehua Iki, and also in the Koolau Mountains from Kaipapau Valley to Aiea Gulch.

Current Distribution

At present *Diellia falcata* is found only in the Waianae Mountains, from Ekahanui Gulch to Manini Gulch. Seven populations, comprising about 7,000 plants, are found in a 22-square-mile area on both state and private land.

Conservation and Recovery

The main threats to *Diellia falcata* are habitat degradation caused by feral pigs, goats, and cattle; the invasion of aggressive alien plant species; and fire.

Feral pigs, which are managed by the state as game animals, have been in the Waianae Mountains for about 150 years and have had a major effect on the native flora. Their rooting destroys plants and opens the habitat to invasive plant species. They also help spread alien species by carrying seed on their bodies and in their feces. Feral goats, also game animals, have been on the island for 170 years. Because of their agility they are able to reach areas inaccessible to pigs and cattle. Although a major control effort greatly reduced the goat population by 1905, remaining animals are still a threat to rare species. Cattle, too, have had a major affect on the native vegetation. Much of the low- to mid-elevation forest between 210 and 550 meters (700 and 1,800 ft) was destroyed by cattle and goats. Most feral cattle were eliminated from the island by the mid-1900s. However, ranching operations continue in the Mokuleia area on the western side of the Waianae Mountains. Some cattle move into the upland forest where they consume native vegetation, threatening *Diellia falcata* and other rare species.

The activities of feral animals help the spread of aggressive alien plant species, several of which are a direct threat to *Diellia falcata* populations. Christmasberry (*Schinus terebinthifolius*), an aggressive tree introduced to Hawaii before 1911, forms dense thickets and may also release chemicals that inhibit the growth of other species. Huehue haole (*Passiflora suberosa*) is a vine that smothers the subcanopy of dryland habitats, and strawberry guava (*Psidium cattleianum*) is an invasive tree that forms dense stands that exclude other species.

Fire is a threat to *Diellia falcata* populations near the U.S. Army's Makua Military Reservation and Schofield Barracks. Within a 14-month period from 1989 to 1990, 10 fires resulted from weapons practice on the reservation. In order to minimize damage from fires, the army has constructed firebreaks between the target areas and the surrounding forest.

Additional Sources

Cuddihy, L. W., and C. P. Stone. 1990. *Alteration of Native Hawaiian Vegetation: Effects of Humans, Their Activities and Introductions.* Cooperative National Park Resources Study Unit, University of Hawaii Press, Honolulu.

Culliney, J. L. 1988. *Islands in a Far Sea: Nature and Man in Hawaii.* Sierra Club Books, San Francisco.

Stone, C. P., and J. M. Scott, eds. 1985. *Hawai'i's Terrestrial Ecosystems: Preservation and Management.* Cooperative National Park Resources Study Unit, University of Hawaii Press, Honolulu.

Wagner, W. L., D. R. Herbst, and S. H. Sohmer. 1990. *Manual of the Flowering Plants of Hawai'i.* University of Hawaii Press and Bishop Museum Press, Honolulu.

Contacts

Regional Office of Endangered Species
U.S. Fish and Wildlife Service
Eastside Federal Complex
911 N.S. 11th Avenue
Portland, Oregon 97232-4181

Derral R. Herbst
U.S. Fish and Wildlife Service
300 Ala Moana Boulevard, Room 6307
P.O. Box 50167
Honolulu, Hawaii 96850

Dubautia herbstobatae

No Common Name

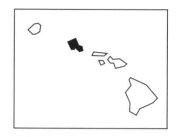

Derral Herbst

Status	Endangered
Listed	October 29, 1991
Family	Asteraceae (Aster)
Description	Small shrub with alternate, elliptic leaves and clusters of yellowish orange flower heads.
Habitat	Rock outcrops in dry shrubland.
Threats	Feral pigs and goats, alien plant species.
Region 1	Hawaii (Oahu)

Description

Dubautia herbstobatae is a small, spreading shrub of the aster family that grows 50 centimeters (20 in) high. The shiny, leathery leaves are alternate, narrowly elliptic, and 2 to 5.5 centimeters (0.8 to 2.2 in) long. Each flower cluster contains 5 to 15 flower heads, which are composed of 4 to 20 yellowish orange, tubular florets. The fruit is a dry seed, covered with silky hairs. The species has also been known by the name *Railliardia herbstobatae*.

Habitat

Dubautia herbstobatae is found only in the Waianae Mountain Range on the west-ern side of the island of Oahu, Hawaii. This island is dominated by the remnants of two ancient volcanoes that have eroded into two "mountain ranges," which consist of long, narrow ridges. The Waianae Range lies on the western side of the island, while the Koolau Range traverses the eastern side. The Waianae Range, which runs northwest to southeast for about 40 miles, lies in the rain shadow of the Koolau Range, and, except for the summit of Mt. Kaala, the highest point on the island, receives much less rainfall.

A variety of plant habitats are found in the Waianae Mountains, ranging from coastal dry shrubland to lowland dry forest to lowland wet forest. *Dubautia herbsto-*

batae occurs on rock outcrops on north-facing ridges in dry shrubland at an elevation of 580 to 910 meters (1,900 to 3,000 ft). Associated plant species include ohia (*Metrosideros polymorpha*) and kawelu (*Eragrostis variabilis*).

The diverse habitats of the Waianae Mountains contain a large number of vulnerable native Hawaiian plant species. In October 1991 the Fish and Wildlife Service (FWS) listed *Dubautia herbstobatae* and 25 other plant species from Oahu's Waianae Mountains as Endangered. This group listing was the result of the settlement of a 1989 lawsuit brought against the FWS by the Sierra Club Legal Defense Fund on behalf of a Hawaii conservation group. The terms of the settlement called for the proposed listing before October 1992 of 186 Hawaiian candidate plant species.

Historic Range

Dubautia herbstobatae was discovered in 1971 in the northern Waianae Mountains in western Oahu, Hawaii. It has not been found in any other area.

Current Distribution

This species is found on Ohikilolo and Kamaileunu ridges in the northern Waianae Mountains. Eight populations, containing less than 100 individual plants, are located in a 1.5-square-mile area of state and private land.

Conservation and Recovery

The main threats to *Dubautia herbstobatae*, as for almost all rare species in the Waianae Mountains, are habitat degradation by feral pigs and goats and competition from invasive alien plant species. The species faces additional threats associated with low numbers and a limited distribution, such as fire and trampling by hikers.

Feral pigs, which are managed by the state as game animals, have been in the Waianae Mountains for about 150 years and have had a major effect on the native flora. Their rooting destroys plants and opens up the habitat to invasive species. They also help spread these alien plants by carrying seed on their bodies and in their feces. Feral goats, which are also game animals, have been on the island for 170 years. Because of their agility they were able to reach areas inaccessible to pigs. Although a major control effort greatly reduced the goat population by 1905, remaining animals are still a threat to rare species, including *Dubautia herbstobatae*.

Invasive alien plant species are a threat to almost all native flora, especially rare species, and *Dubautia herbstobatae* is directly threatened by several. Christmasberry (*Schinus terebinthifolius*), an aggressive tree introduced to Hawaii before 1911, forms dense thickets and may also release chemicals that inhibit the growth of other species. Koa hoale (*Leucaena leucocephala*) is an alien tree that colonizes disturbed lowland areas. This tree makes its own nitrogen and is adaptable to soils with a low nitrogen content, enabling it to compete with native species that have evolved under these conditions. Molasses grass (*Melinus minutiflora*), which ranges from the dry lowlands to the lower wet forests of the leeward ridges, grows in dense mats that smother native vegetation. It is also fire adapted and provides a fuel for spreading wildfires.

Fire is a threat to *Dubautia herbstobatae* populations near the U.S. Army's Makua Military Reservation and Schofield Barracks. Within a 14-month period from 1989 to 1990, 10 fires resulted from weapons practice on the reservation. To minimize damage from fires, the army has constructed firebreaks between the target areas and the surrounding forest.

With fewer than 100 *Dubautia herbstobatae* plants existing in a single small area, the species is vulnerable to extinction from an unpredictable human or natural event. In addition, it occurs near trails and could be trampled by hikers.

Additional Sources

Cuddihy, L. W., and C. P. Stone. 1990. *Alteration of Native Hawaiian Vegetation: Effects of Humans, Their Activities and Introductions.* Cooperative National Park Resources Study Unit, University of Hawaii Press, Honolulu.

Culliney, J. L. 1988. *Islands in a Far Sea: Nature and Man in Hawaii.* Sierra Club Books, San Francisco.

Stone, C. P., and J. M. Scott, eds. 1985. *Hawai'i's Terrestrial Ecosystems: Preservation and Management.* Cooperative National Park Resources Study Unit, University of Hawaii Press, Honolulu.

Carr, Gerald D. "*Dubautia.*" In *Manual of the Flowering Plants of Hawai'i* by W. L. Wagner, D. R. Herbst, and S. H. Sohmer. University of Hawaii Press and Bishop Museum Press, Honolulu.

Contacts

Regional Office of Endangered Species
U.S. Fish and Wildlife Service
Eastside Federal Complex
911 N.S. 11th Avenue
Portland, Oregon 97232-4181

Derral R. Herbst
U.S. Fish and Wildlife Service
300 Ala Moana Boulevard, Room 6307
P.O. Box 50167
Honolulu, Hawaii 96850

Dubautia pauciflorula
No Common Name

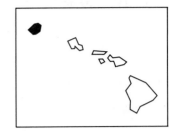

G. Carr

Status . . . . Endangered
Listed . . . . September 20, 1991
Family . . . . Asteraceae (Sunflower)
Description . . . . . . Tall shrub with leaves near the ends of branches and clusters of yellow flower heads.
Habitat . . . . Ridges and stream banks.
Threats . . . . Low numbers, alien plant species.
Region 1 . . . . Hawaii (Kauai)

Description

Dubautia pauciflorula is a shrub in the aster family that grows to a height of 3 meters (10 ft). The opposite leaves, which are clustered near the ends of the branches, are narrowly oblanceolate and from 8 to 21 centimeters (3 to 8 in) long. In August and September, 50 to 500 flower heads, each composed of two to four yellow florets, occur in a cluster. The stems and the bracts of the flower heads are often purple.

Habitat

This species grows on ridges and along a stream bank in the Wahiawa drainage basin on the southern part of the island of Kauai, Hawaii. Kauai has the largest number of endemic plants of all the islands, and the Wahiawa Mountain area is one of the oldest and most diverse montane wet forests in Hawaii. This area, which covers about 1,200 acres, is roughly triangular in shape, with Kapalaoa, Mt. Kahili, and Puuauuka forming the corners. Elevations range from 610 meters (2,000 ft) to 1,000 meters (3,300 ft).

In addition to *Dubautia pauciflorula*, four other plant species endemic to the Wahiawa Stream drainage basin are listed as Endangered: *Cyanea undulata*, *Hesperomannia lydgatei*, kamakahala (*Labordia lydgatei*), and *Viola helenae*. Another 18 extremely rare plant species are also found in this area.

Historic Range

Dubautia pauciflorula was collected in 1909 from a ridge above a tributary to the Wahiawa Stream. There were no subsequent collections until the species was rediscovered in 1979 in the same area. The species is unknown outside the Wahiawa Basin.

Current Distribution

The population rediscovered in 1979 consists of about 30 plants. Two additional populations have been subsequently discovered, one on the Mt. Kahili Ridge consisting of three plants and another small population along the east fork of Wahiawa Stream. The land is owned by a corporation which manages it to preserve the quality of the area's water for agricultural irrigation.

Conservation and Recovery

The main threats to *Dubautia pauciflorula* are the species' low numbers and competition from invasive plant species. With so few surviving plants and a very limited distribution, *Dubautia pauciflorula* is vulnerable to extinction. An unpredictable human or natural event could easily destroy these plants. Although the Wahiawa drainage has been largely undisturbed, invasive plants are now spreading upstream. Strawberry guava (*Psidium cattleianum*) and melastoma (*Melastoma candidum*) are aggressive species that outcompete native species. These species gained a foothold in the basin in 1982 when Typhoon Iwa opened sections of the forest canopy. This invasion is assisted by feral pigs which transport seed and open additional ground

by rooting. Although there are only slight indications of pig activity in the basin, any increase could quickly help spread invading plants.

Additional Sources

Carr, G. D. 1985. "Monograph of the Hawaiian *Madiinae* (Asteraceae): *Argyroxiphium, Daubautia,* and *Wilkesia.*" *Allertonia* 4:1-123.

Cuddihy, L. W., and C. P. Stone. 1990. *Alteration of Native Hawaiian Vegetation: Effects of Humans, Their Activities and Introductions.* Cooperative National Park Resources Study Unit, University of Hawaii Press, Honolulu.

Culliney, J. L. 1988. *Islands in a Far Sea: Nature and Man in Hawaii.* Sierra Club Books, San Francisco.

Stone, C. P., and J. M. Scott, eds. 1985. *Hawai'i's Terrestrial Ecosystems: Preservation and Management.* Cooperative National Park Resources Study Unit, University of Hawaii Press, Honolulu.

St. John, H., and G. D. Carr. 1981. "Two New Species of *Dubautia* (Compositae) from Kauai." *Bulletin of the Torrey Botanical Club* 108:198-204.

Wagner, W. L., D. R. Herbst, and S. H. Sohmer. 1990. *Manual of the Flowering Plants of Hawai'i.* University of Hawaii Press and Bishop Museum Press, Honolulu.

Contacts

Regional Office of Endangered Species
U.S. Fish and Wildlife Service
Eastside Federal Complex
911 N.S. 11th Avenue
Portland, Oregon 97232-4181

Derral R. Herbst
U.S. Fish and Wildlife Service
300 Ala Moana Boulevard, Room 6307
P.O. Box 50167
Honolulu, Hawaii 96850

Kern Mallow
Eremalche kernensis

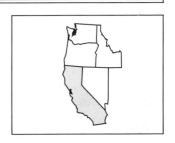

Marianne Austin-McDermon   *Color Plate C-5*

Status	Endangered
Listed	July 19, 1990
Family	Malvaceae (Mallow)
Description	Low-growing annual with white, pink, or lavender flowers.
Habitat	Valley saltbush scrub.
Threats	Conversion of habitat to cropland, oil and gas development, livestock grazing.
Region 1	California

Description

Kern mallow is a small annual that produces a stem 5 to 10 centimeters (2 to 4 in) in height. It bears white or rose-pink to lavender flowers, which resemble hollyhocks. It is distinguished from other species of *Eremalche* by its leaf shape, the type and density of it hairs, color spots on the petals, and the number of seed-bearing structures (carpels). The species has also been known by the name *Malvastrum kernensis*.

Habitat

Kern mallow is endemic to the valley saltbush scrubland at the eastern base of the Temblor Range in Kern County, California. Alien grasses, introduced during the time of the Franciscan missionaries, outcompeted native plant species and came to dominate California valley grasslands. Kern mallow occupies sites with reduced grass cover, such as valley saltbush scrub, a habitat dominated by alkalitolerant species of the Chenopodiaceae (goosefoot) family, including iodinebush (*Allenrolfea occidentalis*) and sea-blight (*Suaeda* spp.). This habitat occurs on gently rolling hills and supports an understory of annual herbs. Three other San Joaquin Valley plants, also listed as Threatened or Endangered, occur in the same habitat: California jewelflower (*Caulanthus californicus*), San Joaquin wooly-threads (*Lem-*

bertia congdonii), and Hoover's wooly-star (*Eriastrum hooveri*).

Historic Range

Kern mallow was first collected in 1937 in the Temblor Valley northwest of McKittrick. It has been found at only six sites in western Kern County. It is no longer found at the site of its discovery or at another site five miles north of Lost Hills.

Current Distribution

Three of the four remaining populations of Kern mallow occur on private land near the South Belridge and Cymric oil fields. One population is on federal land managed by the Bureau of Land Management north of McKittrick.

Conservation and Recovery

Oil and gas exploration destroyed the first known population of Kern mallow; conversion of land to agricultural production is responsible for the loss of the population north of Lost Hills. Remaining populations are near active oil and gas fields and are vulnerable to further development. All surviving populations are in areas grazed by sheep during the winter and spring. If this grazing becomes heavy and is not controlled it would adversely affect the remaining Kern mallow populations.

Additional Sources

Brown, D. E. 1982. "Californian Valley Grassland." *Desert Plants* 4:132-135.

Heady, H. F. 1977. "Valley Grassland." In *Terrestrial Vegetation of California*, edited by M. G. Barbour, and J. Major. John Wiley and Sons, New York.

Hoover, R. F. 1970. *The Vascular Plants of San Luis Obispo County, California*. University of California Press, Berkeley.

McNaughton, S. J. 1968. "Structure and Function in California Grasslands." *Ecology* 49:962-972.

Ornduff, R. 1974. *An Introduction to California Plant Life*. University of California Press, Berkeley.

Taylor, D. W., and W. B. Davilla. 1986. "Status Survey of Three Plants Endemic to the San Joaquin Valley." U.S. Fish and Wildlife Service, Sacramento.

Wester, L. 1981. "Composition of Native Grasslands in the San Joaquin Valley, California." *Madroño* 28:231-241.

Contacts

Regional Office of Endangered Species
U.S. Fish and Wildlife Service
Eastside Federal Complex
911 N.S. 11th Avenue
Portland, Oregon 97232-4181

Jim A. Bartel
U.S. Fish and Wildlife Service
2800 Cottage Way, Room E-1823
Sacramento, California 95825

Hoover's Wooly-Star
Eriastrum hooveri

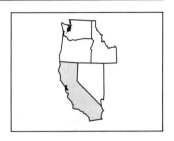

Marianne Austin-McDermon

Status . . . . Threatened
Listed . . . . July 19, 1990
Family . . . . Polemoniaceae (Phlox)
Description . . . . . . Annual with fuzzy, wiry
stems and small, white
flowers.
Habitat . . . . Valley and foothill scrub.
Threats . . . . Oil and gas development,
conversion to cropland,
urbanization, livestock
grazing.
Region 1 . . . . California

Description

Hoover's wooly-star is a small annual of the phlox family that grows to a height of 5 to 7.5 centimeters (2 to 3 in). It has numerous grayish, fuzzy, wire-like branches and bears small, white flowers, 6 millimeters (0.25 in) across. It is distinguished from other species of *Eriastrum* primarily by its flower size and measurements of the flower parts. It has also been known by the name *Huegelia hooveri*.

Habitat

Hoover's wooly-star is endemic to the grassland and adjacent plant communities of California's southern San Joaquin Val-

ley (known as the Tulare Lake Basin) and nearby foothills and valleys. This area lies roughly between Fresno and Bakersfield. Alien grasses, introduced during the time of the Franciscan missionaries, outcompeted native plant species and came to dominate the grasslands. Hoover's wooly-star now occupies sites with reduced grass cover in two native plant communities: valley sink scrub and valley saltbush scrub. Both of these communities are dominated by alkali-tolerant species of the Chenopodiaceae (goosefoot) family, such as iodinebush (*Allenrolfea occidentalis*) and sea-blight (*Suaeda* spp.). Valley sink scrub occurs on the margins of playas and on the heavy clay soils of the valley and produces only a sparse understory. The valley salt-bush scrub community is found on rolling hills in sandy to loamy soils and supports a denser understory. Three other San Joaquin Valley plants, also listed as Threatened or Endangered, occur in the same habitats: Kern mallow (*Eremalche kernensis*), California jewelflower (*Caulanthus californicus*), and San Joaquin wooly-threads (*Lembertia congdonii*).

Historic Range

Hoover's wooly-star was first collected near Little Panoche Creek in Fresno County in 1935. Populations have since been documented at 130 sites in four counties: Fresno, Kern, San Luis Obispo, and Santa Barbara. The species was distributed in the Temblor Range, the Cuyama Valley, and locally in the San Joaquin Valley from Fresno south.

Current Distribution

This species now occurs at 118 sites, nine of which are either in preserves, such as the Paul Paine Preserve or the Alkali Sink Ecological Preserve, or are located in undeveloped foothills. In the Elk Hills area, 33 populations occur on the Naval Petroleum Reserve, managed by the Department of Energy, and six populations occur on land managed by the Bureau of Land Management (BLM). About 40 sites in this area are on private land. On the valley floor about 25 populations are on privately owned land. Most of these sites contain from 5 to 1,000 plants, although some populations consist of up to 40,000 plants.

Conservation and Recovery

The main threats to Hoover's wooly-star are oil and gas development, habitat con-version to cropland, and urbanization. Populations on undeveloped foothills are also threatened by livestock grazing. Although Hoover's wooly-star exists at over 100 sites, some of which contain many thousands of plants, fewer than 10 populations are considered safe. At least 70 sites are directly threatened by oil and gas development, half of them on federal land managed by the Energy Department or BLM. The Energy Department has implemented policies to protect Hoover's wooly-star populations on land under its control and BLM is expected to consult with the Fish and Wildlife Service to avoid damage to the plant. Populations that occur on private land on the valley floor are in danger of being converted to cropland or urban use.

In addition, one large population along Warthan Creek in Fresno County is threatened by a proposed reservoir, as part of the Arroyo Pasajero Project.

Additional Sources

Hoover, R. F. 1970. *The Vascular Plants of San Luis Obispo County, California.* University of California Press, Berkeley.

Taylor, D. W., and W. B. Davilla. 1986. "Status Survey of Three Plants Endemic to the San Joaquin Valley." U.S. Fish and Wildlife Service, Sacramento.

Contacts

Regional Office of Endangered Species
U.S. Fish and Wildlife Service
Eastside Federal Complex
911 N.S. 11th Avenue
Portland, Oregon 97232-4181

Jim A. Bartel
U.S. Fish and Wildlife Service
2800 Cottage Way, Room E-1823
Sacramento, California 95825

Gahnia lanaiensis
No Common Name

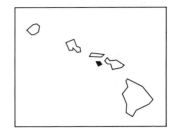

Joel Lau

Status	Endangered
Listed	September 20, 1991
Family	Cyperaceae (Sedge)
Description	Tall, grass-like sedge with solid stems and spirally arranged flowers.
Habitat	Lowland wet forest.
Threats	Low numbers, tourist deveіopment, alien plant species.
Region 1	Hawaii (Lanai)

Description

Gahnia lanaiensis is a tall grass-like member of the sedge family that grows 1.5 to 3 meters (5 to 10 ft) tall. Plants are tufted and grow in clumps. They have spirally arranged flowers, solid stems, and numerous, three-ranked leaves. The seed-like fruits are purplish black when mature.

Habitat

This species grows on the summit of the Lanaihale Ridge on the island of Lanai, Hawaii. A broad ridge runs northwest to southeast across this small island and is commonly known by the name of its highest peak, Lanaihale, which is 1,027 meters (3,370 ft) high. A lowland wet forest plant community is found on the Lanaihale summit and its narrow valleys. Although annual rainfall is only about 94 centimeters (37 in), the area is usually cloud-covered in the afternoon and shrouded in fog at night. Dominant members of the plant community are ohia (*Metrosideros polymorpha*) and uluhe fern (*Dicranopteris linearis*). Three other Endangered plant species, *Cyanea macrostegia* var. *gibsonii*, *Phyllostegia glabra* var. *lanaiensis*, and *Viola lanaiensis*, are also found in this lowland wet forest. A lowland dry shrubland plant community occurs on the leeward slopes and valleys of Lanaihale. This community supports two plant species federally listed as Endangered: *Abutilon eremitopetalum* and *Tetramolopium remyi*. All of these Endangered plant species are endemic to Lanaihale.

Historic Range

Gahnia lanaiensis was first collected in 1964 in a shrubby rainforest east of Munro Trail and north of Lanaihale. It has not been found at any other location.

Current Distribution

The only known population of *Gahnia lanaiensis* is at the site of its first collection. About 15 clumps grow in an area of less than a mile at an altitude of about 1,000 meters (3,200 ft).

Conservation and Recovery

The main threat to *Gahnia lanaiensis* is the species' small population and extremely limited range. With only a very few plants in existence, *Gahnia lanaiensis* is vulnerable to extinction through an unpredictable human or natural event.

In addition the species faces a potential threat from an invasive exotic tree, manuka (*Leptospermum scoparium*). This species is spreading along Lanaihale but has not yet reached the area where *Gahnia lanaiensis* occurs. Plans to develop the island's tourist industry are a long-term threat because the Munro Trail, which runs across Lanaihale, affords a scenic view of the island and is likely to be popular with tourists. This may have a harmful effect on *Gahnia lanaiensis* since about a third of the known plants grow along the trail.

Additional Sources

Cuddihy, L. W., and C. P. Stone. 1990. *Alteration of Native Hawaiian Vegetation: Effects of Humans, Their Activities and Introductions.* University of Hawaii Cooperative National Park Resources Study Unit, Honolulu.

Culliney, J. L. 1988. *Islands in a Far Sea: Nature and Man in Hawaii.* Sierra Club Books, San Francisco.

Koyama, Tetsuo. 1990. "Cyperaceae." In *Manual of the Flowering Plants of Hawai'i*, by W. L. Wagner, D. R. Herbst, and S. H. Sohmer. University of Hawaii Press and Bishop Museum Press, Honolulu.

Contacts

Regional Office of Endangered Species
U.S. Fish and Wildlife Service
Eastside Federal Complex
911 N.S. 11th Avenue
Portland, Oregon 97232-4181

Derral R. Herbst
U.S. Fish and Wildlife Service
300 Ala Moana Boulevard, Room 6307
P.O. Box 50167
Honolulu, Hawaii 96850

Spreading Avens
Geum radiatum

Jessie M. Harris

Status	Endangered
Listed	April 5, 1990
Family	Rosaceae (Rose)
Description	Perennial with a basal rosette of leaves and a cluster of bright yellow, radial flowers.
Habitat	Steep mountaintop slopes and cliffs.
Threats	Hikers, recreational and residential development.
Region 4	North Carolina, Tennessee

Description

Spreading avens is a perennial in the rose family that grows to a height of 20 to 50 centimeters (8 to 20 in). It has a basal rosette of leaves that arise from a horizontal rhizome. The leaves have a large terminal lobe and small laterals. From June through September it produces a cluster of bright yellow, five-petaled, radial flowers. From August through October it produces hemispheric fruits composed of hairy seeds. This species is distinguished from other species of southeastern *Geum* by its large, yellow flowers and leaf shape.

Habitat

Spreading avens is endemic to mountaintop sites in western North Carolina and eastern Tennessee. It is an early successional plant that grows in shallow, acidic soils on sunny slopes, cliffs, and rock outcrops.

Associated species include sand myrtle (*Leiophyllum buxifolium*), minnie-bush (*Menziesia pilosa*), Catawba rhododendron (*Rhododendron catawbiense*), asters, sedges, goldenrod, alumroot (*Heuchera villosa*), mountain saxifrage (*Saxifraga michauxii*), and various grasses. On some sites it occurs along with Heller's blazing star (*Liatris helleri*) and Blue Ridge goldenrod (*Solidago spithamaea*), which are listed as Threatened. It also sometimes occurs with Roan Mountain bluet (*Hedyotis purpurea* var. *montana*), which is listed as Endangered. Surrounding coniferous forest is dominated by red spruce (*Picea rubens*) and Fraser fir (*Abies fraseri*), a candidate for federal listing.

Historic Range

The species was described in 1803 from specimens collected in North Carolina. Sixteen populations have been reported in North Carolina and Tennessee, five of which no longer exist.

Current Distribution

Eleven populations of spreading avens survive, mostly in North Carolina. Three are located in Ashe County, North Carolina, and one each is found in Avery, Buncombe, Transylvania, Watauga, and Yancey counties, North Carolina, and Sevier County, Tennessee. The other two populations are on the Mitchell County, North Carolina/Carter County, Tennessee, line and the Avery/Watauga County line in North Carolina.

Four of these populations are on federal land managed by the Forest Service and Park Service, and one is on North Carolina state park land. The remaining six populations are on privately owned land.

Most populations consist of a small number of plants in a very limited area. Seven of the remaining sites consist of fewer than 50 plants, with three of these having fewer than 10 plants. One site on Forest Service land supports 73 percent of the known species population.

Conservation and Recovery

The main threats to spreading avens are habitat disturbance by hikers and recreational and residential development. Five of the remaining populations are on public land that is heavily used by hikers, rock climbers, and sightseers. Of the six pri-

vately owned sites, one has been developed as a commercial recreational facility and another is currently being developed as a ski resort. The area where the other four privately owned sites are located is being rapidly developed as a tourist center. The construction of recreational facilities such as roads, trails, parking lots, and buildings has probably destroyed local populations and, if the presence of spreading avens is not taken into account in planning, will no doubt destroy more.

Spreading avens faces additional long-term threats from natural processes. As an early successional plant, it is susceptible to invasion by shrubs and trees, which could shade out remaining populations. In addition, the surrounding high elevation forest is suffering a drastic decline caused by air pollution and the invasion of an exotic insect, the balsam wooly aphid. The loss of these forests might allow the habitat to become too arid to support healthy, reproducing spreading avens populations.

Additional Source

Massey, J., P. Whitson, and T. Atkinson. 1980. "Endangered and Threatened Plant Survey of Twelve Species in the Eastern Part of Region Four." U.S. Fish and Wildlife Service.

Contacts

Regional Office of Endangered Species
U. S. Fish and Wildlife Service
Richard B. Russell Federal Building
75 Spring Street, S.W.
Atlanta, Georgia 30303

Nora Murdock
U.S. Fish and Wildlife Service
330 Ridgefield Court
Asheville, North Carolina 28806

Gouania meyenii
No Common Name

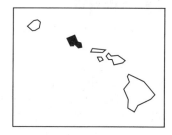

John Obata

Status . . . . Endangered
Listed . . . . October 29, 1991
Family . . . . Rhamnaceae (Buckthorn)
Description . . . . . . Shrub with papery, oval, untoothed leaves and clusters of small, white flowers.
Habitat . . . . Rocky slopes, ridges, and cliffs in dry shrubland.
Threats . . . . Alien plant species, low numbers.
Region 1 . . . . Hawaii (Oahu)

Description

Gouania meyenii is a shrub of the buckthorn family that grows to a height of 2.2 meters (7 ft). The oval leaves are untoothed, 3 to 7 centimeters (1.2 to 2.8 in) long, and papery in texture. Small white flowers appear in clusters arising from the leaf axils. The smooth fruits are winged.

This species has also been known as *Gouania integrifolia, G. orbicularis, G. oliveri,* and *G. gagnei.* Three species of *Gouania* have been known from Hawaii. *G. hillebrandi,* which is found on Maui, was listed as Endangered in 1984. *G. vitifolia* has only been collected seven times. In 1932 it was believed to be on the verge of extinction, and today it is probably extinct.

Habitat

Gouania meyenii is found only in the Waianae Mountain Range on the western side of the island of Oahu, Hawaii. This island is dominated by the remnants of two ancient volcanoes that have eroded into two "mountain ranges" that consist of long, narrow ridges. The Waianae Range lies on the western side of the island, while the Koolau Range traverses the eastern side. The Waianae Mountains, which run northwest to southeast for about 40 miles, lie in the rain shadow of the Koolau Range, and, except for the summit of Mt. Kaala, which is the highest point on Oahu, receive much less rainfall.

A variety of plant habitats are found in

the Waianae Mountains, ranging from coastal dry shrubland to lowland dry forest to lowland wet forest. *Gouania meyenii* is found in dry shrubland on rocky ledges and cliff faces at an elevation of 580 to 820 meters (1,900 to 2,700 ft). Associated plants include 'a'ali'i (*Dodonaea viscosa*), lama (*Diospyros sandwicensis*), kolokolo kuahiwi (*Lysimachia hillebrandii*) and kolomona (*Senna gaudichaudii*).

The diverse habitats of the Waianae Mountains contain a large number of vulnerable native Hawaiian plant species. In October 1991 the Fish and Wildlife Service (FWS) listed *Gouania meyenii* and 25 other plant species from Oahu's Waianae Mountains as Endangered.

This group listing was the result of the settlement of a 1989 lawsuit brought against the FWS by the Sierra Club Legal Defense Fund on behalf of a Hawaii conservation group. The terms of the settlement called for the proposed listing before October 1992 of 186 Hawaiian candidate plant species.

Historic Range

Gouania meyenii was first collected in 1831 from the Waianae Mountains. It has been known from the central and southern portions of the mountain range, from Kamaileunu Ridge to Honouliuli.

Current Distribution

The species is now found only Kamaileunu Ridge and Makaha-Waianae Kai Ridge. Four known populations, totaling about 75 plants, occur over a square mile of state land.

Conservation and Recovery

The main threat to *Gouania meyenii* is competition from alien plant species. Christmasberry (*Schinus terebinthifolius*), an aggressive tree introduced to Hawaii before 1911, forms dense thickets and may also release chemicals that inhibit the growth of other species. Strawberry guava (*Psidium cattleianum*) is an invasive tree that forms dense stands that exclude other species. Molasses grass (*Melinus minutiflora*) grows in dense mats that smother native vegetation. It is also fire adapted and provides a fuel for spreading wildfires.

Gouania meyenii populations lie near the U.S. Army's Makua Military Reservation and Schofield Barracks. Within a 14-month period from 1989 to 1990, 10 fires resulted from weapons practice on the reservation. In order to minimize fire damage, the army has constructed firebreaks between the target areas and the surrounding forest.

With a total known species population of only 75 plants in a very limited range, *Gouania meyenii* is also vulnerable to extinction through unpredictable human or natural events.

Additional Source

Stone, C. P., and J. M. Scott, eds. 1985. *Hawai'i's Terrestrial Ecosystems: Preservation and Management.* Cooperative National Park Resources Study Unit, University of Hawaii Press, Honolulu.

Contact

Derral R. Herbst
U.S. Fish and Wildlife Service
300 Ala Moana Boulevard, Room 6307
P.O. Box 50167
Honolulu, Hawaii 96850

Higo Chumbo
Harrisia portoricensis

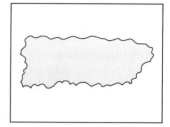

Robert Ross

Status	Threatened
Listed	August 8, 1990
Family	Cactaceae (Cactus)
Description	Slender, spined, columnar cactus, with night-blooming greenish-white flowers.
Habitat	Dry forests.
Threats	Limited range, feral pigs and goats, development.
Region 4	Puerto Rico

Description

Higo chumbo is a slender, columnar cactus, usually unbranched, which grows to a height of 2 meters (6 ft). It can reach 7 centimeters (3 in) in diameter and has from 8 to 11 ribs. The spines, which are from 2 to 9 centimeters (1 to 3 in) long, occur in groups about 2 centimeters (0.7 in) apart. The large, greenish-white flowers are funnel shaped and open at night. The fruit is a round, spineless, yellow berry containing black seeds surrounded by a white pulp. Fruit of higo chumbo are the preferred food of the Endangered yellow-shouldered blackbird (*Agelaius xanthomus*) on the island of Mona. The species has also been known by the name *Cereus portoricensis*.

Habitat

Higo chumbo grows in semi-open dry forests on islands composed of carbonate rock, limestone, dolomite, and reef rock. Rainfall on these islands is only 80 centimeters (31 in) per year.

Historic Range

The species was first collected in 1908 in southern Puerto Rico, west of Ponce. It was also found on three islands off the west coast of Puerto Rico: Mona, Monito, and Desecheo.

Current Distribution

Development has extirpated higo chumbo from the mainland and it is now found only on the three small islands.

Conservation and Recovery

Mona and Monito islands are managed by the commonwealth Department of Natural Resources as wildlife reserves. Mona, which has the vast majority of cactus habitat, is also the home of the Endangered yellow-shouldered blackbird (*Agelaius xanthomus*) and two Threatened species, the Mona ground iguana (*Cyclura stegnegeri*) and the Mona boa (*Epicrates m. monensis*). The principal threat to higo chumbo on Mona is the island's potential for development. In the past there have been proposals to use the island as a superport and oil storage facility, and as a prison. Monito Island is also the habitat of the Endangered Monito gecko (*Sphaerodactylus micropithecus*). Desecheo is protected as a National Wildlife Refuge. However, feral pigs and goats on Desecheo and Mona threaten native vegetation, including higo chumbo. All three islands have been used by the U.S. Navy in the past as bombing ranges.

Additional Sources

Liogier, H. A., and L. F. Martorell. 1982. *Flora of Puerto Rico and Adjacent Islands: A Systematic Synopsis*. University of Puerto Rico Press, Río Piedras.

Vivaldi, J. L., and R. O. Woodbury. 1981. "Status Report on *Harrisia portoricensis* Britton." U.S. Fish and Wildlife Service, Atlanta.

Woodbury, R. C., L. F. Martorell, and J. G. García-Turduri. 1977. *The Flora of Mona and Monito Islands, Puerto Rico (West Indies)*.

Bulletin 252, Agricultural Experiment Station, University of Puerto Rico, Mayaguez.

Contacts

Regional Office of Endangered Species
U. S. Fish and Wildlife Service
Richard B. Russell Federal Building
75 Spring Street, S.W.
Atlanta, Georgia 30303

Susan Silander
U.S. Fish and Wildlife Service
P.O. Box 491
Boquerón, Puerto Rico 00622

Hedyotis degeneri
No Common Name

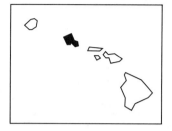

Status	Endangered
Listed	October 29, 1991
Family	Rubiaceae (Coffee)
Description	Prostrate, branched shrub with a peeling, corky bark and clusters of tubular flowers.
Habitat	Moist forest.
Threats	Feral pigs, alien plant species, low numbers.
Region 1	Hawaii (Oahu)

No illustration of this species is available.

Description

Hedyotis degeneri is a prostrate, branching shrub of the coffee family that has a four-sided stem and a peeling, corky bark. Leaf shapes are variable, ranging from long and thin to heart-shaped. Leafy shoots sprout from the leaf axils. Clusters of up to 10 flowers appear at the ends of the stems. The flower petals are fused into a trumpet-shaped tube about 7 millimeters (0.3 in) long ending in four or five lobes. The fruits are round capsules containing dark angled seeds.

Two varieties of *Hedyotis degeneri* are recognized: var. *degeneri*, which is the typical variety, and var. *coprosmifolia*, which has narrower leaves. A photograph or illustra-tion of *Hedyotis degeneri* could not be obtained. It is sufficiently different from other members of its genus that an illustration of a closely-related species would be misleading.

Habitat

Hedyotis degeneri is found only in the Waianae Mountain Range on the western side of the island of Oahu, Hawaii. This island is dominated by the remnants of two ancient volcanoes that have eroded into two "mountain ranges," which consist of long, narrow ridges. The Waianae Range lies on the western side of the island, while the Koolau Range traverses the eastern side. The Waianae Range, which runs northwest to southeast for about 40 miles, lies in the rain shadow of the Koolau Range, and, except for the summit of Mt. Kaala, the highest point on the island, receives much less rainfall..

A variety of plant habitats are found in the Waianae Mountains, ranging from coastal dry shrubland to lowland dry forest to lowland wet forest. *Hedyotis degeneri* is found in diverse moist forest at an elevation of 820 meters (2,700 ft). Associated plants include ohia (*Metrosideros polymorpha*) and manono (*Hedyotis terminalis*).

The diverse habitats of the Waianae Mountains contain a large number of vulnerable native Hawaiian plant species. In October 1991 the Fish and Wildlife Service (FWS) listed *Hedyotis degeneri* and 25 other plant species from Oahu's Waianae Mountains as Endangered. This group listing was the result of the settlement of a 1989 lawsuit brought against the FWS by the Sierra Club Legal Defense Fund on behalf of a Hawaii conservation group. The terms of the settlement called for the proposed listing before October 1992 of 186 Hawaiian candidate plant species.

Historic Range

Hedyotis degeneri was first described in 1943. It has been found only in the Waianae Mountains of Oahu, on Mt. Kaala, and Kamaileunu Ridge.

Current Distribution

The species survives in a single small population of six plants on state land on Kamaileunu Ridge.

Conservation and Recovery

The main threats to *Hedyotis degeneri,* as to most of the rare plant species of the Waianae Mountains, are habitat degradation by feral pigs and competition from aggressive alien plant species.

Feral pigs, which are managed by the state as game animals, have been in the Waianae Mountains for about 150 years and have had a major effect on the native flora. Their rooting destroys plants and opens the habitat to invasive species. They also help spread these alien plants by carrying seed on their bodies and in their feces.

Hedyotis degeneri is directly threatened by several non-native species. Christmasberry (*Schinus terebinthifolius*), an aggressive tree introduced to Hawaii before 1911, forms dense thickets and may also release chemicals that inhibit the growth of other species. Molasses grass (*Melinus minutiflora*) grows in dense mats that smother native vegetation. Strawberry guava (*Psidium cattleianum*) is an invasive tree that forms dense stands that exclude other species.

In addition, with only six known surviving plants in a single population, *Hedyotis degeneri* is extremely vulnerable to extinction through unpredictable human or natural events.

Additional Source

Wagner, W. L., D. R. Herbst, and S. H. Sohmer. 1990. *Manual of the Flowering Plants of Hawai'i*. University of Hawaii Press and Bishop Museum Press, Honolulu.

Contact

Derral R. Herbst
U.S. Fish and Wildlife Service
300 Ala Moana Boulevard, Room 6307
P.O. Box 50167
Honolulu, Hawaii 96850

Hedyotis parvula
No Common Name

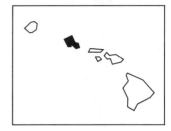

John Obata

Status	Endangered
Listed	October 29, 1991
Family	Rubiaceae (Coffee)
Description	Branched shrub with leathery leaves and tubular white flowers, tipped with pink.
Habitat	Dry cliff bases and ledges.
Threats	Feral pigs, alien plant species, low numbers.
Region 1	Hawaii (Oahu)

Description

Hedyotis parvula is an erect or sprawling, branched shrub of the coffee family with stems up to 30 centimeters (12 in) long. The short, leathery leaves (4 cm; 1.6 in) are uniform in size along the stem. The white flowers consist of a funnel-shaped tube about 1 centimeter (0.4 in) long with purplish pink-tipped lobes. The fruit is a round capsule that contains angled, brown seeds. The species has also been known by the name *Kadua parvula*.

Habitat

Hedyotis parvula is found only in the Waianae Mountain Range on the western side of the island of Oahu, Hawaii. This island is dominated by the remnants of two ancient volcanoes that have eroded into two "mountain ranges," which consist of long, narrow ridges. The Waianae Range lies on the western side of the island, while the Koolau Range traverses the eastern side. The Waianae Range, which runs northwest to southeast for about 40 miles, lies in the rain shadow of the Koolau Range, and, except for the summit of Mt. Kaala, the highest point on the island, receives much less rainfall.

A variety of plant habitats are found in the Waianae Mountains, ranging from coastal dry shrubland to lowland dry forest to lowland wet forest. *Hedyotis parvula* grows in dry habitat on rock outcrops, ledges, and at the bases of cliff faces. Associated plants include 'a'ali'i (*Dodonaea viscosa*), alahe'e (*Canthium odoratum*), and 'ala'ala wai nui or spurflower (*Plectranthus parviflorus*).

The diverse habitats of the Waianae Mountains contain a large number of rare native Hawaiian plant species. In October 1991 the Fish and Wildlife Service (FWS) listed *Hedyotis parvula* and 25 other plant species from Oahu's Waianae Mountains as Endangered. This group listing was the result of the settlement of a 1989 lawsuit brought against the FWS by the Sierra Club Legal Defense Fund on behalf of a Hawaii conservation group. The terms of the settlement called for the proposed listing before October 1992 of 186 Hawaiian candidate plant species.

Historic Range

Hedyotis parvula is known from the central and southern Waianae Mountains on Oahu, from Makaleha Valley to Nanakuli Valley. It has not been found anywhere else.

Current Distribution

This species was found in 1976 on Makua-Keaau Ridge and in 1986 on Makaleha Ridge. No plants have been seen for several years. However, since this species grows on inaccessible cliffs, botanists are hopeful that new populations will eventually be discovered.

Conservation and Recovery

Any surviving *Hedyotis parvula* plants are threatened by habitat degradation by feral pigs and competition with aggressive non-native plant species.

Feral pigs, which are managed by the state as game animals, have been in the Waianae Mountains for about 150 years and have had a major effect on the native flora. Their rooting destroys plants and opens the habitat to invasive species. They also help spread these alien plants by carrying seed on their bodies and in their feces.

Two non-native species are colonizing the area where *Hedyotis parvula* is believed to survive. Christmasberry (*Schinus terebinthifolius*), an aggressive tree introduced to Hawaii before 1911, forms dense thickets and may also release chemicals that inhibit the growth of other species. Molasses grass (*Melinus minutiflora*), which ranges from the dry lowlands to the lower wet forests of the leeward ridges, grows in dense mats that smother native vegetation.

Any surviving plants are extremely vulnerable to extinction through unpredictible human or natural events.

Additional Sources

Cuddihy, L. W., and C. P. Stone. 1990. *Alteration of Native Hawaiian Vegetation: Effects of Humans, Their Activities and Introductions.* Cooperative National Park Resources Study Unit, University of Hawaii Press, Honolulu.

Stone, C. P., and J. M. Scott, eds. 1985. *Hawai'i's Terrestrial Ecosystems: Preservation and Management.* Cooperative National Park Resources Study Unit, University of Hawaii Press, Honolulu.

Contact

Derral R. Herbst
U.S. Fish and Wildlife Service
300 Ala Moana Boulevard, Room 6307
P.O. Box 50167
Honolulu, Hawaii 96850

Roan Mountain Bluet
Hedyotis purpurea var. *montana*

Paul Somers *Color Plate C-1*

Status	Endangered
Listed	April 5, 1990
Family	Rubiaceae (Coffee)
Description	Low-growing perennial with clusters of bright purple flowers.
Habitat	Steep mountaintop slopes and cliffs.
Threats	Hikers, recreational and residential development.
Region 4	North Carolina, Tennessee

Description

Roan Mountain bluet is a low-growing perennial with square, narrowly winged stems, which form loose tufts 10 to 15 centimeters (4 to 6 in) tall. The untoothed leaves are arranged in opposite pairs. Terminal clusters of bright, four-petaled, purple flowers appear in July and early August. The species has also been known by the names *Houstonia montana* and *Houstonia purpurea* var. *montana*.

Habitat

Roan Mountain bluet is endemic to mountaintop sites in western North Carolina and eastern Tennessee. It is an early successional plant that grows in shallow, acidic soils on sunny slopes, cliffs, and rock outcrops.

Associated species include sand myrtle (*Leiophyllum buxifolium*), minnie-bush (*Menziesia pilosa*), Catawba rhododendron (*Rhododendron catawbiense*), asters, sedges, goldenrod, alumroot (*Heuchera villosa*), mountain saxifrage (*Saxifraga michauxii*), and various grasses. On some sites it occurs along with spreading avens (*Geum radiatum*), which is federally listed as Endangered. It is also found with Heller's blazing star (*Liatris helleri*), and Blue Ridge goldenrod (*Solidago spithamaea*), which are listed as Threatened. Surrounding coniferous forest is dominated by red spruce

(*Picea rubens*) and Fraser fir (*Abies fraseri*), a candidate for federal listing.

Historic Range

Roan Mountain bluet was first described in 1903 from specimens collected on Roan Mountain in North Carolina and Tennessee. Only seven populations have been found, six of which still exist.

Current Distribution

Two populations of Roan Mountain bluet are found at the juncture of Avery and Watauga counties, North Carolina; one is at the boundary of Mitchell and Avery counties, North Carolina, and Carter County, Tennessee; two are in Ashe County, North Carolina, and one is in Watauga County, North Carolina.

The surviving populations are small and vulnerable. One site located on Forest Service land contains 41 percent of the known species population.

Conservation and Recovery

The main threats to the Roan Mountain bluet are habitat disturbance by hikers and recreational and residential development. The largest remaining population is on public land heavily used by hikers, rock climbers, and sightseers. Two populations are on sites that have been developed for commercial recreation. The construction of roads, trails, and parking lots threatens the remaining populations. The presence of Roan Mountain bluet needs to be taken into account when construction is planned.

Roan Mountain bluet faces additional long-term threats from natural processes. As an early successional plant, it is susceptible to invasion by shrubs and trees, which would shade out the remaining

populations. In addition, the surrounding high elevation forest is suffering a drastic decline caused by air pollution and the invasion of an exotic insect, the balsam wooly aphid. The loss of these forests might allow the habitat to become too arid to support healthy, reproducing Roan Mountain bluet populations.

Additional Sources

Kral, R. 1983. *A Report on Some Rare, Threatened, or Endangered Forest-related Vascular Plants of the South.* USDA, Forest Service, Technical Publication R8-TP2.

Massey, J., P. Whitson, and T. Atkinson. 1980. "Endangered and Threatened Plant Survey of Twelve Species in the Eastern Part of Region Four." U.S. Fish and Wildlife Service.

Contacts

Regional Office of Endangered Species
U. S. Fish and Wildlife Service
Richard B. Russell Federal Building
75 Spring Street, S.W.
Atlanta, Georgia 30303

Nora Murdock
U.S. Fish and Wildlife Service
330 Ridgefield Court
Asheville, North Carolina 28806

Na Pali Beach Hedyotis
Hedyotis st.-johnii

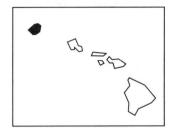

Yevonn Wilson-Ramsey from *Manual of the Flowering Plants of Hawai'i*

Status	Endangered
Listed	September 30, 1991
Family	Rubiaceae (Coffee)
Description	Succulent, slightly woody, trailing perennial, with clusters of green flowers.
Habitat	Sea cliffs.
Threats	Low numbers, feral goats.
Region 1	Hawaii (Kauai)

Description

Na Pali beach hedyotis is a succulent perennial with slightly woody trailing stems up to 30 centimeters (12 in) long. The glossy, dark green leaves, ovate to elliptic, 5.5 to 15 centimeters (2 to 6 in) long and about 5 centimeters (2 in) wide, are clustered near the base. The flowers are borne on stems 7 to 15 centimeters (3 to 6 in) long. What appear to be petals are enlarged, leafy sepals, which reach 11 millimeters (0.4 in) in length. The green petals are fused into an urn-shaped tube about 5 to 8 millimeters (0.2 to 0.3 in) wide. The fruit is a kidney-shaped capsule with dark angular seeds.

Habitat

This hedyotis species grows only on north-facing sea cliffs on the Na Pali Coast of the island of Kauai, Hawaii. It occurs within the spray zone, below about 75 meters (250 ft) elevation. Associated vegetation is sparse, dry coastal scrub; typical species are *Artemisia australis* and the invasive sourbush (*Pluchea symphytifolia*).

Historic Range

Na Pali beach hedyotis was first collected in 1947 from sea cliffs between Kalalau and Honopu valleys on Kauai. The species is only known from a 4.5-mile section of the Na Pali Coast: between Kalalau and

Honopu beaches, from Nualolo Valley, Nualolo Kai, and Milolii Beach. It was probably once more widespread but is now found almost entirely at sites inaccessible to feral goats.

Current Distribution

The species is found today at sites throughout its historic range. It is possible that it no longer occurs at Nualolo Kai, which has not been surveyed in over a decade. The total population is about 250 individual plants, all in the Na Pali Coast State Park.

Conservation and Recovery

The main factor in the decline of Na Pali beach hedyotis has been predation by feral goats. Surviving plants now occur only at sites inaccessible to the animals. About 1,600 goats inhabited the Na Pali Coast in 1982 and they remain abundant. One hedyotis population, behind Kalalau Beach, is still accessible to goats, which degrade the habitat in addition to consuming plants. While feeding, the goats trample the ground, preventing the establishment of new seedlings and clearing the ground for invasion by alien plants. Sourbush threatens some Na Pali beach hedyotis populations.

Because of low numbers, Na Pali beach hedyotis is threatened by catastrophic human or natural events, primarily landslides and wildfires. Recently, cliff vegetation near Honopu Beach was destroyed in a landslide. The amount of dry plant material on the cliffs and prevailing winds also leave the species vulnerable to fires that might originate at nearby recreational areas.

Additional Sources

Corn, C. A. 1984. "Na Pali Botanical Findings, July 16-21, 1984." Division of Forestry and Wildlife, Department of Land and natural Resources, Honolulu, Hawaii.

Cuddihy, L. W., and C. P. Stone. 1990. *Alteration of Native Hawaiian Vegetation: Effects of Humans, Their Activities and Introductions.* Cooperative National Park Resources Study Unit, University of Hawaii Press, Honolulu.

Culliney, J. L. 1988. *Islands in a Far Sea: Nature and Man in Hawaii.* Sierra Club Books, San Francisco.

Stone, B. C., and I. Lane. 1958. "A New *Hedyotis* from Kauai, Hawaiian Islands." *Pacific Science* 12:139-145.

Stone, C. P., and J. M. Scott, eds. 1985. *Hawai'i's Terrestrial Ecosystems: Preservation and Management.* Cooperative National Park Resources Study Unit, University of Hawaii Press, Honolulu.

Wagner, W. L., D. R. Herbst, and S. H. Sohmer. 1990. *Manual of the Flowering Plants of Hawai'i.* University of Hawaii Press and Bishop Museum Press, Honolulu.

Contacts

Regional Office of Endangered Species
U.S. Fish and Wildlife Service
Eastside Federal Complex
911 N.S. 11th Avenue
Portland, Oregon 97232-4181

Joan E. Canfield
U.S. Fish and Wildlife Service
300 Ala Moana Boulevard, Room 6307
P.O. Box 50167
Honolulu, Hawaii 96850

Schweinitz's Sunflower
Helianthus schweinitzii

Nora Murdock

Status	Endangered
Listed	May 7, 1991
Family	Asteraceae (Aster)
Description	Perennial with narrowly lanceolate leaves and yellow flower heads.
Habitat	Clearings, rights-of-way.
Threats	Maintenance activities.
Region 4	North Carolina, South Carolina

Description

Schweinitz's sunflower is a perennial in the aster family that grows from a cluster of carrot-like rhizomes to a height of between 1 and 2 meters (3.3 and 6.6 ft). The stems, which are often deep red, are usually solitary, branching only at mid-height. The narrowly lanceolate, usually untoothed, opposite leaves (becoming alternate on the upper stem) are about 18 centimeters (7 in) long and 2.5 centimeters (1 in) wide. The leaves are roughly hairy above; beneath they are resin-dotted and covered with soft white hairs. The yellow flower heads are about 5.5 centimeters (2 in) wide and bloom from September until the first frost.

This species is distinguished from certain sunflowers by the smaller size of the flower heads, leaf characteristics, and its tuberous root system.

Habitat

Schweinitz's sunflower grows in full sun or light shade in clearings and at forest edges. It is endemic to the piedmont region of the Carolinas, which in colonial times were unforested prairies. It occurs on sandy and gravelly clay and clay-loam soils. Since it cannot grow in shade, this sunflower requires periodic disturbance of its habitat to prevent vegetational succession. Historically the presence of bison and elk, as well as wildfires, provided this disturbance. Schweinitz's sunflower populations now occur mostly at sites that are periodically cleared such as roadsides and powerline cuts.

Historic Range

The species was described in 1841 from specimens collected in North Carolina. It has been found at 21 sites in North Carolina and South Carolina.

Current Distribution

Thirteen Schweinitz's sunflower populations survive in York County, South Carolina, and five North Carolina counties (Cabarrus, Mecklenburg, Rowan, Stanley, and Union). Five populations are along roadways maintained by the state in North Carolina, two are along South Carolina roads. One South Carolina population is on land managed by the Rock Hill Department of Parks, Recreation, and Tourism. Five populations are on privately owned land, usually near utility line rights-of-way.

Conservation and Recovery

About one-third of the known Schweinitz's sunflower populations have been destroyed since the species' discovery, mostly through land development and vegetative succession caused by fire suppression.

The remaining populations are primarily threatened by highway and right-of-way maintenance practices. Over the last three years declines ranging from 9 to 89 percent have been recorded for six of the remaining populations. Two populations have been lost since the species was proposed for listing in July 1990. Three populations

have shown increases of from 14 to 150 percent. The population showing the largest increase is located only a few feet from a paved road and is extremely vulnerable to maintenance activities. Although Schweinitz's sunflower requires the disturbance associated with maintenance activities to preserve its habitat, herbicides should not be used, and mowing must be timed so as not to interfere with seed dispersal. The Fish and Wildlife Service is working with agencies responsible for right-of-way maintenance to ensure the proper management of populations.

Additional Sources

Cronquist, A. 1980. *Vascular Flora of the Southeastern United States. Vol. I (Asteraceae).* University of North Carolina Press, Chapel Hill.

Kral, R. 1983. *A Report on Some Rare, Threatened, or Endangered Forest-related Vascular Plants of the South.* USDA Forest Service, Technical Publication R8-TP-2.

Contacts

Regional Office of Endangered Species
U. S. Fish and Wildlife Service
Richard B. Russell Federal Building
75 Spring Street, S.W.
Atlanta, Georgia 30303

Nora Murdock
U.S. Fish and Wildlife Service
330 Ridgefield Court
Asheville, North Carolina 28806

Hesperomannia arbuscula
No Common Name

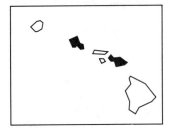

John Obata

Status	Endangered
Listed	October 29, 1991
Family	Asteraceae (Aster)
Description	Shrub with clusters of erect, yellowish brown flower heads.
Habitat	Slopes and ridges in moist to wet forests.
Threats	Feral pigs, alien plant species, low numbers.
Region 1	Hawaii (Maui, Oahu)

Description

Hesperomannia arbuscula is a shrub or small tree in the aster family that grows to 3.3 meters (11 ft). The leaves are alternate, elliptic, and from 10 to 18 centimeters (4 to 7 in) long. The erect flower heads occur in clusters of four or five. Each head is comprised of numerous yellow or yellowish brown florets.

The species has also been known by the names *Hesperomannia arborescens* var. *oahuensis, H. arbuscula* ssp. *oahuensis, H. arbuscula* var. *pearsallii, H. mauiensis,* and *H. oahuensis.*

Habitat

Hesperomannia arbuscula is found in the Waianae Mountain Range on the western side of the island of Oahu and on West Maui, Hawaii. Oahu is dominated by the remnants of two ancient volcanoes that have eroded into two "mountain ranges," which consist of long, narrow ridges. The Waianae Range lies on the western side of the island, while the Koolau Range traverses the eastern side. The Waianae Range, which runs northwest to southeast for about 40 miles, lies in the rain shadow of the Koolau Range, and, except for the summit of Mt. Kaala, the highest point on the island, receives much less rainfall.

A variety of plant habitats are found in the Waianae Mountains, ranging from coastal dry shrubland to lowland dry forest to lowland wet forest. *Hesperomannia arbuscula* grows on slopes and ridges in moist to wet forests at elevations between

350 and 900 meters (1,200 to 3,000 ft). These forests are dominated by koa (*Acacia koa*), and ohia (*Metrosideros polymorpha*). Associated species include ko'oko'olau (*Bidens*), maile (*Alyxia oliviformis*), and kopiko (*Psychotria*).

The diverse habitats of the Waianae Mountains contain a large number of rare native Hawaiian plant species. In October 1991 the Fish and Wildlife Service (FWS) listed *Hesperomannia arbuscula* and 25 other plant species from Oahu's Waianae Mountains as Endangered. This group listing was the result of the settlement of a 1989 lawsuit brought against the FWS by the Sierra Club Legal Defense Fund on behalf of a Hawaii conservation group. The terms of the settlement called for the proposed listing before October 1992 of 186 Hawaiian candidate plant species.

Historic Range

Hesperomannia arbuscula is known from the central and southern Waianae Mountains, from Makaleha to Puu Kanehoa, as well as from West Maui.

Current Distribution

The species is now found on the Makaha-Waianae Kai Ridge on Oahu and in the Iao Valley on West Maui. Three populations, all on state land, consist of a total of about 50 plants.

Conservation and Recovery

As for most rare Hawaiian plants, the main threats to *Hesperomannia arbuscula* are habitat degradation by feral pigs and competition from non-native plant species. Feral pigs, which are managed by the state as game animals, have had a major effect on the native flora. Their rooting destroys plants and opens the habitat to invasive species. They also help spread these alien plants by carrying seed on their bodies and in their feces.

Hesperomannia arbuscula faces direct competiton from several non-native plants. Christmasberry (*Schinus terebinthifolius*), an aggressive tree introduced to Hawaii before 1911, forms dense thickets and may also release chemicals that inhibit the growth of other species. Koster's curse (*Clidemia hirta*), a cultivated shrub that spread to the Waianae Mountains at the beginning of the 1970s, and strawberry guava (*Psidium cattleianum*), an invasive tree, each form dense stands that exclude other species.

The extremely low number of known plants and their limited distribution makes the species vulnerable to extinction through unpredictible human or natural events. In addition, the proximity of some populations to trails exposes plants to an increased danger of collection or trampling by hikers.

Additional Sources

Cuddihy, L. W., and C. P. Stone. 1990. *Alteration of Native Hawaiian Vegetation: Effects of Humans, Their Activities and Introductions.* Cooperative National Park Resources Study Unit, University of Hawaii Press, Honolulu.

Stone, C. P., and J. M. Scott, eds. 1985. *Hawai'i's Terrestrial Ecosystems: Preservation and Management.* Cooperative National Park Resources Study Unit, University of Hawaii Press, Honolulu.

Contact

Derral R. Herbst
U.S. Fish and Wildlife Service
300 Ala Moana Boulevard, Room 6307
P.O. Box 50167
Honolulu, Hawaii 96850

Hesperomannia lydgatei
No Common Name

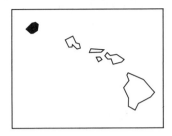

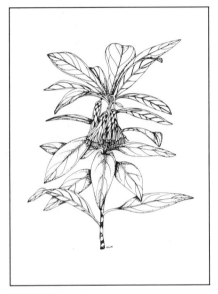

Yevonn Wilson-Ramsey from *Manual of the Flowering Plants of Hawai'i*

Status . . . . Endangered
Listed . . . . September 20, 1991
Family . . . . Asteraceae (Sunflower)
Description . . . . . . Small tree with alternate, lanceolate leaves and clusters of yellow flower heads.
Habitat . . . . Stream banks.
Threats . . . . Low numbers, alien plant species.
Region 1 . . . . Hawaii (Kauai)

Description

Hesperomannia lydgatei is a small tree of the aster family that grows to a height of 3 meters (10 ft). The alternate, elliptic, or lanceolate leaves are 10 to 30 centimeters (4 to 12 in) long. A nodding cluster of four or five yellow flower heads is borne at the ends of branches. The flower heads are 4 to 5 centimeters (1.5 to 2 in) high and are enclosed by circles of overlapping bracts. The inner bracts are silver; the outer ones are brown to purple. Mature fruits have not been described.

Habitat

This species grows along or near stream banks in the Wahiawa drainage basin on the southern part of the island of Kauai, Hawaii. Kauai has the largest number of endemic plants of all the islands, and the Wahiawa Mountain area is one of the oldest and most diverse montane wet forests in Hawaii. This area, which covers about 1,200 acres, is roughly triangular in shape, with Kapalaoa, Mt. Kahili, and Puuauuka forming the corners. Elevations range from 610 meters (2,000 ft) to 1,000 meters (3,300 ft).

In addition to *Hesperomannia lydgatei*, four other plant species endemic to the Wahiawa Stream drainage basin are listed as Endangered: *Cyanea undulata*, *Dubautia pauciflorula*, kamakahala (*Labordia lydgatei*), and *Viola helenae*. Another 18 extremely rare plant species occur in this area.

Historic Range

Hesperomannia lydgatei was first collected in 1908 from the Wahiawa Mountains. There were no other collections after 1909 until the species was rediscovered in 1955 along Wahiawa Stream. The species is unknown outside the Wahiawa Basin.

Current Distribution

Today four populations of *Hesperomannia lydgatei* are known, all from along Wahiawa Stream or its tributaries. One lies above Wahiawa Stream behind Kanaele Bog and consists of four or five trees. In 1972 this population was estimated at 30 to 36 trees. A second population farther upstream consists of 10 to 12 trees. Two other populations occur along tributaries. One consists of 40 to 50 trees; the other has not been surveyed recently. About ten years ago it was estimated to contain between 100 and 125 trees, and it is likely that this population has declined. The land is owned by a corporation which manages it to preserve irrigation resources.

Conservation and Recovery

The main threats to *Hesperomannia lydgatei* are the species' low numbers, limited distribution, and competition from invasive plant species. With so few remaining individuals and an extremely limited distribution, *Hesperomannia lydgatei* is vulnerable to extinction by an unpredictable event. Although the Wahiawa drainage has been largely undisturbed, invasive plants are now spreading upstream. Strawberry guava (*Psidium cattleianum*) and melastoma (*Melastoma candidum*) are aggressive introduced plants that outcompete native

species. These species gained a foothold in the basin in 1982 when Typhoon Iwa opened sections of the forest canopy. This invasion is assisted by feral pigs which transport seed and open additional ground by rooting. Although there are only slight indications of pig activity in the basin, any increase could quickly help spread invading plants.

Additional Sources

Carlquist, S. 1957. "Systematic Anatomy of *Hesperomannia*." *Pacific Science* 11:207-215.

Cuddihy, L. W., and C. P. Stone. 1990. *Alteration of Native Hawaiian Vegetation: Effects of Humans, Their Activities and Introductions*. Cooperative National Park Resources Study Unit, University of Hawaii Press, Honolulu.

Culliney, J. L. 1988. *Islands in a Far Sea: Nature and Man in Hawaii*. Sierra Club Books, San Francisco.

Stone, C. P., and J. M. Scott, eds. 1985. *Hawai'i's Terrestrial Ecosystems: Preservation and Management*. Cooperative National Park Resources Study Unit, University of Hawaii Press, Honolulu.

Wagner, W. L., D. R. Herbst, and S. H. Sohmer. 1990. *Manual of the Flowering Plants of Hawai'i*. University of Hawaii Press and Bishop Museum Press, Honolulu.

Contacts

Regional Office of Endangered Species
U.S. Fish and Wildlife Service
Eastside Federal Complex
911 N.S. 11th Avenue
Portland, Oregon 97232-4181

Derral R. Herbst
U.S. Fish and Wildlife Service
300 Ala Moana Boulevard, Room 6307
P.O. Box 50167
Honolulu, Hawaii 96850

Aupaka
Isodendrion hosakae

Robert Gustafson

Status . . . . Endangered
Listed . . . . January 14, 1991
Family . . . . Violaceae (Violet)
Description . . . . . . Slender shrub with
leathery, toothed leaves
and yellowish green to
white flowers.
Habitat . . . . Cinder cones.
Threats . . . . Cattle grazing, wildfires.
Region 1 . . . . Hawaii (Hawaii)

Description

Aupaka is a slender, branched shrub of the violet family that grows to a height of 46 to 76 centimeters (18 to 30 in). The leathery leaves are narrowly lance-shaped, about 2.5 to 7 centimeters (1 to 2.7 in) long, with toothed margins. The upper part of the stem is covered with leaf stipules. The yellowish green to white flowers are about 1.3 centimeters long (0.5 in) long. The fruit is a green capsule, about 1 centimeter (0.4 in) long, containing olive green seeds.

Isodendrion, a genus comprising four species, is endemic to Hawaii. Three of the species are considered rare and one is extinct.

Habitat

This species is only found on the northeast slopes of three extinct volcanic cinder cones at an elevation between 850 and 1,095 meters (2,800 and 3,600 ft) on the island of Hawaii. The vegetation in the area is open grassland and scrub and the sites are exposed to wind and fog.

Historic Range

Aupaka was first collected in the late 1940s from a cinder cone at Waikoloa (South Kohala District) on the northwestern portion of the island of Hawaii. It was not seen again until it was rediscovered in 1980 in the same area. Surveys for the species over the next two years found additional populations on two other cinder cones. The species has always been extremely limited in its distribution.

Current Distribution

Today there are only three populations of aupaka growing on privately owned cinder cones in the Waikoloa area. They occupy an area of less than 2 acres. One population consists of about 260 plants; the other two have less than 10 plants each.

Conservation and Recovery

Cattle grazing is the main threat to the few existing aupaka plants. Domestic and feral animals have altered the vegetation of the islands since the 1700s. Aupaka occurs in an area prone to drought conditions that force cattle to graze on less palatable plants. In order to save remaining aupaka plants the cinder cone supporting the largest population was fenced in a cooperative effort of the Fish and Wildlife Service, the state wildlife agency, and the landowner. In the past, the land on which aupaka is found was leased to the U.S. military for troop training exercises. Now that the species is listed as Endangered, the Department of Defense would be required to consult with the Fish and Wildlife Service before using the land again.

Additional Sources

Cuddihy, L. W., and C. P. Stone. 1990. *Alteration of Native Hawaiian Vegetation: Effects of Humans, Their Activities and Introductions.* Cooperative National Park Resources Study Unit, University of Hawaii Press, Honolulu.

Culliney, J. L. 1988. *Islands in a Far Sea: Na-*

ture and Man in Hawaii. Sierra Club Books, San Francisco.

Nagata, K. 1982. "Status Survey of *Isodendrion hosakae* St. John (Aupaka)." U.S. Fish and Wildlife Service, Honolulu.

St. John, H. "Monograph of the Genus *Isodendrion* (Violaceaé)." Hawaiian Plant Studies 21. *Pacific Science* 6:213-255.

Stone, C. P., and J. M. Scott, eds. 1985. *Hawai'i's Terrestrial Ecosystems: Preservation and Management.* Cooperative National Park Resources Study Unit, University of Hawaii Press, Honolulu.

Wagner, W. L., D. R. Herbst, and S. H. Sohmer. 1990. *Manual of the Flowering Plants of Hawai'i.* University of Hawaii Press and Bishop Museum Press, Honolulu.

Contacts

Regional Office of Endangered Species
U.S. Fish and Wildlife Service
Eastside Federal Complex
911 N.S. 11th Avenue
Portland, Oregon 97232-4181

Ernest F. Kosaka
U.S. Fish and Wildlife Service
300 Ala Moana Boulevard, Room 6307
P.O. Box 50167
Honolulu, Hawaii 96850

Kamakahala
Labordia lydgatei

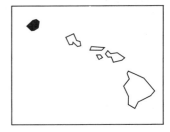

John Obata/National Tropical Botanical Garden

Status	Endangered
Listed	September 20, 1991
Family	Loganiaceae (Strychnine)
Description	Branched shrub with slightly hairy, square stems and pale yellow, funnel-shaped flowers.
Habitat	Near streams in montane wet forests.
Threats	Low numbers, alien plant species.
Region 1	Hawaii (Kauai)

Description

Kamakahala is a branched shrub or small tree of the strychnine family with slightly hairy, square stems. The elliptic to lanceolate leaves, which are from 5 to 10 centimeters (2 to 4 in) long, are smooth above and hairy below. The funnel-shaped, pale yellow flowers appear in clusters of 6 to 21. The fruit is an oval woody capsule.

Habitat

This species grows near stream banks in the Wahiawa drainage basin in the southern part of the island of Kauai, Hawaii. Kauai has the largest number of endemic plants of all the islands, and the Wahiawa Mountain area is one of the oldest and most diverse montane wet forests in Hawaii. This area, which covers about 1,200 acres, is roughly triangular in shape, with Kapalaoa, Mt. Kahili, and Puuauuka forming the corners. Elevations range from 610 to 1,000 meters (2,000 to 3,300 ft).

In addition to kamakahala (*Labordia lydgatei*), four other plant species endemic to the Wahiawa Stream drainage basin are listed as Endangered: *Cyanea undulata, Dubautia pauciflorula, Hesperomannia lydgatei,* and *Viola helenae.* Another 18 extremely rare plant species are found in this area.

Historic Range

Kamakahala was first collected in 1908 or 1909 in the Wahiawa Basin. It was described in 1916 and has only been collected five times. The species is unknown outside the Wahiawa Basin.

Current Distribution

Today kamakahala is known from a single population of about three plants located above one of the tributaries of Wahiawa Stream. The land is owned by a corporation which manages it to preserve irrigation resources.

Conservation and Recovery

The main threats to kamakahala are the species' extremely small population, its limited distribution, and competition from invasive alien plant species. With only three or four surviving individuals at a single site, an unpredictable event could easily destroy all known kamakahala plants. Although the Wahiawa drainage has been largely undisturbed, invasive plants are now spreading upstream. Strawberry guava (*Psidium cattleianum*) and melastoma (*Melastoma candidum*) are aggressive introduced plants that outcompete native species. These species gained a foothold in the basin when in 1982 Typhoon Iwa opened sections of the forest canopy. This invasion is assisted by feral pigs which transport seed and open additonal ground by rooting. Although there are only slight indications of pig activity in the basin, any increase could quickly help spread invading plants.

Additional Sources

Cuddihy, L. W., and C. P. Stone. 1990. *Alteration of Native Hawaiian Vegetation: Effects of Humans, Their Activities and Introductions*. Cooperative National Park Resources Study Unit, University of Hawaii Press, Honolulu.

Culliney, J. L. 1988. *Islands in a Far Sea: Nature and Man in Hawaii*. Sierra Club Books, San Francisco.

Stone, C. P., and J. M. Scott, eds. 1985. *Hawai'i's Terrestrial Ecosystems: Preservation and Management*. Cooperative National Park Resources Study Unit, University of Hawaii Press, Honolulu.

Wagner, W. L., D. R. Herbst, and S. H. Sohmer. 1990. *Manual of the Flowering Plants of Hawai'i*. University of Hawaii Press and Bishop Museum Press, Honolulu.

Contacts

Regional Office of Endangered Species
U.S. Fish and Wildlife Service
Eastside Federal Complex
911 N.S. 11th Avenue
Portland, Oregon 97232-4181

Derral R. Herbst
U.S. Fish and Wildlife Service
300 Ala Moana Boulevard, Room 6307
P.O. Box 50167
Honolulu, Hawaii 96850

Burke's Goldfields
Lasthenia burkei

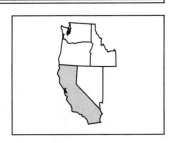

Marianne Austin-McDermon

Status	Endangered
Listed	December 2, 1991
Family	Asteraceae (Aster)
Description	Annual with opposite, lanceolate leaves and yellow flower heads.
Habitat	Vernal pools and swales.
Threats	Residential and agricultural development.
Region 1	California

Description

Burke's goldfields is an annual in the aster family that grows to a height of about 30 centimeters (12 in). The lanceolate leaves are arranged in opposite pairs. Flower heads, consisting of bright yellow ray and disk flowers, bloom from April through June. It is distinguished from similar goldfields species by certain seed characteristics. The species has also been known as *Baeria burkei*.

Habitat

This species is limited to vernal pools and other seasonal wetlands in Lake County, California, and in the Cotati Valley, which lies north of San Francisco. These pools form where non-porus material, such as clay, hardpan, or volcanic stone, underlies surface depressions. In these areas winter rains form pools which gradually dry out during the spring and summer. This unique habitat is not suitable for species that are intolerant of inundation or for aquatic species that require permanent standing water.

Two other Endangered plant species are found in Cotati Valley vernal pools: Sebastapol meadowfoam (*Limnanthes vinculans*) and Baker's sticky seed (*Blennosperma bakeri*). These species occur in an area of Sonoma County about 16 miles long and from 5 to 11 miles wide. This range is bounded on the north by Windsor; on the south by the town of Hessel; on the west by the Laguna de Santa Rosa, a tributary of the Russian River; and on the east by the foothills of the Sonoma and Mayacmas mountains. In the Cotati Valley, vernal pools form on Huichica loam and Clear Lake clay soil types where there is an impervious layer 2 to 3 feet below the surface.

Other plants associated with these vernal pools include fringed downingia (*Downingia concolor*), *Navarretia* spp., smooth lasthenia (*Lasthenia glaberrima*), and Lobb's buttercup (*Ranunculus lobbii*).

Historic Range

Burke's goldfields was first collected in 1886 near Ukiah in Mendocino County, California. It has also been found in Sonoma and Lake counties.

Current Distribution

At present there are 34 known populations of Burke's goldfields, all but one in the Cotati Valley. These sites are concentrated in the northern portion of the valley, near Windsor. Most of the valley's vernal pools are privately owned; however, three are within the rights-of-way owned by the California Department of Transportation, and four are owned by county or city agencies. The species is also found on private property at Manning Flat in Lake County. The discovery site near Ukiah has not been relocated and the continued existence of the species there is unknown.

Conservation and Recovery

The overwhelming threat to Burke's goldfields and other vernal pool species is the destruction of their unique habitats for residential and agricultural development.

So far about 90 percent of the Cotati Valley has been developed. The need for affordable housing within commuting distance of San Francisco has increased developmental pressure throughout the valley.

The construction of housing developments near Windsor is destroying populations of Burke's goldfields. Recently more than a dozen pools have been filled without the landowners obtaining permits from the Army Corps of Engineers required by the federal Clean Water Act. In part because most of the pools are relatively small the Corps of Engineers has been reluctant to involve itself in examining the ecological effects of filling these seasonal wetlands. Now that Burke's goldfields and other vernal pool species have been listed under the Endangered Species Act, the Corps must consult with the Fish and Wildlife Service whenever alteration of their habitat is proposed, regardless of the size of the wetland.

Sonoma County has approved a development plan for Windsor which, if fully implemented, would destroy most, if not all, of the vernal pools in the northern reaches of the valley—about 35 percent of the species' range.

A lesser threat to Burke's goldfields is livestock grazing, which has reduced populations of endemic vernal pool species at many of their historic sites.

Additional Sources

Holland, R. F. 1976. "The Vegetation of Vernal Pools: a Survey." In *Vernal Pools: their Ecology and Conservation*, a symposium sponsored by the Institute of Ecology, University of California, Davis, May 1 and 2, 1976. Institute of Ecology Publication No. 9.

Jain, S. 1976. "Evolutionary Studies in the Meadowfoam Genus *Limnanthes*, an Overview." In *Vernal Pools: their Ecology and*

Conservation, a symposium sponsored by the Institute of Ecology, University of California, Davis, May 1 and 2, 1976. Institute of Ecology Publication No. 9.

Ornduff, R. 1966. "A Biosystematic Survey of the Goldfield Genus *Lasthenia* (Compositae: Heleniae). *University of California Publications in Botany* 40:1-92.

_____. 1977. "Rare Plant Status Report for *Lasthenia burkei.*" California Native Plant Society, Sacramento.

Waaland, M. 1989. "Santa Rosa Plains Endangered Plant Protection Program Report, Section A." Sonoma County Planning Department and California Department of Fish and Game.

Contacts

Regional Office of Endangered Species
U.S. Fish and Wildlife Service
Eastside Federal Complex
911 N.S. 11th Avenue
Portland, Oregon 97232-4181

Jim A. Bartel
U.S. Fish and Wildlife Service
Sacramento Field Office
2899 Cottage Way, Room E-1823
Sacramento, California 95825

San Joaquin Wooly-Threads
Lembertia congdonii

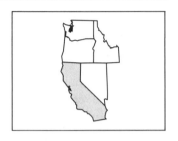

B. "Moose" Peterson   *Color Plate C-4*

Status	Endangered
Listed	July 19, 1990
Family	Asteraceae (Aster)
Description	Trailing annual with white-wooly, branching stems.
Habitat	Valley saltbush scrub.
Threats	Conversion of habitat to cropland, urbanization, livestock grazing.
Region 1	California

Description

San Joaquin wooly-threads is an annual which produces several white-wooly, branching stems, growing to a length of 25 centimeters (10 in) and often trailing along the ground. It is distinguished from its closest relative, *Eatonella nivea*, which is from the Great Basin, by differences in growth habit, flowers, and seeds. It has also been known by the name *Eatonella congdonii*.

Habitat

San Joaquin wooly-threads is found only in the grassland and adjacent plant communities of California's southern San Joaquin Valley (often called the Tulare Lake Basin) and the nearby foothills and valleys. This area lies roughly between Fresno and Bakersfield. Alien grasses, introduced during the time of the Franciscan missionaries, outcompeted native plant species and came to dominate the grasslands. San Joaquin wooly-threads now occupies sites with reduced grass cover, such as valley saltbush scrub. This habitat, which occurs on the gently rolling hills, is dominated by alkali-tolerant species of the Chenopodiaceae (goosefoot) family, such as iodinebush (*Allenrolfea occidentalis*) and sea-blight (*Suaeda* spp.), and supports an understory of annual herbs. Three other San Joaquin Valley plants, also listed as Threatened or Endangered, occur in the same habitat: Kern mallow (*Eremalche kernensis*), California jewelflower (*Caulanthus californicus*), and Hoover's wooly-star (*Eriastrum hooveri*).

Historic Range

San Joaquin wooly-threads has been found at 52 sites in seven southern California counties: Fresno, Kern, Kings, San Benito, San Luis Obispo, Santa Barbara, and Tulare.

Current Distribution

Of the 52 historic populations only 19 survive. Thirty-three populations have been lost, primarily through the conversion of land to agricultural use. Twelve populations remain in an area of the valley that runs from Panoche Pass in San Benito County southeast to Caliente Creek, east of Bakersfield, in Kern County. Seven populations occur in San Luis Obispo County in the Cuyama Valley and Carrizo Plain.

In surveys during 1987 and 1988 plants were observed at nine of the known sites. Populations ranged from 20 to 300 plants. The 10 sites where no plants were found remain suitable habitat and it is hoped that the species will reappear when drought conditions ease.

Three of the 19 sites are on land managed by the Bureau of Land Management (BLM). The Nature Conservancy owns 120 acres at Sand Ridge, east of Bakersfield, which includes a portion of the population there. In 1988 that organization also purchased portions of two population sites as part of their Carrizo Plain Natural Heritage Preserve. That same year the state Department of Water Resources purchased land within a largely abandoned oil field which harbors three populations of San Joaquin wooly-threads. The remaining 10 sites

(and portions of three others) are privately owned.

Conservation and Recovery

The major cause for the decline in San Joaquin wooly-threads has been the conversion of land to agricultural use. This resulted in the loss of 63 percent of the known populations. The remaining unprotected populations remain vulnerable to conversion of land to cropland, urbanization, oil and gas exploration, and overgrazing. BLM, which manages land where three populations occur, will consult with the Fish and Wildlife Service over management plans for the species.

Additional Sources

Heady, H. F. 1977. "Valley Grassland." In *Terrestrial Vegetation of California*, edited by M. G. Barbour and J. Major. John Wiley and Sons, New York.

Hoover, R. F. 1970. *The Vascular Plants of San Luis Obispo County, California*. University of California Press, Berkeley.

Taylor, D. W. 1987. "Status Survey of San Joaquin Wooly-threads (*Lembertia congdonii*)." U.S. Fish and Wildlife Service, Sacramento.

Wester, L. 1981. "Composition of Native Grasslands in the San Joaquin Valley, California." *Madroño* 28:231-241.

Contacts

Regional Office of Endangered Species
U.S. Fish and Wildlife Service
Eastside Federal Complex
911 N.S. 11th Avenue
Portland, Oregon 97232-4181

Jim A. Bartel
U.S. Fish and Wildlife Service
2800 Cottage Way, Room E-1823
Sacramento, California 95825

Lepanthes eltorensis
No Common Name

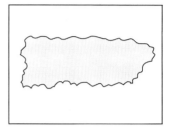

James D. Ackerman

Status	Endangered
Listed	November 29, 1991
Family	Orchidaeae (Orchid)
Description	Small, reddish epiphytic orchid.
Habitat	Moss-covered trees in wet, upper-elevation forests.
Threats	Collectors, low numbers.
Region 4	Puerto Rico

Description

Lepanthes eltorensis is a very small (4 centimeters; 1.5 in) epiphytic orchid that grows on moss-covered trees. Epiphytic plants use other plants, usually trees, for physical support, but not as a source of nutrients. Plants have 3 to 7 sheathed stems, each terminating in a leaf. The smooth, untoothed leaves are from 9 to 24 millimeters (0.3 to 1 in) long and obovate to oblanceolate. The flower is reddish with two-lobed lateral petals and a three-lobed lip petal. Before it was described as a separate species, *Lepanthes eltorensis* and all other *Lepanthes* were considered *L. selenitepala*.

Habitat

Lepanthes eltorensis grows on moss-covered trees in wet, upper-elevation forests in the Luquillo Mountains of northeastern Puerto Rico. The forest is enshrouded in clouds at night and for most of the day. The relative humidity is always over 90 percent; the annual rainfall ranges between 313 and 450 centimeters (122 and 176 in). This orchid species is found at elevations above 850 meters (2,800 ft) in sierra palm, palo colorado, and dwarf forest. It grows on several tree species, all of which support mosses and liverworts.

Historic Range

Lepanthes eltorensis was described as a separate species in 1969. It is found in the vicinity of the El Toro Trail in the Luquillo Mountains of Puerto Rico. Only three populations have been discovered: in the sierra palm forest to the east of El Toro mountain, and in the palo colorado and dwarf forests to the west and south of the peak.

Current Distribution

Lepanthes eltorensis survives at two of the three historic locations. By 1975 collectors had completely eliminated the population in the sierra palm forest. All known sites are within the Caribbean National Forest which is administered by the U.S. Forest Service.

Conservation and Recovery

Even though all *Lepanthes eltorensis* plants occur on Forest Service land, illegal plant collecting has destroyed one population. In such an isolated area, regulations against taking plants are difficult to enforce, and collecting remains the major threat to the species.

In 1989 Hurricane Hugo struck the Caribbean National Forest. Although it did not destroy any of the orchid's host trees, it did fell a large number of huge trees, leaving many new openings in the forest canopy, some near known *Lepanthes eltorensis* populations. This may have an adverse effect on some of the orchids. When a species is as rare as this orchid, the loss of any plants may affect the survival of the species.

Additional Sources

Stimson, W. 1969. "A Revision of the Puerto Rican species of *Lepanthes* (Orchidaceae)." *Brittonia* 21:332-345.

Vivaldi, J. L., R. O. Woodbury, and H. Diaz-Soltero. 1981. "Status Report on *Lepanthes eltorensis* Stimson." U.S. Fish and Wildlife Service, Atlanta.

Contacts

Regional Office of Endangered Species
U. S. Fish and Wildlife Service
Richard B. Russell Federal Building
75 Spring Street, S.W.
Atlanta, Georgia 30303

Susan Silander
Caribbean Field Office
U.S. Fish and Wildlife Service
P.O. Box 491
Boquerón, Puerto Rico 00622

Barneby Ridge-Cress
Lepidium barnebyanum

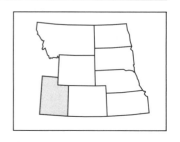

Ben Franklin   *Color Plate C-2*

Status	Endangered
Listed	September 28, 1990
Family	Brassicaceae (Mustard)
Description	Clump-forming perennial with smooth stems, narrow leaves clustered near the base, and cream-colored flowers.
Habitat	Marly shale barrens.
Threats	Off-road vehicles, oil and gas development.
Region 6	Utah

Description

Barneby ridge-cress is a perennial that grows to a height of 5 to 15 centimeters (2 to 6 in) and forms raised clumps up to 20 centimeters (8 in) wide. Smooth, hairless stems rise from a deep, woody taproot; the narrow leaves are clustered at the base of the plant. The four-petaled, cream-colored flowers begin blooming in early May. They are 5 to 7 millimeters (0.25 in) across and alternate along a stem that rises 2.5 to 6 centimeters (1 to 2.5 in) above the plant's base. The very small seeds, carried in elliptical seed pods, are dispersed in June and July.

The species was discovered in 1947 and was first described under the scientific name *Lepidium montanum* ssp. *demissum*. It has also been known by the common name of Barneby pepper cress.

Habitat

The species is restricted to a single known site in Utah, where it grows on marly shale barrens at an elevation of 1,890 to 1,980 meters (6,200 to 6,500 ft). Barneby ridge-cress is a member of the shale barren pulvinate (clump-forming) plant community which is part of the broader pinyon pine-juniper woodland community characteristic of the area. It is found in association with other clump-forming species including stemless gold-flower (*Hymenoxys acaulis*), *Arenaria hookeri, Townsendia mensana,* and *Parthenium ligulatum.* Other associated plant species include *Astragalus spatulatus, Eriogonum batemanii,* and *Castilleja scabrida.*

Historic Range

Since it is limited to a single site, the historic range of Barnaby's ridge-cress is the same as its current distribution.

Current Distribution

Barneby's ridge-cress is known from a single population with four distinct stands on the Uintah and Ouray Ute Indian Reservation in northeast Utah. These stands are on three ridge lines on both sides of Indian Creek on the northeast margin of Indian Creek Canyon about 5 kilometers (3 mi) south of Starvation Reservoir and the town of Duchesne. The total population is estimated at about 5,000 individuals over an area of less than 500 acres. Searches of similar shale barren habitats in the Uinta Basin of northeast Utah and adjacent Colorado have failed to locate additional populations.

Conservation and Recovery

The main threats to Barneby's ridge-cress are disturbances caused by motorcycles and other off-road vehicles, and oil and gas development. Although the Ute Tribe prohibits off-road vehicle use on the reservation, enforcement is difficult. The sole population lies within an oil and gas field where several wells are scheduled to be drilled. The plant grows on the relatively level ridge lines in generally steep terrain. These ridge lines are the preferred routes for off-road vehicles and are likely sites for the construction of roads and the location of wells.

Two federal agencies are involved in any resource development on the Ute Reservation. The Bureau of Indian Affairs is responsible for assisting the tribe in resource development of reservation lands, and the Bureau of Land Management must approve proposed operations on all leaseholds within the reservation. Both agencies are responsible for ensuring that any land action does not jeopardize the continued existence of Barneby's ridge-cress. A Fish and Wildlife Service recovery plan is expected to recommend ways to deal with the threat of off-road vehicles.

Additional Sources

U.S. Fish and Wildlife Service. 1989. "*Lepidium barnebyanum* Supplemental Status Report." Salt Lake City, Utah.

Welsh, S. L. 1978. "Status Report: *Lepidium barnebyanum.*" Brigham Young University Herbarium, Provo, Utah.

Welsh, S. L., N. D. Atwood, S. Goodrich, and L. C. Higgins. 1987. *A Utah Flora.* Great Basin Naturalist Memoirs, No. 9.

Contacts

Regional Office of Endangered Species
U.S. Fish and Wildlife Service
P.O. Box 25486
Denver Federal Center
Denver, Colorado 80225

John L. England
U.S. Fish and Wildlife Service
2078 Administration Building
1745 West 1700 South
Salt Lake City, Utah 84104

Dudley Bluffs Bladderpod
Lesquerella congesta

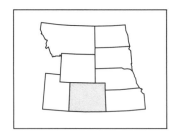

Robert L. Powell   *Color Plate C-3*

Status	Threatened
Listed	February 6, 1990
Family	Brassicaceae (Mustard)
Description	Small, cushion-shaped perennial with yellow flowers and silvery leaves.
Habitat	Oil shale outcrops.
Threats	Mining.
Region 6	Colorado

Description

The Dudley Bluffs bladderpod, a perennial in the mustard family, is a small plant with a cushion growth form. The fruiting stems are only 1 to 3 centimeters (0.4 to 1.2 in) tall. The small, silvery leaves are less than 12 millimeters (0.5 in) in length, linear, and untoothed. The species bears bright yellow, four-petaled flowers and small, rounded, downy fruits.

Habitat

Endemic to barren, white oil shale outcrops in the Piceance Basin of Colorado, Dudley Bluffs bladderpod grows on flat oil shale ridges and on other level outcrops. It is often found in association with another Threatened mustard, the Dudley Bluffs twinpod (*Physaria obcordata*), which grows on the steep oil shale slopes. The species is found at elevations of from 1,860 to 2,010 meters (6,140 to 6,844 ft). The surrounding hills and mesas support pinyon-juniper woodlands.

Historic Range

Dudley Bluffs bladderpod was discovered in 1982 in Rio Blanco County, northwestern Colorado, during a survey of the plant life of the Piceance Basin conducted by the state Natural Heritage Inventory for the Bureau of Land Management (BLM).

The species has not been found outside the Piceance Basin.

Current Distribution

This bladderpod is currently found at five sites in Rio Blanco County, mostly on public land administered by BLM. There are five known populations along Piceance and Yellow creeks on approximately 50 acres over a 10 mile range. The largest population, consisting of about 10,000 plants, is located on BLM land at the junction of Piceance Creek and Ryan Gulch. This site also contains an equal number of the Threatened Dudley Bluffs twinpod. Along Yellow Creek the species occurs on BLM land and state land administered by the Colorado Division of Wildlife.

Conservation and Recovery

The main threat to the Dudley Bluffs bladderpod is the mining of its habitat for rich deposits of oil shale and sodium minerals such as nahcolite and dawsonite. While mining is not imminent, long term mineral development plans clearly threaten the species. As the federal government seeks alternative energy sources to imported petroleum, subsidy programs for oil shale development continue to be proposed in the U.S. Congress.

Yellow Creek, Dudley Bluffs, and Ryan Gulch are on oil shale deposits which could be mined by open-pit methods. A pilot project for an underground nahcolite solution mine has been established between Piceance Creek and Yellow Creek, and a commercial mine, which has been proposed for the area would cover 254 acres. These activities could result in the destruction or modification of the entire Dudley Bluffs bladderpod habitat. At this time BLM has decided not to lease the

commercial mineral rights to the area until improved mining technology is developed, but is still considering leases for non-commercial research purposes. While BLM has designated a section of Dudley Bluffs as an "Area of Critical Environmental Concern," this gives protection to only about 50 acres.

Although Dudley Bluffs bladderpod is locally abundant in its specialized habitat, its extremely limited range renders it vulnerable to any surface disruptions. The Rio Blanco County government and oil shale and nahcolite companies opposed the listing of Dudley Bluffs bladderpod as a Threatened species.

Additional Sources

Bureau of Land Management. 1987. "Piceance Basin Resource Management Plan Record of Decision." U.S. Government Printing Office, Washington, DC.

Colorado Native Plant Society. 1989. *Rare Plants of Colorado*. Colorado Native Plant Society and the Rocky Mountain Nature Association, Estes Park, Colorado.

Colorado Natural Areas Program. 1987. "Status Report for *Physaria obcordata*." Denver, Colorado.

Contacts

Regional Office of Endangered Species
U.S. Fish and Wildlife Service
P.O. Box 25486
Denver Federal Center
Denver, Colorado 80225

John Anderson
U.S. Fish and Wildlife Service
529 25½ Road, Suite B-113
Grand Junction, Colorado 81505

Lyrate Bladder-Pod
Lesquerella lyrata

David H. Webb

Status	Threatened
Listed	September 28, 1990
Family	Brassicaceae (Mustard)
Description	Annual with alternate leaves and small, four-petaled, yellow flowers.
Habitat	Disturbed cedar glades, including farms, pastures, and roadsides.
Threats	Limited range, succession, herbicides.
Region 4	Alabama

Description

An annual in the mustard family, lyrate bladder-pod grows to a height of 10 to 30 centimeters (4 to 12 in). Plants usually branch near the base and the stems are covered with short hairs (pubescent). The leaves are alternate, ovate to elliptic in shape, and have either smooth or toothed margins. There are prominent ear-like projections at the base of the leaves. The flowers are borne on short stalks (12 mm; 0.5 in) and the four yellow petals are about 7 millimeters (0.3 in) long.

Plants flower in March and April and disperse their seed in late April and May. Lyrate bladder-pod is dormant in summer; the seeds germinate in the fall and over-winter as a small circular cluster of leaves (rosette).

Lyrate bladder-pod (*Lesquerella lyrata*) is closely related to *L. densipila*. The two species can be distinguished by their fruits and styles (slender stalks of the pistils). In *L. lyrata* these parts are smooth; in *L. densipila* they are hairy.

Habitat

Lyrate bladder-pod is an early successional plant which occurs in association with limestone outcroppings in cedar glades. These glades are shallow-soiled, open areas sometimes surrounded by cedar woods. Current populations are in glade areas that show some disturbance, such as cultivated fields, pastures, and roadside rights-of-way.

Historic Range

The species is known only from a very limited area in Alabama. It was discovered and named in 1955 from specimens collected from three sites in Franklin County. It was then thought to be extinct until 1984 when it was rediscovered at one of the original sites.

Current Distribution

Following rediscovery of the species, extensive searches were conducted for additional populations, and one other population was found in Colbert County, Alabama. No plants were discovered at two of the original collection sites in Franklin County. Both known populations are on private land and consist of several sites within a quarter- to half-mile radius of one another. The size of the populations vary from year to year, and in some years the sites have supported hundreds to thousands of individual plants.

Conservation and Recovery

Lyrate bladder-pod is vulnerable to extinction because of its extremely limited range and the small number of populations. The two known populations are on private property and are unprotected. The main threats to the species are succession and the application of herbicides.

Since lyrate bladder-pod requires a habitat that is frequently disturbed in order to inhibit plant succession and since it is dormant during the summer, it is compatible with row crop farming. In fact, plowing plays an important part in maintaining the early successional stage that the species requires. There is, however, a danger to the species if plowing or the application of herbicides takes place before plants have set and dispersed their seed. Those populations located in pastures may be harmed by heavy grazing, which might overly compact the soil, or by the introduction of forage grasses which would take over. Mowing along roadways or the use of herbicides before seed dispersal could decimate plant populations at these locations. In addition, privately owned, unprotected sites are always in danger of being destroyed by residential development.

While not in imminent danger of extinction, the species is clearly vulnerable. Current populations have declined in recent years because of succession, and the active management of remaining populations is necessary if the species is to survive.

Additional Sources

McDaniel, S. T. 1987. "Status Report on *Lesquerella lyrata*." U.S. Fish and Wildlife Service, Jackson, Mississippi.

Webb, D. H., and R. Kral. 1986. "Recent Collections and Status of *Lesquerella lyrata* Rollins (Cruciferae)." *Sida* 11:347-351.

Contacts

Regional Office of Endangered Species
U. S. Fish and Wildlife Service
Richard B. Russell Federal Building
75 Spring Street, S.W.
Atlanta, Georgia 30303

Cary Norquist
U.S. Fish and Wildlife Service
300 Woodrow Wilson Avenue, Suite 316
Jackson, Mississippi 39213

Sebastopol Meadowfoam
Limnanthes vinculans

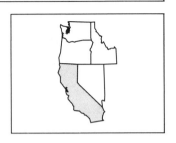

Marianne Austin-McDermon   *Color Plate C-3*

Status	Endangered
Listed	December 2, 1991
Family	Limnanthaceae
	(False Mermaid)
Description	Annual with pinnate leaves
	and white flowers.
Habitat	Vernal pools and swales.
Threats	Residential and agricultural
	development.
Region 1	California

Description

Sebastopol meadowfoam is an annual in the false mermaid (meadow foam) family that grows to a mature height of about 30 centimeters (12 in). Its multiple stems bear long-stemmed, pinnately divided leaves comprising three to five leaflets. Single white flowers bloom at the ends of the stems.

Habitat

This species is limited to vernal pools and other seasonal wetlands in the Cotati Valley, California, which lies north of San Francisco. These pools occur where a non-porous material, such as clay, hardpan, or volcanic stone, lies under surface depressions. In these areas winter rains form pools which gradually dry out during the spring and summer. This unique habitat is not suitable for plant species that are intolerant of inundation or for aquatic species that require permanent standing water.

Sebastopol meadowfoam is found in Cotati Valley vernal pools along with two other Endangered plants: Burke's goldfields (*Lasthenia burkei*) and Baker's sticky seed (*Blennosperma bakeri*). These species occur is an area of Sonoma County about 16 miles long and from 5 to 11 miles wide. This range is bounded on the north by the town of Windsor; on the south by the town of Hessel; on the west by the Laguna de

Santa Rosa, a tributary of the Russian River; and on the east by the foothills of the Sonoma and Mayacmas mountains. In the Cotati Valley, vernal pools form on Huichica loam and Clear Lake clay soil types where there is an impervious layer a few feet below the surface.

Other plants that grow in these vernal pools include fringed downingia (*Downingia concolor*), *Navarretia* spp., smooth lasthenia (*Lasthenia glaberrima*), and Lobb's buttercup (*Ranunculus lobbii*).

Historic Range

Sebastopol meadowfoam was first described in 1969 from specimens collected in 1966 along Todd Road in Sonoma County. The species has never been recorded outside of the Cotati Valley.

Current Distribution

At present there are 19 populations of Sebastopol meadowfoam in vernal pools in the southern portion of the Cotati Valley, Sonoma County. These scattered sites stretch from the vicinity of Santa Rosa south to Hessel. Most of the vernal pools are privately owned. One site, the Todd Road Reserve, is owned by the California Department of Fish and Game. It contains a population of Sebastopol meadowfoam as well as the Endangered Baker's sticky seed (*Blennosperma bakeri*). Four other sites are owned by county or city agencies.

Conservation and Recovery

The overwhelming threat to Sebastopol meadowfoam and other vernal pool species is the destruction of these unique habitats for residential and agricultural development. So far about 90 percent of the Cotati Valley has been developed. The

need for affordable housing within commuting distance of San Francisco has increased developmental pressure throughout the valley.

The construction of housing developments near Santa Rosa is destroying populations of Sebastopol meadowfoam, as well as Burke's goldfields (*Lasthenia burkei*) and Baker's sticky seed (*Blennosperma bakeri*). Recently more than a dozen pools have been filled without the landowners obtaining permits from the Army Corps of Engineers as required by the federal Clean Water Act. In part because most of the pools are relatively small, the Corps of Engineers has been reluctant to examine the ecological effects of destroying these seasonal wetlands. Now that Sebastopol meadowfoam and other vernal pool species have been listed under the Endangered Species Act, the Corps is required to consult with the Fish and Wildlife Service whenever alteration of their wetland habitat is proposed, regardless of size.

Sebastopol meadowfoam faces an additional threat related to development. Santa Rosa is planning to expand its wastewater treatment facility to accommodate its growing population. Currently, treated wastewater is used to irrigate about 4,500 acres of cropland. Expansion plans call for the construction of a series of terraces planted with water-tolerant grasses and flooded with wastewater for treatment. The water would then be recycled for irrigation. The plan calls for the wastewater capacity to be increased to irrigate 7,500 acres. Even if vernal pools were not directly flooded, the increase in residential and agricultural development, as well as the probable spread of the semi-aquatic grasses, would threaten Sebastopol meadowfoam and other vernal pool species.

A lesser threat to Sebastopol meadowfoam is livestock grazing, which has reduced populations of endemic vernal pool species at many of their historic sites.

Additional Sources

Brown, C., and S. K. Jain. 1977. "Rare Plant Status Report: *Limnanthes vinculans.*" California Native Plant Society, Sacramento.

Holland, R. F. 1976. "The Vegetation of Vernal Pools: a Survey." In *Vernal Pools: their Ecology and Conservation,* a symposium sponsored by the Institute of Ecology, University of California, Davis, May 1 and 2, 1976. Institute of Ecology Publication No. 9.

Jain, S. 1976. "Evolutionary Studies in the Meadowfoam Genus *Limnanthes, an Overview.* In *Vernal Pools: their Ecology and Conservation,* a symposium sponsored by the Institute of Ecology, University of California, Davis, May 1 and 2, 1976. Institute of Ecology Publication No. 9.

Ornduff, R. 1969. *"Limnanthes vinculans, a New California Endemic." Brittonia* 21:11-14.

Waaland, M. 1989. "Santa Rosa Plains Endangered Plant Protection Program Report, Section A." Sonoma County Planning Department and California Department of Fish and Game.

Wainright, T. C. 1984. "Status Report on Sebastopol Meadowfoam, *Limnanthes vinculans* Ornduff." U.S. Fish and Wildlife Service, Sacramento.

Contacts

Regional Office of Endangered Species
U.S. Fish and Wildlife Service
Eastside Federal Complex
911 N.S. 11th Avenue
Portland, Oregon 97232-4181

Jim A. Bartel
U.S. Fish and Wildlife Service
Sacramento Field Office
2899 Cottage Way, Room E-1823
Sacramento, California 95825

Lipochaeta lobata
var. leptophylla
No Common Name

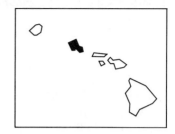

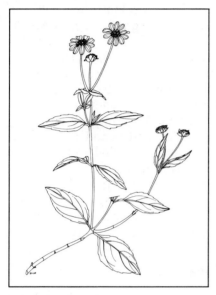

Yevonn Wilson-Ramsey from *Manual of the Flowering Plants of Hawai'i*

Status	Endangered
Listed	October 29, 1991
Family	Asteraceae (Aster)
Description	Somewhat woody, nearly prostrate perennial with narrow leaves and and yellow flower heads.
Habitat	Dry shrubland.
Threats	Alien plant species, low numbers.
Region 1	Hawaii (Oahu)

Description

Lipochaeta lobata var. *leptophylla* is a somewhat woody perennial of the aster family with nearly prostrate stems up to 150 centimeters (59 in) long. The closely spaced leaves are narrowly lance-shaped to linear. The flower heads, which appear singly or in small clusters, consist of 8 to 15 yellow ray florets surrounding 20 to 65 yellow disk florets.

A photograph or drawing of *Lipochaeta lobata* var. *leptophylla* could not be obtained. The drawing above is of *L. l.* var. *lobata*, which differs from the listed variety by having broader leaves which are more widely spaced along the stems.

Habitat

Lipochaeta lobata var. *leptophylla* is found only in the Waianae Mountain Range on the western side of the island of Oahu, Hawaii. This island is dominated by the remnants of two ancient volcanoes that have eroded into two "mountain ranges," which consist of long, narrow ridges. The Waianae Range lies on the western side of the island, while the Koolau Range traverses the eastern side. The Waianae Range, which runs northwest to southeast for about 40 miles, lies in the rain shadow of the Koolau Range, and, except for the summit of Mt. Kaala, the highest point on the island, receives much less rainfall.

A variety of plant habitats are found in the Waianae Mountains, ranging from coastal dry shrubland to lowland dry forest to lowland wet forest. *Lipochaeta lobata* var. *leptophylla* is found in dry shrubland at elevations between 460 and 760 meters (1,500 to 2,000 ft).

The diverse habitats of the Waianae Mountains contain a large number of vulnerable native Hawaiian plant species. In October 1991 the Fish and Wildlife Service (FWS) listed *Lipochaeta lobata* var. *leptophylla* and 25 other plant species from Oahu's Waianae Mountains as Endangered. This group listing was the result of the settlement of a 1989 lawsuit brought against the FWS by the Sierra Club Legal Defense Fund on behalf of a Hawaii conservation group. The terms of the settlement called for the proposed listing of 186 Hawaiian candidate plant species.

Historic Range

Lipochaeta lobata var. *leptophylla* was first collected in 1915 from the Waianae Mountains of Oahu. It has only been found in the southern portions of the mountains, from Kolekole Pass to Lualualei.

Current Distribution

The species now occurs on Lualualei-Nanakuli Ridge and at Kolekole Pass. Two populations, about 4.2 miles apart on state and federal land, contain about 25 to 50 plants.

Conservation and Recovery

The major threat to *Lipochaeta lobata* var. *leptophylla* is competition from alien plant species, a threat shared by almost all rare native Hawaiian flora. Direct threats include Christmasberry (*Schinus terebinthifolius*), an aggressive tree that forms dense thickets and may also release chemicals that inhibit the growth of other species; koa haole (*Leucaena leucocephala*), another aggressive tree that creates its own nitrogen, allowing it to colonize low nitrogen soils; and molasses grass (*Melinus minutiflora*), which grows in dense mats that smother native vegetation. Molasses grass is also fire adapted and provides fuel for spreading wildfires.

Lipochaeta lobata var. *leptophylla* populations lie near the U.S. Army's Makua Military Reservation and Schofield Barracks. Within a 14-month period from 1989 to 1990, 10 fires resulted from weapons practice on the reservation. In order to minimize damage from fires, the army has constructed firebreaks between the target areas and the surrounding forest.

Additional Sources

Culliney, J. L. 1988. *Islands in a Far Sea: Nature and Man in Hawaii*. Sierra Club Books, San Francisco.

Wagner, W. L., D. R. Herbst, and S. H. Sohmer. 1990. *Manual of the Flowering Plants of Hawai'i*. University of Hawaii Press and Bishop Museum Press, Honolulu.

Contacts

Regional Office of Endangered Species
U.S. Fish and Wildlife Service
Eastside Federal Complex
911 N.S. 11th Avenue
Portland, Oregon 97232-4181

Derral R. Herbst
U.S. Fish and Wildlife Service
300 Ala Moana Boulevard, Room 6307
P.O. Box 50167
Honolulu, Hawaii 96850

Lipochaeta tenuifolia
No Common Name

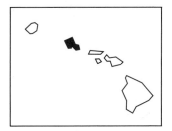

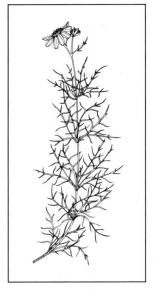

Yevonn Wilson-Ramsey from
*Manual of the Flowering Plants
of Hawai'i*

Status	Endangered
Listed	October 29, 1991
Family	Asteraceae (Aster)
Description	Perennial with long, trailing stems and yellow flower heads.
Habitat	Ridges and bluffs in moist forest.
Threats	Feral pigs and goats, alien plant species.
Region 1	Hawaii (Oahu)

Description

Lipochaeta tenuifolia is a somewhat woody member of the aster family with 3 meter (10 ft) stems that partially trail along the ground. The paired, opposite leaves are so deeply lobed that they appear to be six separate leaves. The flower heads, which occur singly or in pairs, contain 8 to 10 yellow ray florets and 20 to 30 yellow disk florets. The small seeds are slightly winged.

Habitat

Lipochaeta tenuifolia is found only in the Waianae Mountain Range on the western side of the island of Oahu, Hawaii. This island is dominated by the remnants of two ancient volcanoes that have eroded into two "mountain ranges," which consist of long, narrow ridges. The Waianae Range lies on the western side of the island, while the Koolau Range traverses the eastern side. The Waianae Range, which runs northwest to southeast for about 40 miles, lies in the rain shadow of the Koolau Range, and, except for the summit of Mt. Kaala, the highest point on the island, receives much less rainfall.

A variety of plant habitats are found in the Waianae Mountains, ranging from coastal dry shrubland to lowland dry forest to lowland wet forest. *Lipochaeta tenuifolia* grows on open ridgetops and bluffs in moist forest at elevations between 370 and 900 meters (1,200 to 1,300 ft). The habitat is dominated by Christmasberry (*Schinus terebinthifolius*) and ohia (*Metrosideros polymorpha*). Associated species include ko'oko'olau (*Bidens*), molasses grass (*Melinus minutiflora*), and Hamakua pamakani or spreading mist flower (*Ageratina riparia*).

The diverse habitats of the Waianae Mountains contain a large number of vulnerable native Hawaiian plant species. In October 1991 the Fish and Wildlife Service (FWS) listed *Lipochaeta tenuifolia* and 25 other plant species from Oahu's Waianae Mountains as Endangered. This group listing was the result of the settlement of a 1989 lawsuit brought against the FWS by the Sierra Club Legal Defense Fund on behalf of a Hawaii conservation group. The terms of the settlement called for the proposed listing before October 1992 of 186 Hawaiian candidate plant species.

Historic Range

Lipochaeta tenuifolia was first collected in 1840 from Oahu. It has been found in the northern Waianae Mountians, from Kaluakauila Gulch to Kamaileunu Ridge and east to Mt. Kaala. It has been found nowhere else.

Current Distribution

Reduced numbers continue to occur throughout the historic range. Seven known populations over a 30-square-mile area contain an estimated 400 to 600 plants. All populations are on state land.

Conservation and Recovery

The main threats to *Lipochaeta tenuifolia* are habitat degradation by feral pigs and goats and competition from non-native plant species. Feral pigs, which are managed by the state as game animals, have been in the Waianae Mountains for about 150 years and have had a major effect on the native flora. Their rooting destroys plants and opens the habitat to invasive species. They also help the spread of these plants by carrying seed on their bodies and in their feces. Feral goats, also game animals, have been on the island for 170 years. Because of their agility they are able to reach areas inaccessible to pigs and cattle. Although a major control effort greatly reduced the goat population by 1905, remaining animals still pose a threat to rare species.

Lipochaeta tenuifolia is directly threatened by several non-native plant species. Christmasberry (*Schinus terebinthifolius*), an aggressive tree introduced to Hawaii before 1911, forms dense thickets and may also release chemicals that inhibit the growth of other species. Koa haole (*Leucaena leucocephala*), another aggressive tree species, makes its own nitrogen, enabling it to colonize nitrogen poor habitats and displace species adapted to that environment. Molasses grass (*Melinus minutiflora*) grows in dense mats that smother native vegetation; strawberry guava (*Psidium cattleianum*) forms dense stands that exclude other species.

Populations of *Lipochaeta tenuifolia* lie near the U.S. Army's Makua Military Reservation and Schofield Barracks. Within a 14-month period from 1989 to 1990, 10 fires resulted from weapons practice on the reservation. In order to minimize damage from fires, the army has constructed firebreaks between the target areas and the surrounding forest.

Additional Sources

Cuddihy, L. W., and C. P. Stone. 1990. *Alteration of Native Hawaiian Vegetation: Effects* of Humans, Their Activities and Introductions. Cooperative National Park Resources Study Unit, University of Hawaii Press, Honolulu.

Culliney, J. L. 1988. *Islands in a Far Sea: Nature and Man in Hawaii.* Sierra Club Books, San Francisco.

Stone, C. P., and J. M. Scott, eds. 1985. *Hawai'i's Terrestrial Ecosystems: Preservation and Management.* Cooperative National Park Resources Study Unit, University of Hawaii Press, Honolulu.

Wagner, W. L., D. R. Herbst, and S. H. Sohmer. 1990. *Manual of the Flowering Plants of Hawai'i.* University of Hawaii Press and Bishop Museum Press, Honolulu.

Contacts

Regional Office of Endangered Species
U.S. Fish and Wildlife Service
Eastside Federal Complex
911 N.S. 11th Avenue
Portland, Oregon 97232-4181

Derral R. Herbst
U.S. Fish and Wildlife Service
300 Ala Moana Boulevard, Room 6307
P.O. Box 50167
Honolulu, Hawaii 96850

Lobelia niihauensis
No Common Name

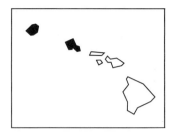

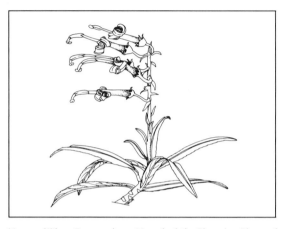

Yevonn Wilson-Ramsey from *Manual of the Flowering Plants of Hawai'i*

Status	Endangered
Listed	October 29, 1991
Family	Campanulaceae (Bellflower)
Description	Shrub with terminal rosettes of narrowly elliptic leaves and clusters of magenta flowers.
Habitat	Exposed moist to dry cliffs.
Threats	Feral pigs and goats, alien plant species.
Region 1	Hawaii (Kauai, Oahu)

Description

Lobelia niihauensis is a low, branched shrub of the bellflower family. Each branch ends with a rosette of narrowly elliptic leaves, 7 to 15 centimeters (3 to 6 in) long. Clusters of magenta flowers appear at the ends of the branches. The fruits are egg-shaped capsules containing numerous brown seeds.

The species has been known by a variety of scientific names: *Lobelia niihauensis* var. *forbesii, L. niihauensis* var. *meridiana, L. tortuosa, L. tortuosa* f. *glabrata, L. tortuosa* var. *haupuensis,* and *L. tortuosa* var. *intermedia.*

Habitat

Lobelia niihauensis grows on exposed moist to dry cliffs at elevations between 125 and 830 meters (410 to 2,720 ft) in the Waianae Mountain Range on the western side of the island of Oahu and on the western portion of the island of Kauai, Hawaii.

The diverse habitats of the Waianae Mountains contain a large number of vulnerable native Hawaiian plant species. In October 1991 the Fish and Wildlife Service (FWS) listed *Lobelia niihauensis* and 25 other plant species from Oahu's Waianae Mountains as Endangered. This group listing was the result of the settlement of a

1989 lawsuit brought against the FWS by the Sierra Club Legal Defense Fund on behalf of a Hawaii conservation group. The terms of the settlement called for the proposed listing before October 1992 of 186 Hawaiian candidate plant species.

Historic Range

Lobelia niihauensis was first described in 1931 from a specimen collected on the island of Niihau in 1912. The species was also found in the Waianae Mountains of Oahu, from Uluhulu Gulch to Nanakuli Valley; on western Kauai, from Limahuli Valley to near the Hanapepe River; and on eastern Kauai at Nounou Mountain.

Current Distribution

The species survives only on Kauai and Oahu. On Kauai it is found in Waimea Canyon, on Polihale Ridge, and along the Na Pali Coast. On Oahu plants survive on Kamaileunu Ridge, Makaha-Waianae Kai Ridge, Makua-Keaau Ridge, and in Nanakuli Valley. Nineteen populations, which occur on both state and private land, contain from 400 to 1,300 plants.

Conservation and Recovery

The main threats to *Lobelia niihauensis* are habitat degradation by feral pigs and goats and competition from alien plant species. Feral pigs, which are managed by the state as game animals, have had a major effect on the native flora. Their rooting destroys plants and opens the habitat to invasive species. They also help spread these alien plants by carrying seed on their bodies and in their feces. Feral goats are able to reach areas inaccessible to pigs. Although a major control effort greatly reduced the goat population by 1905, re-

maining animals still pose a danger to rare species.

Aggressive non-native species are a threat to all native Hawaiian flora, especially rare species. *Lobelia niihauensis* is directly threatened by several. Christmasberry (*Schinus terebinthifolius*), a tree introduced to Hawaii before 1911, forms dense thickets and may also release chemicals that inhibit the growth of other species. The koa haole tree (*Leucaena leucocephala*) is able to make its own nitrogen, enabling it to compete with native species adapted to low nitrogen soils. Molasses grass (*Melinus minutiflora*) grows in dense mats that smother native vegetation.

In addition, some populations of *Lobelia niihauensis* on Oahu are located near the U.S. Army's Makua Military Reservation and Schofield Barracks. Within a 14-month period from 1989 to 1990, 10 fires resulted from weapons practice on the reservation. In order to minimize damage from fires, the army has constructed firebreaks between the target areas and the surrounding forest.

Additional Source

Cuddihy, L. W., and C. P. Stone. 1990. *Alteration of Native Hawaiian Vegetation: Effects of Humans, Their Activities and Introductions.* Cooperative National Park Resources Study Unit, University of Hawaii Press, Honolulu.

Contact

Derral R. Herbst
U.S. Fish and Wildlife Service
300 Ala Moana Boulevard, Room 6307
P.O. Box 50167
Honolulu, Hawaii 96850

Walker's Manioc
Manihot walkerae

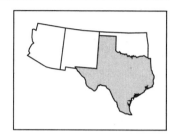

Paul Montgomery   Color Plate C-1

Status . . . . Endangered
Listed . . . . October 2, 1991
Family . . . . Euphorbiaceae (Spurge)
Description . . . . . . Branched perennial with
                              alternate, palmate leaves
                              and fleshy, white flowers.
Habitat . . . . South Texas native
                              brushland.
Threats . . . . Brush clearing, grazing.
Region 2 . . . . Texas

Description

Walker's manioc is a multi-branched perennial in the spurge family that grows to a height of about 50 centimeters (18 in). The alternate leaves are palmately five-lobed. Separate male and female flowers are fleshy and white, about 1 centimeter (0.4 in) long. The fruit is a capsule, about a centimeter (0.4 in) in diameter, containing three seeds.

Habitat

This species grows in loamy and sandy-loamy soil along the Rio Grande in south Texas. It has also been found in Mexico on sandy prairie overlying caliche, a hard desert soil containing calcium carbonate. Walker's manioc occurs in Tamaulipan brushland which is dominated by acacia, mesquite (*Prosopis glandulosa*), Texas ebony (*Pithecellobium flexicaule*), and cenizo (*Leucophyllum frutescens*).

Historic Range

Walker's manioc was first collected in 1853 at Ringgold Barracks, Starr County, Texas, but was misidentified. It was not described as a new species until 1942. Plants have been found at seven sites in Starr and Hidalgo counties, Texas, and the State of Tamaulipas, Mexico.

Current Distribution

The species is now found at a single site in the United States. Despite extensive searches in the late 1980s, no Walker's manioc plants were found at historic sites. However, in 1990 the species was discovered at a new site in Hidalgo County, Texas. Plants may still exist in Mexico, but their status is unknown. Botanists familiar with the area around the Rio Grande are hopeful that new populations will eventually be discovered.

Conservation and Recovery

The main threat to this extremely rare species is the clearing of its unique habitat for agriculture, urban development, and recreation. It is endemic to Tamaulipan brushland, which is found only in south Texas and northeastern Mexico. During this century, 95 percent of this habitat has been cleared for development. Along the Rio Grande 99 percent of native brushland has been destroyed. Almost all remaining native vegetation is on land that is being heavily grazed by livestock.

Because Walker's manioc is related to cassava (*Manihot esculenta*), an important food plant in the tropics, it is a possible source of genetic material valuable in improving cultivated strains of cassava. Often wild species are able to confer increased resistance to disease or harsh climatic conditions to cultivated plants. Walker's manioc plants are currently under cultivation at the University of Texas, Austin, and at the San Antonio Botanical Gardens.

Although this species is not found on federally owned land, two federal agencies are active in areas where there is hope of finding additional plants. The Army Corps of Engineers has jurisdiction over pipeline construction in the area, and the International Boundary Commission is in charge of brush clearing to maintain canals on the U.S. side of the Rio Grande. Any Walker's manioc plants discovered on federal land administered by these agencies will require them to consult with the Fish and Wildlife Service about ways to conserve the species.

Additional Sources

Collins, K. 1984. "Status and Management of Native South Texas Brushlands." U.S. Fish and Wildlife Service, Corpus Christi, Texas.

Jahrsdoerfer, S. E., and D. M. Leslie, Jr. 1988. "Tamaulipan Brushland of the Lower Rio Grande Valley of South Texas: Description, Human Impacts, and Management Options." U.S. Fish and Wildlife Service, Biological Report 88(36).

Rogers, D. J., and S. G. Appan. 1973. "*Manihot*, Manihotoides (Euphorbiaceae)." *Flora Neotropica, Monograph No. 13*, Hafner Press, New York.

Contacts

Regional Office of Endangered Species
U.S. Fish and Wildlife Service
P.O. Box 1306
Albuquerque, New Mexico 87103

Philip Clayton
U.S. Fish and Wildlife Service
c/o Corpus Christi State University
Campus Box 338
6300 Ocean Drive
Corpus Christi, Texas 78412

Michigan Monkey-Flower
Mimulus glabratus var. *michiganensis*

Status	Endangered
Listed	June 21, 1990
Family	Scrophulariaceae (Snapdragon)
Description	Semi-aquatic perennial with yellow, two-lipped, tubular flowers.
Habitat	Cold, saturated soils along seepages, streams, and lakeshores.
Threats	Recreational and residential development.
Region 3	Michigan

Michigan Natural Features Inventory   *Color Plate C-1*

Description

Michigan monkey-flower is an aquatic or semi-aquatic perennial in the snapdragon family. The smooth, prostrate stems average 36 centimeters (14 in) in length. The leaves are round, opposite, coarsely toothed, and evenly distributed along the stem. From mid-June to mid-July (sometimes into August) yellow flowers, ranging from 1.6 to 2.7 centimeters (0.6 to 1.1 in) long, bloom on stalks that emerge from the upper leaf axils. The tubular flowers have a two-lobed upper lip and a three-lobed lower lip; the lower lip and tube are spotted with red. Reproduction is primarily vegetative; the lower stem nodes root and produce clumps of up to several hundred individual stems.

Close relatives of Michigan monkey-flower are *M. glabratus* var. *fremontii* and *M. guttatus*. While these species are extremely similar in appearance, they can be distinguished through the measurements of floral parts. Those of var. *michiganensis* are larger than those of var. *fremontii* but generally smaller than those of *M. guttatus*. *M. guttatus* and var. *michiganensis* can also be differentiated by the shape of some of the flower parts.

Habitat

The species grows in mucky soil and sand that is saturated or covered by cold, flowing spring water. Nearly all known populations occur near the present or past shorelines of the Great Lakes. Northern white-cedar (*Thuja occidentalis*) is usually the dominant tree; common associates include touch-me-not (*Impatiens biflora*), forget-me-not (*Myosotis scorpioides*), watercress (*Nasturtium officinale*), spearmint (*Mentha arvensis*), and liverwort (*Conocephalum conicum*).

Historic Range

Michigan monkey-flower has been found at sixteen sites in the Mackinac Straits and Grand Traverse regions of Michigan. It was first collected in Harbor Springs (Emmet County) in 1890, but was not described until 1980. The type specimen (from which the first published description was made) was collected in 1925 along Niger Creek, near Topinabee (Cheboygan County). Other populations were discovered in Benzie, Leelanau, Charlevoix, and Mackinac counties.

Current Distribution

The species survives at twelve sites, two of which contain only one or two plants. Two-thirds of the plants occur on private land. Sites with some degree of protection include Sleeping Bear Dunes National Lakeshore and the University of Michigan Biological Station, which contain the three most abundant populations. The species also occurs in a township park and on land owned by the Michigan Nature Association, a private conservation group. The Maple River site in Emmet County contains the most significant population on private land. Plants at that site are the only ones that are producing viable pollen and setting seed. Along with another private site, it is registered with the Michigan chapter of The Nature Conservancy, affording it some informal protection.

While population estimates of species that reproduce clonally are difficult to make, only four of the twelve existing sites support more than ten clumps of Michigan monkey-flower.

Conservation and Recovery

The principal threat to Michigan monkey-flower is the loss of its specialized habitat through recreational and residential development. Increased construction of vacation homes along lake and stream shores is known to have been responsible for the destruction of three populations; two others have been severely affected.

Besides direct disturbance, Michigan monkey-flower is vulnerable to any disturbance to its water supply. Road construction or other activites that alter water drainage patterns may affect populations.

Although there does not appear to be an organized commercial trade in Michigan monkey-flower, some collecting has occurred. In fact, one population was discovered when a botanist was served a sprig of Michigan monkey-flower as a garnish on a restrauant dinner plate.

Additional Source

Penskar, M. R. 1991. "Michigan Monkey-Flower (*Mimulus glabratus* var. *michiganensis*) Recovery Plan." U.S. Fish and Wildlife Service, Twin Cities, Minnesota.

Contact

William F. Harrison
U.S. Fish and Wildlife Service
Federal Building, Fort Snelling
Twin Cities, Minnesota, 55111

Neraudia angulata
No Common Name

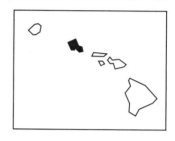

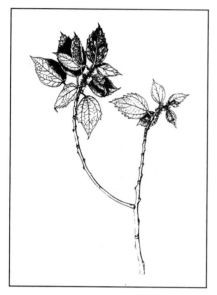

From Cowan, R. *Pacific Science* 3 (1949).

Status	Endangered
Listed	October 29, 1991
Family	Urticaceae (Nettle)
Description	Erect shrub with elliptic leaves; male and female flowers on separate plants.
Habitat	Slopes, ledges, and gulches in moist forest.
Threats	Feral pigs and goats, alien plant species.
Region 1	Hawaii (Oahu)

Description

Neraudia angulata is an erect shrub of the nettle family that grows 3 meters (10 ft) tall. The elliptic leaves, 7 to 15 centimeters (3 to 6 in) long, are slightly hairy above and moderately hairy below. Male and female flowers occur on different plants. Two varieties of this Endangered plant are recognized: *N. a.* var. *angulata*, which has untoothed leaves and *N. a.* var. *dentata*, which has toothed leaves. The drawing above is var. *dentata*.

Habitat

Neraudia angulata is found only in the Waianae Mountain Range on the western side of the island of Oahu, Hawaii. This island is dominated by the remnants of two ancient volcanoes that have eroded into two "mountain ranges," which consist of long, narrow ridges. The Waianae Range lies on the western side of the island, while the Koolau Range traverses the eastern side. The Waianae Range, which runs northwest to southeast for about 40 miles, lies in the rain shadow of the Koolau Range, and, except for the summit of Mt. Kaala, the highest point on the island, receives much less rainfall.

A variety of plant habitats are found in the Waianae Mountains, ranging from coastal dry shrubland to lowland dry forest to lowland wet forest. *Neraudia angu-*

lata grows on slopes, ledges, or gulches in diverse moist forest dominated by lama (*Diospyros sandwicensis*) at elevations between 370 and 820 meters (1,200 to 2,700 ft). Associated species include aulu (*Sapindus oahuensis*), Christmasberry (*Schinus terebinthifolius*), and olopua (*Nestegis sandwicensis*).

The diverse habitats of the Waianae Mountains contain a large number of vulnerable native Hawaiian plant species. In October 1991 the Fish and Wildlife Service (FWS) listed *Neraudia angulata* and 25 other plant species from Oahu's Waianae Mountains as Endangered. This group listing was the result of the settlement of a 1989 lawsuit brought against the FWS by the Sierra Club Legal Defense Fund on behalf of a Hawaii conservation group. The terms of the settlement called for the proposed listing before October 1992 of 186 Hawaiian candidate plant species.

Historic Range

Neraudia angulata was first collected in 1912 from Oahu. It has been found throughout most of the Waianae Mountains, from Kaluakauila Gulch almost to Puu Manawahua.

Current Distribution

The species is now found at Kahana-haiki-Makua Ridge, Kaluakauila Gulch, Makaha-Waianae Kai Ridge, Puu Kanehoa, and Puu Kumakalii. These five populations, which occur on federal, state, and private land, are estimated to contain fewer than 15 plants.

Conservation and Recovery

The main threats to *Neraudia angulata* are habitat degradation by feral pigs and goats and competition with aggressive alien plant species. Pigs, which are managed by the state as game animals, have been in the Waianae Mountains for about 150 years and have had a major effect on the native flora. Their rooting destroys plants and opens the habitat to invasive species. They also help spread these plant species by carrying seed on their bodies and in their feces. Feral goats, also game animals, have been on the island for 170 years. Because of their agility they are able to reach areas inaccessible to pigs. Although a major control effort greatly reduced the goat population by 1905, remaining animals are still a threat to rare species.

Non-native plants threaten almost all native Hawaiian flora, especially rare species. *Neraudia angulata* is directly threatened by several. Christmasberry (*Schinus terebinthifolius*), an aggressive tree introduced to Hawaii before 1911, forms dense thickets and may also release chemicals that inhibit the growth of other species. Molasses grass (*Melinus minutiflora*) grows in dense mats that smother native vegetation. Strawberry guava (*Psidium cattleianum*) is an invasive tree that forms dense stands that exclude other species.

Some *Neraudia angulata* plants lie near the U.S. Army's Makua Military Reservation and Schofield Barracks. Within a 14-month period from 1989 to 1990, 10 fires resulted from weapons practice on the reservation. A fire in July 1989 may have destroyed a *Neraudia angulata* population. In order to minimize damage from fires, the army has constructed firebreaks between the target areas and the surrounding forest.

With only 15 *Neraudia angulata* plants known to exist in five populations, the species is extremely vulnerable to extinction through unpredictable human or natural events.

Additional Sources

Cuddihy, L. W., and C. P. Stone. 1990. *Alteration of Native Hawaiian Vegetation: Effects of Humans, Their Activities and Introductions.* Cooperative National Park Resources Study Unit, University of Hawaii Press, Honolulu.

Culliney, J. L. 1988. *Islands in a Far Sea: Nature and Man in Hawaii.* Sierra Club Books, San Francisco.

Stone, C. P., and J. M. Scott, eds. 1985. *Hawai'i's Terrestrial Ecosystems: Preservation and Management.* Cooperative National Park Resources Study Unit, University of Hawaii Press, Honolulu.

Wagner, W. L., D. R. Herbst, and S. H. Sohmer. 1990. *Manual of the Flowering Plants of Hawai'i.* University of Hawaii Press and Bishop Museum Press, Honolulu.

Contacts

Regional Office of Endangered Species
U.S. Fish and Wildlife Service
Eastside Federal Complex
911 N.S. 11th Avenue
Portland, Oregon 97232-4181

Derral R. Herbst
U.S. Fish and Wildlife Service
300 Ala Moana Boulevard, Room 6307
P.O. Box 50167
Honolulu, Hawaii 96850

Nototrichium humile
No Common Name

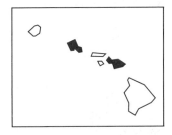

Status	Endangered
Listed	October 29, 1991
Family	Amaranthaceae (Amaranth)
Description	Branched, hairy shrub with opposite leaves and a slender flower spike at the stem ends.
Habitat	Gulches, steep slopes, and cliff faces in open dry forest.
Threats	Feral pigs, goats, and cattle; alien plant species.
Region 1	Hawaii (Maui, Oahu)

Robert Gustafson

Description

Nototrichium humile is a branched, upright to trailing shrub of the amaranth family with stems up to 1.5 meters (5 ft) long. The stems and leaves are covered with short hairs. The opposite, oblong leaves are 3 to 9 centimeters (1.2 to 3.5 in) long. Stalkless flowers appear on a slender spike 3 to 14 centimeters (1.2 to 5.5 in) long at the stem ends. The species has also been known as *Psilotrichum humile*.

Habitat

Amost all populations of *Nototrichium humile* are found in the Waianae Mountain Range on the western side of the island of Oahu, Hawaii. This island is dominated by the remnants of two ancient volcanoes that have eroded into two "mountain ranges," which consist of long, narrow ridges. The Waianae Range lies on the western side of the island, while the Koolau Range traverses the eastern side. The Waianae Range, which runs northwest to southeast for about 40 miles, lies in the rain shadow of the Koolau Range, and, except for the summit of Mt. Kaala, the highest point on the island, receives much less rainfall.

A variety of plant habitats are found in the Waianae Mountains, ranging from coastal dry shrubland to lowland dry forest to lowland wet forest. *Nototrichium humile* grows in gulches, on steep slopes, and on cliff faces in remnants of open dry forest at elevations between 60 and 700 meters (200 and 2,300 ft). The vegetation is dominated by aulu or soapberry (*Sapindus oahuensis*) and lama (*Diospyros sandwicensis*). Associated species include Christmasberry (*Schinus terebinthifolius*), kukui or candlenut (*Aleurites moluccana*), and olopua (*Nestegis sandwicensis*).

The diverse habitats of the Waianae Mountains contain a large number of vulnerable native Hawaiian plant species. In October 1991 the Fish and Wildlife Service (FWS) listed *Nototrichium humile* and 25 other plant species from Oahu's Waianae Mountains as Endangered. This group listing was the result of the settlement of a 1989 lawsuit brought against the FWS by the Sierra Club Legal Defense Fund on behalf of a Hawaii conservation group. The terms of the settlement called for the proposed listing before October 1992 of 186 Hawaiian candidate plant species.

Historic Range

Nototrichium humile was first described in 1888. It has been known from the entire length of the Waianae Mountains, from near Kaena Point to Nanakuli Valley. It has also been collected from Lualailua Hills on East Maui.

Current Distribution

The species is currently found in the Waianae Mountains at Kahanahaiki Valley, Dealia, Makaha-Waianae Kai Ridge, Makua Valley, and Nanakuli Valley. A single population occurs on state land in Maui's Lualailua Hills. On Oahu *Nototrichium humile* populations occur over a 26-square-mile area of state and private land. The total species population is estimated to be between 1,500 and 3,000 plants.

Conservation and Recovery

As is the case for almost all rare Hawaiian flora, the main threats to the species are habitat degradation by feral pigs, goats, and cattle and competition from invasive non-native plant species.

Feral pigs, which are managed by the state as game animals, have been in the Waianae Mountains for about 150 years and have had a major effect on native flora. Their rooting destroys plants and opens the habitat to invasive species. They also help spread these alien plants by carrying seed on their bodies and in their feces. Feral goats, which are also managed as game animals, have been on the island for 170 years. Because of their agility they are able to reach areas inaccessible to pigs and cattle. Although a major control effort greatly reduced the goat population by 1905, remaining animals are still a threat to rare species.

Cattle, too, have had a major affect on the native vegetation. Much of the low- to mid-elevation forest between 210 and 550 meters (700 and 1,800 ft) was destroyed by cattle and goats. Most feral cattle were eliminated from the island by the mid-1900s. However, ranching operations contine in the Mokuleia area on the west side of the Waianae Mountains. Some cattle move into the upland forest where they consume native vegetation, threatening *Nototrichium humile* and other rare species.

Aggressive non-native plant species are continuing to displace native Hawaiian flora, and *Nototrichium humile* is directly threatened by several. Christmasberry (*Schinus terebinthifolius*), an aggressive tree introduced to Hawaii before 1911, forms dense thickets and may also release chemicals that inhibit the growth of other species. Koa haole (*Leucaena leucocephala*) is another alien tree which is able to colonize poor soils because of its ability to manufacture nitrogen. Strawberry guava (*Psidium cattleianum*) is an invasive tree that forms dense stands that exclude other species. Molasses grass (*Melinus minutiflora*), grows in dense mats that smother native vegetation. It is also fire adapted and provides fuel for spreading wildfires.

Such fires are an additional threat to *Nototrichium humile* populations which lie near the U.S. Army's Makua Military Reservation and Schofield Barracks. Within a 14-month period from 1989 to 1990, 10 fires resulted from weapons practice on the reservation. In July 1989 a 300-acre fire came within a quarter of a mile of a population of *Nototrichium humile*. In order to minimize damage from fires, the army has constructed firebreaks between the target areas and the surrounding forest.

Contacts

Regional Office of Endangered Species
U.S. Fish and Wildlife Service
Eastside Federal Complex
911 N.S. 11th Avenue
Portland, Oregon 97232-4181

Derral R. Herbst
U.S. Fish and Wildlife Service
300 Ala Moana Boulevard, Room 6307
P.O. Box 50167
Honolulu, Hawaii 96850

Additional Sources

Cuddihy, L. W., and C. P. Stone. 1990. *Alteration of Native Hawaiian Vegetation: Effects of Humans, Their Activities and Introductions*. Cooperative National Park Resources Study Unit, University of Hawaii Press, Honolulu.

Culliney, J. L. 1988. *Islands in a Far Sea: Nature and Man in Hawaii*. Sierra Club Books, San Francisco.

Stone, C. P., and J. M. Scott, eds. 1985. *Hawai'i's Terrestrial Ecosystems: Preservation and Management*. Cooperative National Park Resources Study Unit, University of Hawaii Press, Honolulu.

Wagner, W. L., D. R. Herbst, and S. H. Sohmer. 1990. *Manual of the Flowering Plants of Hawai'i*. University of Hawaii Press and Bishop Museum Press, Honolulu.

Bakersfield Cactus
Opuntia treleasei

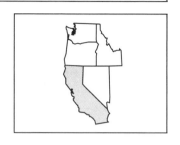

Susan Middleton and David Liittschwager   *Color Plate C-5*

Status	Endangered
Listed	July 19, 1990
Family	Cactaceae (Cactus)
Description	Prickly-pear cactus with large magenta flowers and spines arising from aureoles.
Habitat	Grasslands, scrub.
Threats	Agricultural and urban development, oil and gas drilling.
Region 1	California

Description

The low-growing Bakersfield cactus spreads to form dense thickets. Its pad-like flattened stems are 7.7 to 10.2 centimeters (3 to 4 in) wide and 12.7 to 17.8 centimeters (5 to 7 in) long. Spines, which vary in length and number, arise from aureoles (circular areas) on the flattened stems. The surface of the stem which is nearly cylindrical at the base, is smooth. Plants bear large, attractive, magenta flowers.

Habitat

The Bakersfield cactus is endemic to the grassland and adjacent plant communities of California's southern San Joaquin Valley and nearby foothills and valleys. Alien grasses, introduced during the time of the Franciscan missionaries, outcompeted native plant species and came to dominate the grasslands. Bakersfield cactus persists in these annual grasslands as well as at sites with reduced grass cover. It occurs mainly on annual grassland in sandy or sandy-loamy soils. Four other Threatened or Endangered plants occur in the San Joaquin Valley: Kern mallow (*Eremalche kernensis*), California jewelflower (*Caulanthus californicus*), Hoover's wooly-star (*Eriastrum hooveri*), and San Joaquin wooly-threads (*Lembertia congdonii*).

Historic Range

Bakersfield cactus was first collected in 1892 in Kern County, east of Caliente. It grew on the hills northeast of Oildale along the valley floor to the foothills of the Tehachapi Mountains. It was once extremely abundant on the mesas east of Bakersfield, and thick growths of the cactus along Caliente Creek were noted as late as 1937.

Current Distribution

Today Bakersfield cactus survives only in isolated colonies which can be grouped into five general areas: oil fields northeast of Oildale, the Kern River Bluffs northeast of Bakersfield, the bluffs and hills west and north of Caliente Creek east of Bakersfield, Comanche Point on the Tejon Ranch southeast of Arvin, and northwest of the town of Wheeler Ridge.

Conservation and Recovery

This once abundant species was reduced by conversion of much of its habitat to potato and cotton cultivation, oil development, and urbanization. This array of development activities continues to threaten the species. The colonies north of Oildale are threatened by oil and gas development, while those on the Kern River Bluffs are subject to urban sprawl from Bakersfield. The colonies near Caliente Creek are vulnerable to disturbance from off-road vehicles and sand mining.

The Nature Conservancy owns a portion of the Sand Ridge colony at Caliente Creek, but a proposed flood control project would destroy some of these plants. The Army Corps of Engineers, which is involved in the project, has been consulting with the Fish and Wildlife Service to determine the impact upon two other federally listed species: the San Joaquin kit fox (*Vulpes macrotis mutica*) and the blunt-nosed leopard lizard (*gambelia silus*). The colony near Wheeler Ridge is threatened by conversion to agriculture, urbanization,

off-road vehicles, and various maintenance activities. One population near Wheeler Ridge is on land administered by the state Department of Water Resources.

Additional Sources

Benson, L. 1969. *The Native Cacti of California*. Stanford University Press, Palo Alto.

Heady, H. F. 1977. "Valley Grassland." In *Terrestrial Vegetation of California*, edited by M. G. Barbour, and J. Major. John Wiley and Sons, New York.

Hoover, R. F. 1970. *The Vascular Plants of San Luis Obispo County, California*. University of California Press, Berkeley.

Wester, L. 1981 "Composition of Native Grasslands in the San Joaquin Valley, California." *Madroño* 28:231-241.

Contacts

Regional Office of Endangered Species
U.S. Fish and Wildlife Service
Eastside Federal Complex
911 N.S. 11th Avenue
Portland, Oregon 97232-4181

Jim A. Bartel
U.S. Fish and Wildlife Service
2800 Cottage Way, Room E-1823
Sacramento, California 95825

Palo de Rosa
Ottoschulzia rhodoxylon

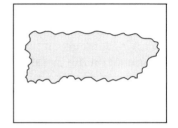

William M. Houghton/Fairchild Tropical Garden

Status	Endangered
Listed	April 10, 1990
Family	Icacinaceae (Icacina)
Description	Small, evergreen tree with alternate, untoothed, leathery leaves.
Habitat	Seasonal and dry forests.
Threats	Low numbers, deforestation.
Region 4	Puerto Rico

Description

Palo de rosa is a small, evergreen tree that can reach a height of 3.6 to 4.6 meters (12 to 15 ft). Its thick, leathery leaves are elliptic to ovate, alternate, untoothed, and rounded at the tip and the base. The flowers have not been observed, but other members of the genus bear solitary or clustered flowers, which have a tubed corolla with five lobes. The fleshy fruit contains a single seed. The heartwood of the tree is reddish.

Habitat

The few remaining palo de rosa trees grow in semi-evergreen, seasonal forests and semi-deciduous, dry forests on limestone soils and in lower montane, semi-evergreen forests on serpentine soils.

Historic Range

Palo de rosa was first collected in 1876 near Mayaguez, Puerto Rico. The species is found only in Puerto Rico and Hispaniola and apparently has always been rare. Puerto Rico has been heavily deforested and much of the remaining forest is secondary growth. It is not known how many palo de rosa trees were lost to deforestation. The species is also considered rare in the Dominican Republic.

Current Distribution

Nine palo de rosa trees are known to survive in Puerto Rico at three locations. The species is found on the north coast in a limestone hill area near Bayamón, on the south coast in the Guánica Commonwealth Forest, and in the Maricao Commonwealth Forest.

Conservation and Recovery

The north coast site is near the expanding metropolitan area of San Juan and any undiscovered palo de rosa trees are likely to be cut. Some trees in the Guánica Commonwealth Forest occur in dry streams and along roads and could be harmed by forest maintenance practices. Palo de rosa flower and fruit production appears erratic, and no seedlings are known to exist. The extreme rarity of the species, coupled with apparent reproductive failure, increase the importance of every remaining tree in the struggle against extinction.

Additional Sources

Liogier, H. A., and L. F. Martorell. 1982. *Flora of Puerto Rico and Adjacent Islands: A Systematic Synopsis.* University of Puerto Rico, Río Piedras.

Little, E. L., Jr., R. O. Woodbury, and F. H. Wadsworth. 1974. *Trees of Puerto Rico and the Virgin Islands.* vol. 2. Agriculture Handbook No. 449. U.S.D.A., Forest Service.

Contacts

Regional Office of Endangered Species
U. S. Fish and Wildlife Service
Richard B. Russell Federal Building
75 Spring Street, S.W.
Atlanta, Georgia 30303

Susan Silander
U.S. Fish and Wildlife Service
P.O. Box 491
Boquerón, Puerto Rico 00622

Texas Trailing Phlox

Phlox nivalis ssp. *texensis*

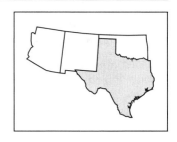

Paul M. Montgomery   *Color Plate C-4*

Status	Endangered
Listed	September 30, 1991
Family	Polemoniaceae (Phlox)
Description	Trailing, hairy, evergreen perennial, bearing clusters of purple, pink, or white flowers.
Habitat	Sandy soil in longleaf pine savannah.
Threats	Low numbers, residential and silvacultural development.
Region 2	Texas

Description

Texas trailing phlox is a clump-forming perennial with spreading, evergreen, hairy shoots that grow to a height of 30 centimeters (12 in). Sterile shoots have needle-like leaves, while fertile shoots have short, lanceolate leaves. The purple-lavender, deep pink, rose, or white flowers occur in clusters of three to six in late March and early April. The fruit capsule has three chambers, each containing a single seed.

Habitat

The species is endemic to the Big Thicket Forest in eastern Texas, north and west of Beaumont. It has been found in open, grassy longleaf pine (*Pinus paulstra*) savannah in sandy soil. It often grows in association with *Bothriochloa* spp., hickory (*Carya* spp.), and yaupon (*Ilex vomitoria*).

Historic Range

Texas trailing phlox was first collected in 1931 in Hardin County, Texas. It has been found in Hardin, Tyler, and Polk counties. In the 1940s it was collected from seven localities in Tyler County, and was considered abundant in the pinelands between Woodville and Warren. In 1980 the species was found at only five sites: three in Tyler County, and two in Hardin County.

Current Distribution

The most current survey (1989) documented only two surviving populations. The largest is in Hardin County on land owned by The Nature Conservancy, where a few hundred plants occur in sandy soil in a former pine plantation. The Tyler County population consists of only six clumps of plants at the edge of a pine plantation.

Conservation and Recovery

Texas trailing phlox has shown a significant decline over recent decades, primarily because of land clearing for housing construction and the establishment of pine plantations. A population on land adjacent to The Nature Conservancy land was destroyed by construction of a pipeline.

Active management is necessary to keep suitable habitat from changing through natural succession. The Nature Conservancy is conducting a program of prescribed burning and slash pine removal to maintain the plant's habitat.

Additional Sources

Mahler, W. F. 1980. "Status Report, *Phlox nivalis* ssp. *texensis*. Lindell." U.S. Fish and Wildlife Service, Albuquerque.

Wherry, E. T. 1966. "Polemoniaceae." In *Flora of Texas*, edited by C. L. Lundell. 1(3): 283-321.

Contacts

Regional Office of Endangered Species
U.S. Fish and Wildlife Service
P.O. Box 1306
Albuquerque, New Mexico 87103

Phillip Clayton
U.S. Fish and Wildlife Service
c/o Corpus Christi State University
Campus Box 338
6300 Ocean Drive
Corpus Christi, Texas 78412

Phyllostegia glabra var. lanaiensis

No Common Name

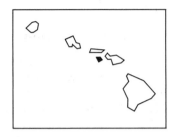

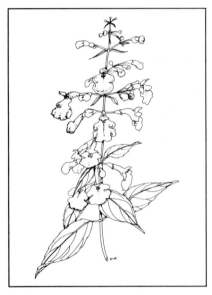

Yevonn Wilson-Ramsey from *Manual of the Flowering Plants of Hawai'i*

Status . . . . Endangered
Listed . . . . September 20, 1991
Family . . . . Lamiaceae (Mint)
Description . . . . . . Tall perennial with red-veined leaves and white flowers, sometimes tinged with purple.
Habitat . . . . Lowland wet forest.
Threats . . . . Low numbers, alien plant species, axis deer.
Region 1 . . . . Hawaii (Lanai)

Description

Phyllostegia glabra var. *lanaiensis* is an erect to reclining perennial of the mint family that grows from 1 to 5 meters (3.3 to 16.4 ft) high. The thin, lance-shaped leaves are 8 to 24 centimeters (3 to 9.5 in) long, toothed, and often reddish or with red veins. The white flowers, sometimes tinged with reddish purple, appear in clusters of 6 to 10 in the leaf axils.

A photograph or drawing of *Phyllostegia glabra* var. *lanaiensis* could not be obtained. The illustration above is of *P. g.* var. *glabra* which differs from the listed variety by having a longer calyx and wider leaves.

Habitat

This species grows on the slopes of the gulches of the Lanaihale Ridge on the island of Lanai, Hawaii. A broad ridge runs northwest to southeast across this small island and is commonly known by the name of its highest peak, Lanaihale, which is 1,027 meters (3,370 ft) high. A lowland wet forest community is found on the Lanaihale summit and its narrow valleys. Although annual rainfall is only about 94 centimeters (37 in), the area is usually cloud-covered in the afternoon and shrouded in fog at night. Dominant members of the plant community are ohia

(*Metrosideros polymorpha*) and uluhe fern (*Dicranopteris linearis*). Three other Endangered plant species, *Cyanea macrostegia* var. *gibsonii*, *Gahnia lanaiensis*, and *Viola lanaiensis*, are also found in this lowland wet forest. A lowland dry shrubland community occurs on the leeward slopes and valleys of Lanaihale. This community supports two plant species listed as Endangered: *Abutilon eremitopetalum* and *Tetramolopium remyi*. All of these Endangered plant species are endemic to Lanaihale.

Historic Range

This species was first collected in 1864 or 1865 from the mountains of Lanai. It has seldom been collected and is not known from anywhere else.

Current Distribution

The last sighting of *Phyllostegia glabra* var. *lanaiensis* was made in the 1980s when a single plant was found in a gulch leading into Maunalei Valley. Even though the species has not been found in recent years, botanists are hopeful that plants will be discovered. Lanaihale valleys and gulches are rugged and not regularly surveyed.

Conservation and Recovery

The main threat to *Phyllostegia glabra* var. *lanaiensis* is its extremely low numbers and very limited range. With no recently documented plant sites, any *Phyllostegia glabra* var. *lanaiensis* plants that exist would be extremely vulnerable to extinction through an unpredictable event.

Like other native plants endemic to Lanai, *Phyllostegia glabra* var. *lanaiensis* is threatened by invasive alien plant species that compete with it for available space and light, as well as browsing axis deer.

Additional Sources

Cuddihy, L. W., and C. P. Stone. 1990. *Alteration of Native Hawaiian Vegetation: Effects of Humans, Their Activities and Introductions*. University of Hawaii Cooperative National Park Resources Study Unit, Honolulu.

Culliney, J. L. 1988. *Islands in a Far Sea: Nature and Man in Hawaii*. Sierra Club Books, San Francisco.

Wagner, W. L., D. R. Herbst, and S. H. Sohmer. 1990. *Manual of the Flowering Plants of Hawai'i*. University of Hawaii Press and Bishop Museum Press, Honolulu.

Contacts

Regional Office of Endangered Species
U.S. Fish and Wildlife Service
Eastside Federal Complex
911 N.S. 11th Avenue
Portland, Oregon 97232-4181

Derral R. Herbst
U.S. Fish and Wildlife Service
300 Ala Moana Boulevard, Room 6307
P.O. Box 50167
Honolulu, Hawaii 96850

Phyllostegia mollis
No Common Name

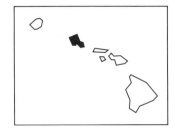

Status	Endangered
Listed	October 29, 1991
Family	Lamiaceae (Mint)
Description	Sparsely branched with hairy stems; opposite leaves; and lipped, tubular white flowers.
Habitat	Slopes and gulches in moist to wet forest.
Threats	Alien plant species, low numbers.
Region 1	Hawaii (Oahu)

John Obata

Description

Phyllostegia mollis is a sparsely branched, nonaromatic, perennial of the mint family with stems that are densely covered with short hairs. The opposite, oval leaves have rounded teeth and are 10 to 24 centimeters (4 to 9.4 in) long. Lipped, tubular white flowers appear, usually in groups of six, at intervals along the stems. The fruits are fleshy, dark nutlets.

The species has also been known by the names *Phyllostegia haliakaloe, P. honolulensis, P. parviflora* var. *honolulensis*, and *P. parviflora* var. *mollis*.

Habitat

Phyllostegia mollis is found only in the Waianae Mountain Range on the western side of the island of Oahu, Hawaii. This island is dominated by the remnants of two ancient volcanoes that have eroded into two "mountain ranges," which consist of long, narrow ridges. The Waianae Range lies on the western side of the island, while the Koolau Range traverses the eastern side. The Waianae Range, which runs northwest to southeast for about 40 miles, lies in the rain shadow of the Koolau Range, and, except for the summit of Mt. Kaala, the highest point on the island, receives much less rainfall.

A variety of plant habitats are found in the Waianae Mountains, ranging from coastal dry shrubland to lowland dry forest to lowland wet forest. *Phyllostegia mollis* grows on steep slopes and in gulches in moist to wet forest at elevations between

450 and 800 meters (1,500 and 2,800 ft). Associated plant species include kopiko (*Psychotria*), papala kepau (*Pisonia*), raspberry (*Rubrus*), and various ferns.

The diverse habitats of the Waianae Mountains contain a large number of vulnerable native Hawaiian plant species. In October 1991 the Fish and Wildlife Service (FWS) listed *Phyllostegia mollis* and 25 other plant species from Oahu's Waianae Mountains as Endangered. This group listing was the result of the settlement of a 1989 lawsuit brought against the FWS by the Sierra Club Legal Defense Fund on behalf of a Hawaii conservation group. The terms of the settlement called for the proposed listing before October 1992 of 186 Hawaiian candidate plant species.

Historic Range

Phyllostegia mollis was first described in 1831. It has been known from Oahu where it occurred in the central and southern Waianae Mountains, from Mt. Kaala to Honoliuli, and at Makiki in the Koolau Mountains. It was also found on Molokai and East Maui.

Current Distribution

Today *Phyllostegia mollis* survives only at Kaluaa Gulch and on Puu Kaua in Oahu's Waianae Mountains. These two populations, which occur on federal and private lands, contain less than 50 plants.

Conservation and Recovery

The major threats to *Phyllostegia mollis* are competition from an aggressive non-native plant species and its extremely low population and limited distribution. The species' habitat is being invaded by Christmasberry (*Schinus terebinthifolius*), an ag-

gressive tree that forms dense thickets and may also release chemicals that inhibit the growth of other species.

With a total species' population of less than 50 plants and an extremely limited distribution, *Phyllostegia mollis* is vulnerable to extinction through unpredictible human or natural events.

Additional Sources

Cuddihy, L. W., and C. P. Stone. 1990. *Alteration of Native Hawaiian Vegetation: Effects of Humans, Their Activities and Introductions.* Cooperative National Park Resources Study Unit, University of Hawaii Press, Honolulu.

Culliney, J. L. 1988. *Islands in a Far Sea: Nature and Man in Hawaii.* Sierra Club Books, San Francisco.

Stone, C. P., and J. M. Scott, eds. 1985. *Hawai'i's Terrestrial Ecosystems: Preservation and Management.* Cooperative National Park Resources Study Unit, University of Hawaii Press, Honolulu.

Wagner, W. L., D. R. Herbst, and S. H. Sohmer. 1990. *Manual of the Flowering Plants of Hawai'i.* University of Hawaii Press and Bishop Museum Press, Honolulu.

Contacts

Regional Office of Endangered Species
U.S. Fish and Wildlife Service
Eastside Federal Complex
911 N.S. 11th Avenue
Portland, Oregon 97232-4181

Derral R. Herbst
U.S. Fish and Wildlife Service
300 Ala Moana Boulevard, Room 6307
P.O. Box 50167
Honolulu, Hawaii 96850

Dudley Bluffs Twinpod
Physaria obcordata

Robert L. Powell   *Color Plate C-4*

Status	Threatened
Listed	February 6, 1990
Family	Brassicaceae (Mustard)
Description	Low-growing perennial with hairy leaves and yellow, four-petaled flowers.
Habitat	Oil shale outcrops.
Threats	Mining.
Region 6	Colorado

Description

The Dudley Bluffs twinpod is a low-growing perennial in the mustard family that reaches a height of 12 to 18 centimeters (4.8 to 7.2 in). The hairy leaves, which are oblanceolate and untoothed, appear silvery. Plants bear small, yellow, four-petaled flowers and heart shaped fruits.

Habitat

Found only in the Piceance Basin of Colorado, Dudley Bluffs twinpod grows on the slopes of barren, white oil shale outcrops. It is often found near another Threatened mustard, the Dudley Bluffs bladderpod (*Lesquerella congesta*), which grows on level shale outcrops. The species occurs at elevations of from 1,806 to 2,255 meters (5,960 to 7,440 ft). The surrounding hills and mesas support pinyon-juniper woodlands.

Historic Range

Dudley Bluffs twinpod was discovered in 1982 in Rio Blanco County, northwestern Colorado, during a survey of the flora of the Piceance Basin conducted by the state Natural Heritage Inventory for the Bureau of Land Management (BLM). The species has not been found outside this basin.

Current Distribution

This twinpod is currently found at five sites in Rio Blanco County, mostly on federal land administered by BLM. There are three known populations along Piceance and Yellow creeks and two populations on Calamity Ridge. These five populations cover approximately 250 acres over a 15-mile range. The largest population, consisting of about 10,000 plants, is on BLM land at the junction of Piceance Creek and Ryan Gulch. This site also supports a similar number of the Dudley Bluffs bladderpod (*Lesquerella obcordata*). At the Dudley Bluffs site the species occurs on both BLM land and private land.

Conservation and Recovery

The main threat to the Dudley Bluffs twinpod is the mining of its habitat for rich deposits of oil shale and sodium minerals, such as nahcolite and dawsonite. While mining is not imminent, long term mining plans are clearly a threat to the species. As the federal government seeks alternative energy sources to imported petroleum, subsidy programs for oil shale development continue to be proposed in the U.S. Congress.

Yellow Creek, Dudley Bluffs, and Ryan Gulch are on oil shale deposits which could be mined by open-pit methods. A pilot project for an underground nahcolite solution mine has been established between Piceance Creek and Yellow Creek, and a commercial mine has been proposed for the area which would cover 254 acres. These activities could result in the destruction or modification of almost three-quarters of the entire Dudley Bluffs twinpod habitat. BLM has decided not to lease the commercial mineral rights to the area until improved mining technology is developed, but is still considering leases for noncommercial research purposes. While BLM has designated the federal portion of the Dudley Bluffs site and one of the Calamity ridge sites as "areas of critical environmental concern," this protects only about 250 acres of twinpod habitat.

Although Dudley Bluffs twinpod is locally abundant in its specialized habitat, its extremely limited range makes it vulnerable to surface disturbance. The Rio Blanco County government, as well as oil shale and nahcolite companies opposed the listing of Dudley Bluffs twinpod as a Threatened species.

Additional Sources

Bureau of Land Management. 1987. "Piceance Basin Resource Management Plan Record of Decision." U.S. Government Printing Office, Washington, DC.

Colorado Native Plant Society. 1989. *Rare Plants of Colorado*. Colorado Native Plant Society and the Rocky Mountain Nature Association, Estes Park, Colorado.

Colorado Natural Areas Program. 1987. "Status Report for *Physaria obcordata*." Denver, Colorado.

Contacts

Regional Office of Endangered Species
U.S. Fish and Wildlife Service
P.O. Box 25486
Denver Federal Center
Denver, Colorado 80225

John Anderson
U.S. Fish and Wildlife Service
529 25½ Road, Suite B-113
Grand Junction, Colorado 81505

Eastern Prairie Fringed Orchid
Platanthera leucophaea

Jessie M. Harris

Status	Threatened
Listed	September 28, 1989
Family	Orchidaceae (Orchid)
Description	Perennial orchid with up to 40 large, white, fringed flowers.
Habitat	Prairies and open wetlands.
Threats	Conversion of habitat to cropland, hay mowing, natural succession.
Region 3	Illinois, Iowa, Michigan, Ohio, Wisconsin
Region 5	Maine, Virginia
Canada	Ontario

Description

The eastern prairie fringed orchid is a perennial which, following winter dormancy, sends up leaves and a flower spike in May. The alternate leaves are lanceolate to linear and are 10 to 20 centimeters (4 to 8 in) long. The upper leaves are much smaller than the lower. As many as 40 large white flowers are borne on the stem which grows to a height of 120 centimeters (47 in). The flowers have extremely long spurs and a deeply fringed three-part lower lip. They become fragrant after sunset and are pollinated by night-flying hawkmoths.

The eastern prairie fringed orchid forms a species pair with the closely related western prairie fringed orchid (*Platanthera praeclara*), also listed as a Threatened species. Before *P. praeclara* was described, the two species were both known as *P. leucophaea*. The species has also been known as *Habenaria leucophaea*. These two orchids are distinguished by details of flower structure and their respective pollination strategies. The eastern species places its pollen on the proboscis of visiting moths; the western species has larger flowers, which deposit pollen on the moths' eyes.

Habitat

The eastern prairie fringed orchid grows in tallgrass calcareous silt loam or moist sand prairies. It is also found in open portions of calcareous wetlands, such as fens, marshes, and bogs. The species requires full sunlight and is vulnerable to natural succession.

Historic Range

This orchid once occurred throughout much of the grasslands and open wetlands of the upper Midwest and eastern United States. Its range extended from Nebraska to Maine and south to Oklahoma and possibly Arkansas. West of the Mississippi River, the species no longer occurs in Oklahoma, Arkansas, Nebraska, or Missouri. In the East it has been extirpated from New York, Pennsylvania, New Jersey, Indiana, and possibly Virginia. Overall, the species has declined about 70 percent according to historic county records.

Current Distribution

The eastern prairie fringed orchid is now known from about 50 populations in seven states: Illinois, Iowa, Maine, Michigan, Ohio, Virginia, and Wisconsin. The small Virginia population, which consisted of three plants on private land in 1983, has been seen only intermittently since then. Additional populations are found in Canada (Ontario and New Brunswick). In the United States the orchid is most numerous in Michigan. Moderate populations occur in Wisconsin and Illinois.

In Michigan there are 18 populations in nine counties. A 1984 survey counted 1,322 flowering stems. Several populations numbering over 100 plants occur on prairies that border Saginaw Bay. Three other large populations, totalling about 900 plants, are found on upland prairies along Lake Erie. These sites are owned by the state of Michigan. Southern Michigan

populations are small and occur in isolated wetland habitats.

Nine small populations occur in eight counties in south and southeast Wisconsin. A single large population of several hundred plants is found in Kenosha County on a protected sand prairie bordering Lake Michigan.

In Ohio, three declining populations survive. The largest contained about 60 plants in 1987, a decline from 367 plants in 1982. Another population declined from 46 plants in 1984 to two plants in 1988. The third population is located on land frequently flooded by Lake Erie; in 1988 it contained 14 plants.

Illinois, which historically supported the largest populations of the orchid, has suffered the greatest decline. The species formerly grew in 33 counties across the upper two-thirds of the state, but now occurs in only 18 populations in eight counties in the Chicago area. Two additional populations occur in cemetery prairies in eastern and western Illinois. Only two populations, located in a county bordering Lake Michigan, contain over 100 plants.

One small population, consisting of three plants, remains in Iowa. The single Maine population, which occurs on low, swampy land, contains about 20 plants.

Conservation and Recovery

The decline of the eastern prairie fringed orchid has been the result of the conversion of prairie habitat to cropland. Although most conversions have already taken place, this process continues to pose a threat to surviving populations.

Perhaps the greatest continuing threat to the orchid is natural succession. Many of the largest populations occur on land that also supports successional vegetation. Without proper management orchid numbers on these sites are likely to decline. Other populations occur on small prairie remnants, which limits the possibility of population increase.

Although the species is not known to occur on federal land, a number of important populations are offered state protection. About half of the sites in Michigan are protected, as is the largest Wisconsin population. Most of the Illinois populations are under some form of protection.

Additional Sources

Bowles, M. L. 1983. "The Tallgrass Prairie Orchids *Platanthera leucophaea* and *Cyripedium candidum* Muhl. ex Wilid.: Some Aspects of Their Status, Biology, and Ecology, and Implications Toward Management." *Natural Areas Journal* 3:14-37.

Case, F. W., Jr. 1987. "Orchids of the Western Great Lakes Region." Cranbrook Institute of Science, Bulletin 48.

Luer, C. A. 1975. *The Native Orchids of the United States and Canada, Excluding Florida.* New York Botanical Garden.

Sheviak, C. J. 1974. "An Introduction to the Ecology of the Illinois Orchidaceae." Illinois State Museum, Scientific Paper 14.

Sheviak, C. J., and M. L. Bowles. 1986. "The Prairie Fringed Orchids: a Pollinator-Isolated Species Pair." *Rhodora* 88:267-290.

Contact

James M. Engel
Regional Office of Endangered Species
U.S. Fish and Wildlife Service
Federal Building, Fort Snelling
Twin Cities, Minnesota 55111

Western Prairie Fringed Orchid

Platanthera praeclara

Welby Smith   *Color Plate C-2*

Status	Threatened
Listed	September 28, 1989
Family	Orchidaceae (Orchid)
Description	Perennial orchid displaying up to 40 large, white, fringed flowers.
Habitat	Prairie.
Threats	Conversion of habitat to cropland, hay mowing, overgrazing.
Region 3	Iowa, Minnesota, Missouri
Region 6	Kansas, Nebraska, North Dakota
Canada	Manitoba

Description

The western prairie fringed orchid is a perennial which, following winter dormancy, sends up leaves and a flower spike in May. The alternate leaves are lanceolate to linear and are 10 to 20 centimeters (3.9 to 7.8 in) long. The upper leaves are much smaller than the lower. As many as 40 large white flowers are borne on the stem which grows to a height of 120 centimeters (47 in). The flowers have extremely long spurs and a deeply fringed three-part lower lip. The flowers become fragrant after sunset and are pollinated by night-flying hawkmoths.

The western prairie fringed orchid forms a species pair with the closely related east-ern prairie fringed orchid (*Platanthera leucophaea*), also listed as a Threatened species. Before *P. praeclara* was described, the two species were both known as *P. leucophaea*. They are distinguished by details of flower structure and their pollination mechanics. The western species has larger flowers, and its pollen is deposited on the eyes of a visiting moth; the eastern species places its pollen on the moth's proboscis.

Habitat

This orchid grows in tallgrass calcareous silt loam or moist sand prairies; many populations are found in hay meadows. The species requires full sunlight and is vulnerable to natural succession.

Historic Range

The western fringed orchid occurred in the plains and grasslands of the central United States, almost exclusively west of the Mississippi River. Its range extended from southern Manitoba (Canada) through North Dakota and Minnesota and south to Oklahoma and Missouri. According to county records, populations have experienced a 60 percent decline.

Current Distribution

Today this orchid is known from about 37 populations in six states: North Dakota, Nebraska, Kansas, Minnesota, Iowa, and Missouri. It also survives in Manitoba, Canada. It is no longer found in South Dakota, and the two populations that were discovered in Oklahoma during the 1970s have not been observed since then.

In North Dakota the western prairie fringed orchid occurs in a single large, scattered population of about 2,000 plants on the Sheyenne National Grassland, in the southeastern counties of Ransom and Richland. This land is administered by the Forest Service and is leased to the Sheyenne Valley Grazing Association for livestock production.

Five populations of the orchid are known to occur in Nebraska. Two small populations (less than 20 plants) are in the western portion of the state: one along a railroad right-of-way and another in the Valentine National Wildlife Refuge in Cherry County. The three other populations are in the eastern part of the state on public land or private land managed for conservation. The largest of these populations contains about 150 plants.

In Kansas eight populations are known to exist, seven in private hay meadows and one in a University of Kansas research area. Minnesota has six populations in four counties. The largest of these, containing about 500 plants, is protected. In Iowa there are 13 known populations, containing a total of about 600 plants. Two small populations survive in Missouri.

Conservation and Recovery

The decline of the western prairie fringed orchid was the result of conversion of its prairie habitat to cropland. Although most land conversions have already taken place, this process continues to pose a threat to the species. In the 1970s, the orchid was discovered in four hay meadows in eastern Kansas; they have since been converted to cropland.

Perhaps the greatest continuing threat to this orchid is the intensive mowing of hay meadows. Over 35 percent of known populations are found on hay meadows. Annual mowing removes the seed capsules before seed can be dispersed, resulting in a gradual decline in the local population. Additional threats to the species are overgrazing by livestock and natural succession.

The large North Dakota population on the Sheyenne National Grassland is subject to grazing. The orchid occurs on almost half of the leased grazing allotments. While moderate grazing does not appear to have harmed the species as much as conversion of habitat to cropland or hay mowing, management is necessary to prevent overgrazing. The Forest Service is initiating an interim management plan to ensure that livestock grazing on federal land does not adversely effect orchid populations. The recovery plan for the species is expected to recommend federal policies on grazing management. The Fish and Wild-life Service is also evaluating management policies for the orchid population on the Valentine National Wildlife refuge in western Nebraska to prevent overgrazing or succession.

Throughout its current range the western fringed orchid receives some degree of protection. Many of the populations, including most of the largest, are on federal or state lands, or private lands that are managed for conservation.

Additional Sources

Bowles, M. L. 1983. "The Tallgrass Prairie Orchids *Platanthera leucophaea* and *Cyripedium candidum* Muhl. ex Wilid.: Some Aspects of Their Status, Biology, and Ecology, and Implications Toward Management." *Natural Areas Journal* 3:14-37.

Case, F. W., Jr. 1987. "Orchids of the Western Great Lakes Region." Cranbrook Institute of Science, Bulletin 48.

Luer, C. A. 1975. *The Native Orchids of the United States and Canada, Excluding Florida.* New York Botanical Garden.

Sheviak, C. J. 1974. "An Introduction to the Ecology of the Illinois Orchidaceae." Illinois State Museum, Scientific Paper 14.

Sheviak, C. J., and M. L. Bowles. 1986. "The Prairie Fringed Orchids: a Pollinator-Isolated Species Pair." *Rhodora* 88:267-290.

Contacts

James M. Engel
Regional Office of Endangered Species
U.S. Fish and Wildlife Service
Federal Building, Fort Snelling
Twin Cities, Minnesota 55111

Little Aguja Pondweed
Potamogeton clystocarpus

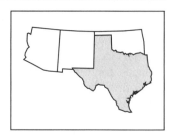

Paul M. Montgomery

Status	Endangered
Listed	November 14, 1991
Family	Potamogetonaceae (Pondweed)
Description	Slender, aquatic plant with submerged leaves and emergent whorls of flowers.
Habitat	Scattered, quiet pools in an intermittent stream.
Threats	Low numbers, trampling, decline in water quality.
Region 2	Texas

Description

Little Aguja pondweed is a slender, aquatic plant. Its branched stem usually has two small translucent glands at the stem nodes. The submerged, translucent light green leaves are linear, about 5 to 12 centimeters (2 to 4.5 in) long. The flower spikes, which have two or three whorls of flowers, emerge from the water, but submerge when fruiting. The fruits, which have distinctive warty protuberances at the base, develop from early May to October.

Habitat

This species is limited to a few scattered pools of an intermittent stream that flows through Little Aguja Canyon in the Davis Mountains (Jeff Davis County) of west Texas. The stream flows mostly underground through gravel bars. Plants root in the pools in igneous derived alluvium. Although there are many pools in the canyon streambed, this pondweed species is found in only two.

Historic Range

This pondweed was first collected in 1931. Thorough surveys of the area, conducted during the 1980s, failed to discover other populations.

Current Distribution

Little Aguja pondweed is only found in two quiet pools of the Little Aguja Canyon streambed. The entire known species population occurs on a ranch owned by the Boy Scouts of America.

Conservation and Recovery

The main threat to this rare pondweed is the low number of known plants. During alternating periods of drought and flooding plants are reduced to stem pieces and seeds, and the entire population must regenerate itself. Severe natural events may cause the population to fall below the level at which it can sustain itself. In addition, such low numbers make the species vulnerable to trampling by horses and wildlife and to any decline in water availability or quality. The landowner has been notified by the Fish and Wildlife Service of the pondweed's presence and rarity.

Additional Sources

Gould, F. W. 1975. *Texas Plants: A Checklist and Ecological Summary.* Texas Agricultural Experiment Station, Texas A&M University, College Station, Texas.

Haynes, R. R. 1974. "A Revision of North American *Potamogeton* Subsection Pusilli (Potamogetonaceae)." *Rhodora* 76:624-626.

Rowell, C. M., Jr. 1983. "Status Report, *Potamogeton clystocarpus* Fern." U.S. Fish and Wildlife Service, Albuquerque.

Contacts

Regional Office of Endangered Species
U.S. Fish and Wildlife Service
P.O. Box 1306
Albuquerque, New Mexico 87103
(505) 766-2321

Rogelio Perez
U.S. Fish and Wildlife Service
c/o Corpus Christi State University
Campus Box 338
6300 Ocean Drive
Corpus Christi, Texas 78412
(512) 888-3346

Remya kauaiensis
No Common Name

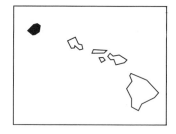

Robert Gustafson

Status	Endangered
Listed	January 14, 1991
Family	Asteraceae (Aster)
Description	Sprawling shrub with hairy leaves bunched at the stem ends and clusters of small, yellow flowers.
Habitat	Steep slopes in moist forests.
Threats	Domestic and feral animals, alien plant species, low numbers.
Region 1	Hawaii (Kauai)

Description

Remya kauaiensis is a small, sprawling to weakly erect perennial shrub that grows to a height of 90 centimeters (35 in). The branches are covered with a tan fuzz near the tips. The coarsely toothed, elliptic to ovate leaves are about 15 centimeters (6 in) long and are bunched near the ends of the branches. The leaf undersides are covered with white hairs. The small, dark yellow flowers (0.7 cm; 0.3 in) are clustered at the stem ends.

Remya is an endemic Hawaiian genus comprising three species. *R. montgomeryi*, discovered on Kauai in 1985, and *R. mauiensis*, found on Maui, are also listed as Endangered. The underside of the leaves of *R. montgomeryi* lack white hairs. The leaves of *R. mauiensis* are more narrowly elliptic.

Habitat

This species is found in Kokee State Park on the island of Kauai in mixed moist forests, mainly on steep north or northeast facing slopes at elevations between 850 and 1,250 meters (2,800 to 4,100 ft). One population grows on steep cliffs below the rim of Kalalau Valley, a considerably wetter habitat.

Historic Range

Remya kauaiensis was first collected on Kauai before 1871. It was next seen in 1952 in Kokee State Park and, after that, was considered extinct until two small populations were rediscovered in the park in 1983. Five additional small populations have been found since then. The few collections suggest that the species has never been common.

Current Distribution

Seven populations of *Remya kauaiensis* are known from the Kokee area of Kauai, all on state land. Because the plant sprawls and grows amid dense vegetation, exact population figures are difficult to estimate. It is believed that there are about 200 plants distributed over an area of two acres. Individual populations range in size between fewer than 10 plants to fewer than a hundred.

Conservation and Recovery

Although species with such low numbers always face the risk of extinction from any number of man-made or natural events, the main threat to *Remya kauaiensis* is habitat destruction through introduced animals and plants. Since man's arrival on the islands, introduced domestic and feral animals have radically altered the islands' flora. These animals consume the plants directly and disrupt the native vegetative cover, allowing alien plant species to invade. The fact that remaining populations of *Remya kauaiensis* occur on steep slopes may afford them some protection from animal grazing and trampling.

Additional Sources

Cuddihy, L. W., and C. P. Stone. 1990. *Alteration of Native Hawaiian Vegetation: Effects of Humans, their Activities and Introductions*. Cooperative National Park Resources Study Unit, University of Hawaii, Honolulu

Herbst, D. R. 1988. "Status Survey of the Genus *Remya*." U.S. Fish and Wildlife Service, Honolulu.

Wagner, W. L., and D. R. Herbst. 1987. "A New Species of *Remya* (Asteraceae: Astereae) on Kaua'i and a Review of the Genus." *Systematic Botany* 12(4):601-608.

Wagner, W. L., D. R. Herbst, and S. H. Sohmer. 1990. *Manual of the Flowering Plants of Hawai'i*. University of Hawaii Press and Bishop Museum Press, Honolulu.

Contacts

Regional Office of Endangered Species
U.S. Fish and Wildlife Service
Eastside Federal Complex
911 N.S. 11th Avenue
Portland, Oregon 97232-4181

Ernest F. Kosaka
U.S. Fish and Wildlife Service
300 Ala Moana Boulevard, Room 6307
P.O. Box 50167
Honolulu, Hawaii 96850

Maui Remya
Remya mauiensis

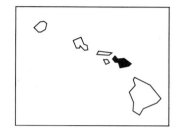

Robert Gustafson

Status . . . . Endangered
Listed . . . . January 14, 1991
Family . . . . Asteraceae (Aster)
Description . . . . . . Sprawling shrub with
leaves bunched at stem
ends and clusters of small,
yellow flowers.
Habitat . . . . Steep slopes in moist
forests.
Threats . . . . Domestic and feral
animals, alien plant
species, low numbers.
Region 1 . . . . Hawaii (Maui)

Description

Maui remya is a small, sprawling to weakly erect perennial shrub that grows to a height of 90 centimeters (35 in). The branches are covered with a tan fuzz near the tips. The coarsely toothed, elliptic leaves are about 15 centimeters (6 in) long and are bunched near the ends of the branches. The leaf undersides are covered with white hairs. The small, dark yellow flowers (0.7 cm; 0.3 in) are clustered at the stem ends.

Remya is an endemic Hawaiian genus comprising three species. *R. montgomeryi*, discovered on Kauai in 1985, and *R. kauaiensis*, both found on Kauai, are also listed as Endangered. The underside of the leaves of *R. montgomeryi* lack white hairs. The leaves of *R. mauiensis* are more narrowly elliptic than those of *R. kauaiensis*.

Habitat

This species is found on West Maui in mixed moist forests, mainly on steep north or northeast facing slopes at elevations between 850 and 1,250 meters (2,800 to 4,100 ft).

Historic Range

Maui remya was collected on West Maui twice between 1851 and 1871, and again in 1920. It was then believed extinct until rediscovered on the slopes of Manawainui Gulch, West Maui, in 1971. A second population has since been discovered nearby. The few collections suggest that the species has never been common.

Current Distribution

Two very small populations of Maui remya are known from West Maui, both on state land. One population consists of seven plants; the other contains only two.

Conservation and Recovery

Although species with such low numbers always face the risk of extinction from any number of man-made or natural events, the main threat to Maui remya is habitat destruction through introduced animals and plants. Since man's arrival on the islands, introduced domestic and feral animals have radically altered the islands' flora. These animals consume the plants directly and disrupt the native vegetative cover, allowing alien plant species to invade. The fact that remaining populations of Maui remya occur on steep slopes may afford them some protection from animal grazing and trampling. The state Division of Wildlife and Forestry has fenced one of the populations to protect it from browsing cattle.

Additional Sources

Cuddihy, L. W., and C. P. Stone. 1990. *Alteration of Native Hawaiian Vegetation: Effects of Humans, their Activities and Introductions.* Cooperative National Prak Resources Study Unit, University of Hawaii, Honolulu

Herbst, D. R. 1988. "Status Survey of the Genus *Remya.*" U.S. Fish and Wildlife Service, Honolulu.

Wagner, W. L., and D. R. Herbst. 1987. "A New Species of *Remya* (Asteraceae: Astereae) on Kaua'i and a Review of the Genus." *Systematic Botany* 12(4):601-608.

Wagner, W. L., D. R. Herbst, and S. H. Sohmer. 1990. *Manual of the Flowering Plants of Hawai'i.* University of Hawaii Press and Bishop Museum Press, Honolulu.

Contacts

Regional Office of Endangered Species
U.S. Fish and Wildlife Service
Eastside Federal Complex
911 N.S. 11th Avenue
Portland, Oregon 97232-4181

Ernest F. Kosaka
U.S. Fish and Wildlife Service
300 Ala Moana Boulevard, Room 6307
P.O. Box 50167
Honolulu, Hawaii 96850

Remya montgomeryi
No Common Name

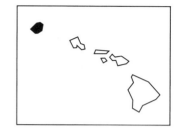

Yevonn Wilson-Ramsey from *Manual of the Flowering Plants of Hawai'i*

Status . . . . Endangered
Listed . . . . January 14, 1991
Family . . . . Asteraceae (Aster)
Description . . . . . . Sprawling shrub with leaves bunched at stem ends and clusters of small, yellow flowers.
Habitat . . . . Wet, steep cliffs.
Threats . . . . Domestic and feral animals, alien plant species, low numbers.
Region 1 . . . . Hawaii (Kauai)

Description

Remya montgomeryi is a small, sprawling to weakly erect perennial shrub that grows to a height of 90 centimeters (35 in). The coarsely toothed, narrowly elliptic leaves are about 15 centimeters (6 in) long and are bunched near the ends of the branches. The leaf undersides are smooth. The small, dark yellow flowers (0.7 cm; 0.3 in) are clustered at the stem ends.

Remya is an endemic Hawaiian genus comprising three species. *R. kauaiensis*, also from Kauai, and *R. mauiensis*, found on Maui, are also federally listed as Endangered. The underside of the leaves of *R. kauaiensis* and *R. mauiensis* are covered with white hairs.

Habitat

The only known population of this species is found on a wet, steep cliff below the upper rim of Kalalau Valley on Kauai at an elevation of about 1,035 meters (3,395 ft).

Historic Range

Remya montgomeryi was discovered in 1985 and described as a new species in 1987. No additional populations have been found.

Current Distribution

The one known population is on state land. It is estimated that is consists of fewer than 50 plants over half an acre.

Conservation and Recovery

Although species with such low numbers of individuals always face the risk of extinction from any number of man-made or natural events, the main threat to *Remya montgomeryi* is habitat destruction through introduced animals and plants. Since man's arrival on the islands, introduced domestic and feral animals have radically altered the islands' flora. These animals consume the plants directly and disrupt the native vegetative cover, allowing alien plant species to invade. The fact that the only population of *Remya montgomeryi* occurs on a virtually inaccessible sheer cliff may give it some protection.

Additional Sources

Cuddihy, L. W., and C. P. Stone. 1990. *Alteration of Native Hawaiian Vegetation: Effects of Humans, their Activities and Introductions.* Cooperative National Prak Resources Study Unit, University of Hawaii, Honolulu

Herbst, D. R. 1988. "Status Survey of the Genus *Remya*." U.S. Fish and Wildlife Service, Honolulu.

Wagner, W. L., and D. R. Herbst. 1987. "A New Species of *Remya* (Asteraceae: Astereae) on Kaua'i and a Review of the Genus." *Systematic Botany* 12(4):601-608.

Wagner, W. L., D. R. Herbst, and S. H. Sohmer. 1990. *Manual of the Flowering Plants of Hawai'i.* University of Hawaii Press and Bishop Museum Press, Honolulu.

Contacts

Regional Office of Endangered Species
U.S. Fish and Wildlife Service
Eastside Federal Complex
911 N.S. 11th Avenue
Portland, Oregon 97232-4181

Ernest F. Kosaka
U.S. Fish and Wildlife Service
300 Ala Moana Boulevard, Room 6307
P.O. Box 50167
Honolulu, Hawaii 96850

Michaux's Sumac

Rhus michauxii

From *Garden and Forest* Vol. 8, No. 398 (1895)

Status	Endangered
Listed	September 28, 1989
Family	Anacardiaceae (Cashew)
Description	Low-growing shrub with compound leaves and clusters of greenish yellow to white flowers.
Habitat	Disturbed areas with sandy or rocky soil.
Threats	Succession, loss of habitat, low numbers.
Region 4	Georgia, North Carolina

Description

Michaux's sumac is a low-growing shrub in the cashew family. The stems grow from an underground rhizome to a height of about 40 centimeters (15.6 in). Each compound leaf consists of from 9 to 13 stalkless, lance-shaped, toothed leaflets. The entire plant is densely covered with downy hairs. In June, small greenish yellow to white flowers bloom in dense, terminal clusters. The species is dioecious (individual plants bearing either male or female flowers). Red, fleshy fruits, which are covered by short hairs and containing a single large seed, are borne on female plants from August to September.

Because of its superficial similarity to poison sumac (*Rhus vernix*) Michaux's sumac is sometimes known as False poison sumac. It is distinguished from similar sumac species by its short stature; toothed leaves; and dense, overall hairiness.

Habitat

This species grows in sandy or rocky soil in open woods. It is not tolerant of shade and requires periodic disturbance of its habitat, once provided by naturally occurring forest fires, to prevent the formation of an overstory. Michaux's sumac is now found on land which is artificially disturbed, such as highway and railroad rights-of-way, and the edges of cultivated fields.

Historic Range

First described in 1895, the range of Michaux's sumac is limited to the inner coastal plain and lower piedmont of Georgia, South Carolina, and North Carolina. Thirty-two populations of the species have been known, only 16 of which survive.

In Georgia, four historic populations—in Cobb, Columbia, Newton, and Rabun counties—no longer survive. The only two known South Carolina populations, in Florence and Kershaw counties, no longer exist. In North Carolina 10 populations of Michaux's sumac have been lost, one from each of the following counties: Durham, Franklin, Hoke, Lincoln, Mechlenberg, Moore, Orange, Robeson, Wake, and Wilson.

Current Distribution

Michaux's sumac is currently known from 15 sites in North Carolina and one site in Georgia. Population sizes vary considerably; seven sites have over 100 plants, nine have less than 100 with three of these supporting fewer than a dozen plants. Only two of the surviving populations contain both male and female plants.

The Georgia site is in Elbert County on land owned by the Army Corps of Engineers. It contains only four plants and is leased to the Georgia Department of Natural Resources as part of the Board River Wildlife Management Area.

In North Carolina populations of Michaux's sumac are found in the following counties: Davie, Franklin, Hoke, Richmond, Robeson, Scotland, and Wake. Three populations are in Hoke County: one, consisting of several hundred female plants, is on privately owned land; a second is on the Ft. Bragg Military Reservation and contains 23 plants; the third,

partially owned by The Nature Conservancy and partially privately owned, consists of only four plants.

Six populations are located in Richmond County. One (two plants) is privately owned; four populations (three with less than 50 plants and one with 137) are on the Sandhills Gamelands, which is administered by the state wildlife agency; the sixth population (eight plants) is on the Ft. Bragg Military Reservation.

Two large populations lie within the Sandhills Gamelands in Scotland County. Although several hundred plants remain in these populations, each contains only individuals of one sex.

A population in Franklin County is located on privately owned land and contains more than 250 plants of both sexes. Thirty plants occupy a privately owned site in Davie County. Several hundred male plants, also on private land, constitute the Robeson County population. In Wake County, the City of Raleigh owns land that holds 279 plants of both sexes.

Because Michaux's sumac also reproduces asexually, the number of individual plants surveyed may be somewhat misleading. Botanists estimate that the number of genetically distinct individuals is actually below 50.

Conservation and Recovery

Michaux's sumac is threatened by fire suppression, development, and the geographical isolation of its remaining populations. The species requires periodic disturbance of its habitat to thrive. Otherwise natural succession will eventually produce an overstory which shades out the species. The periodic forest fires which maintained the open habitat in the past are now suppressed. Surviving populations are now almost exclusively limited to land regularly disturbed by human activities.

Many of the historic populations were lost to conversion of the land to crop and tree farming, as well as industrial and residential development. The Fish and Wildlife Service estimates that 14 of the remaining 16 sites are vulnerable to habitat alteration.

A potential threat to the species, particularly the smaller populations, is hybridization with closely related sumac species. Such hybrids have been discovered at two locations, which formerly supported Michaux's sumac.

Because of prescribed burning programs on North Carolina state lands, the outlook for populations there is more favorable than elsewhere. Overall, however, the large number of same sex populations and the need for periodic habitat disturbance make long term recovery of Michaux's sumac problematic. Much depends on the ability to protect the larger populations that contain both male and female plants.

Additional Sources

Cooper, J., S. Robinson, and J. Funderburg. 1977. *Endangered and Threatened Plants and Animals of North Carolina: Proceedings of the Symposium on Endangered and Threatened Biota of North Carolina.* North Carolina State Museum of Natural History, Raleigh.

Hardin, J., and L. Phillips. 1965 "Hybridization in Eastern North American *Rhus* (Anacardiaceae)." *Association of Southeastern Biologists Bulletin* 32(3):99-100.

Radford, A., H. Ahles, and C. Bell. 1964. *Manual of the Vascular Flora of the Carolinas.* University of North Carolina Press, Chapel Hill.

Contacts

Regional Office of Endangered Species
U. S. Fish and Wildlife Service
Richard B. Russell Federal Building
75 Spring Street, S.W.
Atlanta, Georgia 30303

Nora Murdock
U.S. Fish and Wildlife Service
330 Ridgefield Court
Asheville, North Carolina 23806

Knieskern's Beaked-Rush
Rhynchospora knieskernii

Dana Peters

Status	Threatened
Listed	July 18, 1991
Family	Cyperaceae (Sedge)
Description	Aquatic grass with narrow leaves and small, white flowers.
Habitat	Bog iron deposits and muddy, disturbed areas.
Threats	Natural succession, change in groundwater supply.
Region 5	New Jersey

Description

Knieskern's beaked-rush is an annual sedge that grows from 1.5 centimeters (0.6 in) to 60 centimeters (23.4 in) and has short, narrowly linear leaves. Between July and September it bears clusters of numerous, small, white flowers at intervals along its stem.

Habitat

This species is restricted to natural wetlands and disturbed muddy areas. It is an early successional plant that requires frequent disturbance to its habitat to survive. Until recently it was believed to occur only in bog iron deposits within pitch pine lowland marshy areas (swales) and pine barren grasslands (savannas). Such bog iron deposits consist of iron-coated soil formed by the oxidation of iron-rich sediments at surfaces such as streams and wetlands. Within the last decade, Knieskern's beaked-rush has also been found growing in muddy, disturbed areas, such as abandoned clay pits and cranberry bogs, rights-of-way, and other areas that have been reduced to an early stage of plant succession.

Historic Range

All known populations of Knieskern's beaked-rush have been found in the Pinelands area of New Jersey, where 38 sites were known. The validity of a site in Sussex Country, Delaware, where a specimen was allegedly collected in 1875, is now questioned by botanists.

Current Distribution

At present, the species survives at approximately 27 sites in four New Jersey counties (Atlantic, Burlington, Ocean, and Monmouth). Population sizes vary from about a dozen plants in a few square feet of habitat to large patches that cover more than two acres.

Seven of the existing sites occur on state land (six on bog iron deposits), two are on federal land, and the rest are on privately owned land. One federally owned site is on land administered by the Federal Aviation Administration in Ocean and Burlington counties; another is on Naval Weapons Station Earle in Monmouth County.

The New Jersey Natural Heritage Program surveyed the known sites in 1984 and 1985 and judged only five of the local populations, all on bog iron habitats, to be self-sustaining. Populations on man-made habitats are considered more at risk to natural succession or disturbance and will require periodic maintenance.

Conservation and Recovery

The principal threats to Knieskern's beaked-rush are natural and man-made succession and the loss or degradation of its wetland habitat. Plants associated with later stages of succession, such as red maple, honeysuckle, poison ivy, Virginia creeper, and greenbriar, easily crowd out this sedge.

Although bog iron habitats are subject to erosion and other processes that tend to maintain them in an early successional stage, pollutants such as agricultural fertilizers, pesticides, herbicides, and organic wastes have changed water quality and led to changes in the flora of the New Jersey Pinelands region. At least one bog iron habitat site is vulnerable to succession.

Plant populations in man-made disturbed areas are at greater risk and are in need of management to survive. Natural succession is more likely there than in bog iron habitats. In addition, mowing, the application of pesticides, or the conversion of these sites to other uses, such as cranberry cultivation, could destroy populations.

Since Knieskern's beaked-rush requires wet conditions to survive, any change in the water table is a potential threat to the species. The draining of wetlands for agricultural or residential development or the pumping of groundwater for irrigation would destroy remaining plants.

In addition to the listing of Knieskern's beaked-rush as Threatened under the federal Endangered Species Act, state laws provide some degree of protection. New Jersey's Pinelands Protection Act lists the plant as "endangered" and prohibits development that would have an adverse impact on local populations. However, the act has exceptions which could allow the conversion of wetlands to cranberry or blueberry production. Another state law designed to protect the fragile New Jersey shoreline (the Coastal Area Facility Review Act) also protects rare plant and animal species. However, only one population of the species occurs within the jurisdiction of this law.

Conservation of Knieskern's beaked-rush requires active monitoring and management of existing population sites to maintain the required early successional habitat. Planned construction of communications facilities on federal land where populations occur will be reviewed to ensure that there will be no disturbance to the species.

Additional Sources

Pinelands Commission. 1980. "Comprehensive Management Plan for the Pinelands National Reserve and Pinelands Area." Pinelands Commission, New Lisbon, New Jersey.

Robichaud, B. 1980. "A Conceptual Framework for Pinelands Decision Making." Center for Coastal and Environmental Studies, Rutgers University, New Brunswick, New Jersey.

Roman, C., and R. Good. 1983. "Pinelands Wetlands: Values, Function, and Man's Impacts." Center for Coastal and Environmental Studies, Rutgers University, New Brunswick, New Jersey.

Snyder, D., and E. Vivian. 1981. "Rare and Endangered Vascular Plant Species in New Jersey." The Conservation and Environmental Studies Center.

Stone, W. 1973. *The Plants of Southern New Jersey.* Quarterman Publications, Boston.

Contacts

Regional Office of Endangered Species
U.S. Fish and Wildlife Service
One Gateway Center, Suite 700
Newton Corner, MA 02158

Dana Peters
U.S. Fish and Wildlife Service
927 North Main Street, Building D
Pleasantville, New Jersey 08232

Kral's Water-Plantain
Sagittaria secundifolia

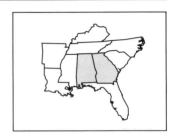

William R. Bowen

Status	Threatened
Listed	April 13, 1990
Family	Alismataceae (Water-plantain)
Description	Aquatic perennial with narrow to quill-like leaves and white flowers.
Habitat	Shallow shoals and pools.
Threats	Habitat loss, limited distribution, poor reproduction.
Region 4	Alabama, Georgia

Description

Kral's water-plantain is an aquatic perennial that grows from a stiff, elongated rhizone, which is up to 10 centimeters (4 in) long. Plants produce two different types of leaves, depending on the depth and flow of the water in which they grow. In shallow, swift water the leaves are linear and sickle-shaped; in deeper, quiet water the linear leaves are longer, more tapered, and quill-like. Both male and female flowers are produced on a single stalk. While female flowers have inconspicuous petals, male flowers have white petals 1 to 1.5 centimeters (0.4 to 0.6 in) long. Flowering is infrequent and occurs from May into July and intermittently into the fall. The fruit consists of a cluster of small, hard seed pods, known as achenes.

Habitat

This aquatic species is found on frequently exposed river shoals and in quiet pools up to 1 meter (3 ft) deep. Plants grow in pure stands or in association with other aquatic species. At several population sites two Endangered plants—green pitcher plant (*Sarracenia oreophilia*) and harperella (*Ptilimnium nodosum*)—also occur.

Historic Range

Kral's water-plantain was first described in 1982 from material collected in the early

1970s from the Little River in Alabama. Previous collections were made in 1899 from the Little River and in 1951 from Town Creek on Sand Mountain in DeKalb County, Alabama.

Current Distribution

This plant is only known to occur in the free-flowing upper reaches of the the Little River drainage system on Lookout Mountain in northwest Georgia and northeast Alabama. Almost all plants are found in Cherokee and DeKalb counties, Alabama, in a dozen or more local populations scattered over a 25-mile stetch of river. Eight populations occur in areas with partial canopy cover. The number of plants at these sites range from 5 to 40. Four larger populations on shallow river shoals support from 75 to several hundred plants. Specimens have also been collected from a site in the East Fork of the Little River in Chattooga County, Georgia.

About 40 percent of the suitable habitat in Little River is owned by the Alabama Power Company; another 20 percent lies within the state of Alabama's DeSoto State Park. A recent survey of suitable habitat in Alabama and Georgia failed to discover new populations.

Conservation and Recovery

Since Kral's water-plantain occurs in only a single river system, it is vulnerable to a number of threats, especially the elimination or modification of its habitat. Clearing of the streamside banks for agriculture, mining, or residential-recreational development would increase turbidity and siltation and harm plant populations.

Some Kral's water-plantain populations may be adversely affected by large summer algal blooms. Leaking sewage systems increase organic nutrients in the water, reducing the level of dissolved oxygen (eutrophication); this promotes algal blooms which often completely cover plants.

Impoundments on the Little River are common over areas of suitable habitat and may have destroyed undocumented populations. If a pump storage facility proposed for the Little River were constructed, it would destroy approximately a third of the current habitat along with the local populations located there. Additionally, much of the current reproductive activity of Kral's water-plantain is clonal, rather than sexual, which suggests that the species may be losing genetic variability. Efforts to maintain suitable habitat is necessary to encourage sexual reproduction.

Additional Sources

Kral, R. 1982. "A New Phyllodial-leaved *Sagittaria* (Alismaceae) from Alabama." *Brittonia* 34:12-17.

Whetstone, R. D. 1988. "Status Survey of *Sagittaria secundifolia*." U.S. Fish and Wildlife Service, Atlanta.

Contacts

Regional Office of Endangered Species
U. S. Fish and Wildlife Service
Richard B. Russell Federal Building
75 Spring Street, S.W.
Atlanta, Georgia 30303

Cary Norquist
U.S. Fish and Wildlife Center
6578 Dogwood View Parkway, Suite A
Jackson, Mississippi 39213

Sanicula mariversa
No Common Name

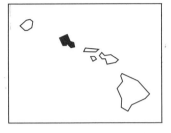

Joel Lau

Status	Endangered
Listed	October 29, 1991
Family	Apiaceae (Parsley)
Description	Upright plant with leathery, lobed leaves and clusters of yellow flowers.
Habitat	Well-drained, dry slopes.
Threats	Feral goats, alien plant species, low numbers.
Region 1	Hawaii (Oahu)

Description

Sanicula mariversa is an upright herb in the parsley family that grows 40 to 70 centimeters (16 to 28 in) tall. Leathery, lobed, heart- to kidney-shaped leaves grow from the base. They become smaller and more deeply lobed as they ascend the stem. Male and hermaphroditic yellow flowers appear in clusters of 10 to 20 at the stem end or from the leaf axils. The egg-shaped fruit is covered with hooked prickles and contains two seeds.

Habitat

Sanicula mariversa is found only in the Waianae Mountain Range on the western side of the island of Oahu, Hawaii. This island is dominated by the remnants of two ancient volcanoes that have eroded into two "mountain ranges," which consist of long, narrow ridges. The Waianae Range lies on the western side of the island, while the Koolau Range traverses the eastern side. The Waianae Range, which runs northwest to southeast for about 40 miles, lies in the rain shadow of the Koolau Range, and, except for the summit of Mt. Kaala, the highest point on the island, receives much less rainfall.

A variety of plant habitats are found in the Waianae Mountains, ranging from coastal dry shrubland to lowland dry forest to lowland wet forest. *Sanicula mari-*

versa is found on well-drained dry slopes at an elevation of 750 to 850 meters (2,500 to 2,800 ft). Associated plant species include Hamakua pamakani or spreading mist flower (*Ageratina riparia*), kawelu (*Eragrostis variabilis*), and ohia (*Metrosideros polymorpha*).

The diverse habitats of the Waianae Mountains contain a large number of vulnerable native Hawaiian plant species. In October 1991 the Fish and Wildlife Service (FWS) listed *Sanicula mariversa* and 25 other plant species from Oahu's Waianae Mountains as Endangered. This group listing was the result of the settlement of a 1989 lawsuit brought against the FWS by the Sierra Club Legal Defense Fund on behalf of a Hawaii conservation group.

Historic Range

Sanicula mariversa was discovered in 1981 in the Waianae Mountains of Oahu. It has been known from the central area of the mountains, from Makau-Keaau Ridge to Kaluaa-Lualualei Summit Ridge. It has not been found on any other island in Hawaii.

Current Distribution

The species survives at two sites at Makau-Keaau Ridge on state land. These populations are less than half a mile apart and together contain fewer than 100 plants.

Conservation and Recovery

The main threats to *Sanicula mariversa* are habitat degradation by feral goats, competition from non-native plant species, and the low number of surviving plants. Feral goats, which are managed as game animals, have been on the island for 170 years. Because of their agility they are able to reach areas inaccessible to feral pigs and cattle.

Most rare Hawaiian flora are threatened by competiton with aggressive non-native species. Remaining *Sanicula mariversa* plants are directly threatend by Christmasberry (*Schinus terebinthifolius*) and molasses grass (*Melinus minutiflora*). Christmasberry is an aggressive tree that forms dense thickets and may also release chemicals that inhibit the growth of other species. Molasses grass grows in dense mats that smother native vegetation. It is also fire adapted and provides fuel for spreading wildfires.

Fire is a special danger to *Sanicula mariversa* populations which occur near the U.S. Army's Makua Military Reservation and Schofield Barracks. Within a 14-month period from 1989 to 1990, 10 fires resulted from weapons practice on the reservation. In order to minimize damage from fires, the army has constructed firebreaks between the target areas and the surrounding forest.

Additional Sources

Cuddihy, L. W., and C. P. Stone. 1990. *Alteration of Native Hawaiian Vegetation: Effects of Humans, Their Activities and Introductions.* Cooperative National Park Resources Study Unit, University of Hawaii Press, Honolulu.

Culliney, J. L. 1988. *Islands in a Far Sea: Nature and Man in Hawaii.* Sierra Club Books, San Francisco.

Contact

Derral R. Herbst
U.S. Fish and Wildlife Service
300 Ala Moana Boulevard, Room 6307
P.O. Box 50167
Honolulu, Hawaii 96850

Ma'oli'oli
Schiedea apokremnos

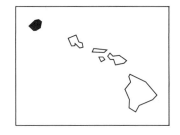

David Lorence

Status . . . . Endangered
Listed . . . . September 30, 1991
Family . . . . Caryophyllaceae (Pink)
Description . . . . . . Low, branching shrub, with fleshy, oblong leaves and clusters of flowers lacking petals.
Habitat . . . . Sea cliffs and inland rock outcrops.
Threats . . . . Feral goats, low numbers.
Region 1 . . . . Hawaii (Kauai)

Description

Ma'oli'oli is a low, branching shrub that grows between 20 and 50 centimeters (8 to 20 in) tall. The smooth, fleshy leaves are oblong, about 3 to 5 centimeters (1 to 2 in) in length, and oppositely arranged. The flowers, which appear in clusters, lack petals; the bracts and sepals are green, often tinged with purple. Round to kindney-shaped seeds are produced in capsules.

Habitat

This species of *Schieda* occurs on the island of Kauai in the crevices of steep sea cliffs and for about a third of a mile inland on cliffs and rock outcrops at elevations from 60 to 330 meters (200 to 1,100 ft). The associated vegetation is dry coastal scrub, including *Artemisia australis*, sourbush (*Pluchea symphytifolia*), akoko (*Chamaesyce celastroides*), and *Lobelia nihauensis*. Inland, the habitat is dominated by koa haole (*Leucaena leucocephala*).

Historic Range

Ma'oli'oli was first collected in the early 1900s at an unrecorded location on Kauai. It was not collected again until 1965 when it was found at Nualolo Kai on the Na Pali Coast. It has since been found at Kaaweiki Ridge and along the Na Pali Coast at Milolii Valley, Kalalau Beach, and between Kaalahin and Manono Ridges.

Current Distribution

The species currently exists at all its historic locations except for Nualolo Kai. The status at Kalalau and Milolii is unknown as these sites have not been surveyed for over six years. Only about 100 individuals are believed to exist, with only the population at Kaalahina-Manono numbering more than five plants. The species occurs only on state land in Na Pali Coast State Park and Puu Ka Pele Forest Reserve (one population).

Conservation and Recovery

The main threat to ma'oli'oli is predation by feral goats, which are abundant in the area. Although plants continue to be browsed by goats, most of the remaining populations are situated at relatively inaccessible sites. Besides directly consuming plants, the goats disturb the habitat, making it more difficult for seedlings to become established. They also open the ground for invasion by exotic species. Koa haole (*Leucaena leucocephala*) and comb hyptis (*Hyptis pectinata*) are common invasive alien species at the Kaaweiki Ridge site.

With such a low species population, ma'oli'oli is vulnerable to catastrophic human and natural events, expecially landslides and wildfires.

Additional Sources

Corn, C. A. 1984. "Na Pali Botanical Findings, July 16-21, 1984." Division of Forestry and Wildlife, Department of Land and Natural Resources, Honolulu, Hawaii.

Cuddihy, L. W., and C. P. Stone. 1990. *Alteration of Native Hawaiian Vegetation: Effects of Humans, Their Activities and Introductions*. Cooperative National Park Resources Study Unit, University of Hawaii Press, Honolulu.

Culliney, J. L. 1988. *Islands in a Far Sea: Nature and Man in Hawaii*. Sierra Club Books, San Francisco.

St. John, H. 1970. "The 'Staminodia' of the Genus *Schiedea* (Caryophyllaceae) and Three New Hawaiian Species." Hwaaiian Plant Studies 32 (i.e. 33). *Pacific Science* 24:245-254.

Stone, C. P., and J. M. Scott, eds. 1985. *Hawai'i's Terrestrial Ecosystems: Preservation and Management*. Cooperative National Park Resources Study Unit, University of Hawaii Press, Honolulu.

Wagner, W. L., D. R. Herbst, and S. H. Sohmer. 1990. *Manual of the Flowering Plants of Hawai'i*. University of Hawaii Press and Bishop Museum Press, Honolulu.

Contacts

Regional Office of Endangered Species
U.S. Fish and Wildlife Service
Eastside Federal Complex
911 N.S. 11th Avenue
Portland, Oregon 97232-4181

Joan E. Canfield
U.S. Fish and Wildlife Service
300 Ala Moana Boulevard, Room 6307
P.O. Box 50167
Honolulu, Hawaii 96850

Schiedea kaalae
No Common Name

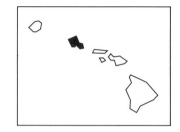

Yevonn Wilson-Ramsey from *Manual of the Flowering Plants of Hawai'i*

Status	Endangered
Listed	October 29, 1991
Family	Caryophyllaceae (Pink)
Description	Perennial with a short woody stem, elliptic leaves, and a scattered cluster of flowers with purple bracts and sepals.
Habitat	Moist forest.
Threats	Feral pigs and goats, alien plant species, low numbers.
Region 1	Hawaii (Oahu)

Description

Schiedea kaalae is a perennial of the pink family with a short, woody stem less than 20 centimeters (8 in) long. Elliptic leaves, 24 centimeters (9.5 in) long are bunched at the top of the stem. The flowers, which lack petals but have purple bracts and sepals, are carried on a branched stem, 20 to 40 centimeters (8 to 16 in) long. The fruits are capsules containing dark gray seeds.

Habitat

Schiedea kaalae is found only in the Waianae Mountain Range on the western side of the island of Oahu, Hawaii. This island is dominated by the remnants of two ancient volcanoes that have eroded into two "mountain ranges," which consist of long, narrow ridges. The Waianae Range lies on the western side of the island, while the Koolau Range traverses the eastern side. The Waianae Range, which runs northwest to southeast for about 40 miles, lies in the rain shadow of the Koolau Range, and, except for the summit of Mt. Kaala, the highest point on the island, receives much less rainfall.

A variety of plant habitats are found in the Waianae Mountains, ranging from coastal dry shrubland to lowland dry forest to lowland wet forest. *Schiedea kaalae* grows on steep slopes and shaded sites in moist forest at elevations between 210 and 790 meters (700 and 2,600 ft). Associated plant species include kukui or candlenut

(*Aleurites moluccana*), *Athyrium sandwicensis*, *Delissea subcordata*, and papala kepau (*Pisonia umbellifera*).

The diverse habitats of the Waianae Mountains contain a large number of vulnerable native Hawaiian plant species. In October 1991 the Fish and Wildlife Service (FWS) listed *Schiedea kaalae* and 25 other plant species from Oahu's Waianae Mountains as Endangered. This group listing was the result of the settlement of a 1989 lawsuit brought against the FWS by the Sierra Club Legal Defense Fund on behalf of a Hawaii conservation group. The terms of the settlement called for the proposed listing before October 1992 of 186 Hawaiian candidate plant species.

Historic Range

Schiedea kaalae was first collected in 1870 from the slopes of Mt. Kaala on Oahu. It has been found in the north-central and south-central Waianae Mountains and in the northern Koolau Mountains. It is not known from any other island.

Current Distribution

The species survives at Huliwai, Makaleha, Mokuleia, Pahole Gulch, and Puu Hapapa in the Waianae Mountains and at Kaipapau and Punaluu in the Koolau Mountains. The Waianae Mountain populations are distributed over a 10-mile area. The two populations in the Koolau Mountains are about 3 miles apart. Together, these populations total fewer than 100 plants.

Conservation and Recovery

As is the case with most rare Hawaiian flora, *Schiedea kaalae* is threatened by habitat degradation by feral pigs and goats and competition from aggressive non-native plant species. Feral pigs, which are managed by the state as game animals, have been in the Waianae Mountains for about 150 years and have had a major effect on the native flora. Their rooting destroys plants and opens the habitat to invasive species. They also help spread these alien species by carrying seed on their bodies and in their feces. Feral goats, also game animals, have been on the island for 170 years. Because of their agility they are able to reach areas inaccessible to pigs. Although a major control effort greatly reduced the goat population by 1905, remaining animals are still a threat to rare species.

Throughout Hawaii alien plant species are a threat to the native flora, especially rare species, and *Schiedea kaalae* is directly threatened by several. Christmasberry (*Schinus terebinthifolius*), an aggressive tree introduced to Hawaii before 1911, forms dense thickets and may also release chemicals that inhibit the growth of other species. Huehue haole (*Passiflora suberosa*) is a vine that smothers the subcanopy of dryland habitats. Koster's curse (*Clidemia hirta*) is a cultivated shrub that spread to the Koolau Mountains in the 1960s and the Waianae Mountains at the beginning of the 1970s. It forms a dense understory that replaces native species. Firetree (*Myrica faya*) was planted in the Waianae Mountains during a reforestation project. Besides forming a dense closed canopy that excludes other species, it produces its own nitrogen, enabling it to colonize areas to which native species have become adapted. Molasses grass (*Melinus minutiflora*) grows in dense mats that smother native vegetation. It is also adapted to fire and provides fuel for spreading wildfires.

These fires are a threat to *Schiedea kaalae* populations which lie near the U.S. Army's

Makua Military Reservation and Schofield Barracks. Within a 14-month period from 1989 to 1990, 10 fires resulted from weapons practice on the reservation. In order to minimize damage from fires, the army has constructed firebreaks between the target areas and the surrounding forest.

The low number of surviving plants and their limited distribution makes *Schiedea kaalae* vulnerable to extinction through unpredictible human or natural events.

Additional Sources

Cuddihy, L. W., and C. P. Stone. 1990. *Alteration of Native Hawaiian Vegetation: Effects of Humans, Their Activities and Introductions.* Cooperative National Park Resources Study Unit, University of Hawaii Press, Honolulu.

Culliney, J. L. 1988. *Islands in a Far Sea: Nature and Man in Hawaii.* Sierra Club Books, San Francisco.

Stone, C. P., and J. M. Scott, eds. 1985. *Hawai'i's Terrestrial Ecosystems: Preservation and Management.* Cooperative National Park Resources Study Unit, University of Hawaii Press, Honolulu.

Wagner, W. L., D. R. Herbst, and S. H. Sohmer. 1990. *Manual of the Flowering Plants of Hawai'i.* University of Hawaii Press and Bishop Museum Press, Honolulu.

Contacts

Regional Office of Endangered Species
U.S. Fish and Wildlife Service
Eastside Federal Complex
911 N.S. 11th Avenue
Portland, Oregon 97232-4181

Derral R. Herbst
U.S. Fish and Wildlife Service
300 Ala Moana Boulevard, Room 6307
P.O. Box 50167
Honolulu, Hawaii 96850

Schoepfia arenaria
No Common Name

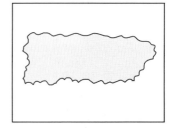

William M. Houghton/Fairchild Tropical Garden

Status	Threatened
Listed	April 19, 1991
Family	Olacaceae (Olax)
Description	Evergreen shrub with alternate leaves and tubular, white flowers.
Habitat	Limestone hills.
Threats	Urban development, quarrying.
Region 4	Puerto Rico

Description

Schoepfia arenaria is a evergreen shrub or small tree with multiple trunks, which attain a diameter of about 10 centimeters (4 in) and grow to a height of about 7 meters (23 ft). The alternate leaves have a slightly shiny, green upper surface and are light green underneath. In the spring and fall, light yellow, tubular flowers occur at the end of the stalk in the leaf bases. The shiny red, elliptic fruit is single-seeded.

Habitat

This rare tree grows in coastal thickets and in low elevation forests on the limestone hills of northern Puerto Rico.

Historic Range

Schoepfia arenaria was first collected in 1899 from sandy coastal thickets at San José Lagoon, Santurce, Puerto Rico. Additional populations have been found at Isabela, Fajardo, and in the Piñones and Rio Abajo Commonwealth forests.

Current Distribution

Fewer than 200 *Schoepfia arenaria* trees are known to survive in northern Puerto Rico. The San José Lagoon population has been destroyed by urban and industrial development. Near Isabela about 100 trees of differing ages are found on the upper slopes of hills to the west of the mouth of the Guajataca Gorge. About 30 mature plants and numerous seedlings are located at Punta Maldonado in the Piñones Commonwealth Forest. Another population in that forest at Punta Vacia Talega has not been observed since 1981 and is presumed lost. About 50 trees are located on limestone hills at El Convento, Fajardo, on property owned by the Commonwealth for the governor's beach house. A single plant is found at "cuesta de los perros" in the Rio Abajo Commonwealth Forest.

Conservation and Recovery

Deforestation for development and the leveling of limestone hills for building material are the main threats to surviving *Schoepfia arenaria* trees. Urban and industrial development was responsible for the loss of the San José Lagoon population. In the Isabela area hills have been leveled for highway construction, and a resort development is planned which would include the construction of seven hotels, five golf courses, thirty-six tennis courts, and thirteen hundred housing units.

Additional Sources

Little, E. L., R. O. Woodbury, and F. H. Wadsworth. 1974. *Trees of Puerto Rico and the Virgin Islands.* U.S. Department of Agriculture, Washington, D.C.

Contacts

Regional Office of Endangered Species
U. S. Fish and Wildlife Service
Richard B. Russell Federal Building
75 Spring Street, S.W.
Atlanta, Georgia 30303

Marelisa T. Rivera
Caribbean Field Office
U.S. Fish and Wildlife Service
P.O. Box 491
Boquerón, Puerto Rico 00622

Northeastern Bulrush
Scirpus ancistrochaetus

Bruce A. Sorrie   *Color Plate C-3*

Status	Endangered
Listed	May 7, 1991
Family	Cyperaceae (Sedge)
Description	Tall, leafy perennial with flowers surrounded by barbed bristles.
Habitat	Shallow depressions, ponds, sinkholes.
Threats	Development, water pollution.
Region 5	Massachusetts, Maryland, Pennsylvania, Vermont, Virginia, West Virginia

Description

Northeastern bulrush is a tall, perennial sedge, which grows 80 to 120 centimeters (30 to 47 in) in height. Its thin leaves are 40 to 60 times as long as they are wide. The plant produces an arching cluster of flowers, each surrounded by bristles which have sharp, downward-pointing barbs. The flowers bloom from mid-June to July and the yellow-brown fruits set between July and September. This species is also known as barbed bristle bulrush.

Habitat

This bulrush is found at widely scattered small wetlands such as natural ponds, sinkholes, or wet depressions in low-lying areas of hilly country in the mid-Atlantic and northeastern states. It grows at the unshaded margins of these wetlands in water that is acidic to almost neutral. The water levels in these wetlands vary seasonally, and they sometimes completely dry up.

Historic Range

Northeastern bulrush was first discovered in 1962 at Rockingham, Windham County, Vermont. Historical records indicate that the species has been known from Maryland, Massachusetts, New York, Pennsylvania, Vermont, Virginia, and West Virginia. Four collection sites in Pennsylvania (Blair, Lehigh, Monroe, and North-ampton counties) and one in New York (Washington County) no longer support the species.

Current Distribution

At present, a total of 13 populations of northeastern bulrush are found in Maryland, Massachusetts, Pennsylvania, Vermont, Virginia, and West Virginia. Nine populations contain less than 70 plants, and six of those have less than 25. All but two are on privately owned land; one is on state land in Pennsylvania, another is on federal land in Virginia.

In Virginia four counties (Alleghany, Augusta, Bath, and Rockingham) have single populations of northeastern bulrush. All are found in shallow sinkholes overlying sandstone in the Blue Ridge Mountains. Three sites are on private land; one is in the George Washington National Forest. In West Virginia there are two populations in Berkeley County, both on private land. One consists of 1,400 plants in two ponds; at the other, 400 plants occur in three patches in a single pond. In Maryland a single site with about 100 plants is located in Frederick County on private land adjacent to a state wildlife management area.

Two northeastern bulrush populations in Pennsylvania (Clinton and Lackawanna counties) have not been seen in the last few years. The Clinton County site is within the Bald Eagle State Forest. These populations, which consisted of only one and two plants respectively, may now be lost. In Monroe County a newly discovered population in a shallow lake on privately owned land consists of between 25 and 50 clumps. In Massachusetts a population of four plants occurs in a privately owned shallow depression in Franklin County. In Vermont two populations occur in Windham

County. An emergent marsh on the Connecticut River supports a population that has declined from 69 plants to 10 since 1985. Although the land is privately owned, The Nature Conservancy has worked out a management agreement with the owner. The second Vermont population is on a privately owned wetland complex of shallow pools and abandoned beaver ponds. In 1989 and 1990 none of the twelve plants counted in 1985 could be found.

Conservation and Recovery

The greatest threat to the northeastern bulrush is the destruction of its fragile wetland habitat for agricultural, residential, or recreational development. The habitat is also threatened by water pollution, excavation, and, when dry, by off-road vehicle use. Development pressures are especially strong in the southern portion of the species' range. In Virginia almost half of the ponds considered suitable habitat for the species have been degraded by fill, excavation, or pollution. The West Virginia populations are located near an area undergoing residential development. Nearby land has already been subdivided and is being sold as home sites.

These small, wetland habitats are currently exempted from many of the permit requirements of the Clean Water Act. However, if they support a federally listed species such as northeastern bulrush, the Army Corps of Engineers, which administers the act, must consult with the Fish and Wildlife Service before issuing a permit to alter the wetland. The Fish and Wildlife Service has notified the Corps of Engineers of the location of northeastern bulrush populations so that remaining sites can be protected.

Additional Sources

Bartgis, R. 1989. "Status Survey Summary: *Scirpus ancistrochaetus* in Maryland and West Virginia." Maryland Natural Heritage Program, Annapolis, Maryland.

Crow, G. E. 1982. "New England's Rare and Endangered Vascular Plants." U.S. Fish and Wildlife Service, Newton Corner, Massachusetts.

Rawinski, T. 1990. "Final Status Survey Report: Distribution and Abundance of Northeastern Bulrush (*Scirpus ancistrochaetus*)." The Nature Conservancy, Eastern Heritage Task Force.

Schuyler, A. E. 1962. "A New Species of *Scirpus* in the Northeastern United States." *Rhodora* 64:43-49.

_____. 1964. "Notes on Five Species of *Scirpus* in Eastern North America." *Bartonia* 33:1-6.

_____. 1967. "A Taxonomic Revision of North American Leafy Species of *Scirpus.*" *Proceedings of the Academy of Natural Science of Philadelphia* 119:295-323.

Contacts

Regional Office of Endangered Species
U.S. Fish and Wildlife Service
One Gateway Center, Suite 700
Newton Corner, Massachusetts 02158

Susanna L. von Oettingen
U.S. Fish and Wildlife Service
22 Bridge Street
Concord, New Hampshire 03301

Silene perlmanii
No Common Name

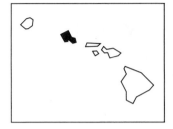

John Obata

Status	Endangered
Listed	October 29, 1991
Family	Caryophyllaceae (Pink)
Description	Branched perennial with narrowly elliptic leaves and clusters of deeply notched, white flowers.
Habitat	Moist forest cliffs.
Threats	Alien plant species, low numbers.
Region 1	Hawaii (Oahu)

Description

Silene perlmanii is a branched perennial in the pink family. A large number of stems rise from a woody base to a height of 30 to 50 centimeters (12 to 20 in). The narrowly elliptic leaves are 5 to 10.5 centimeters (2 to 4 in) long. A few deeply notched, white flowers are borne in clusters at the ends of the stems.

Habitat

Silene perlmanii is found only in the Waianae Mountain Range on the western side of the island of Oahu, Hawaii. This island is dominated by the remnants of two ancient volcanoes that have eroded into two "mountain ranges," which consist of long, narrow ridges. The Waianae Range lies on the western side of the island, while the Koolau Range traverses the eastern side. The Waianae Range, which runs northwest to southeast for about 40 miles, lies in the rain shadow of the Koolau Range, and, except for the summit of Mt. Kaala, the highest point on the island, receives much less rainfall.

A variety of plant habitats are found in the Waianae Mountains, ranging from coastal dry shrubland to lowland dry forest to lowland wet forest. *Silene perlmanii* grows on cliff faces in moist forest at an elevation of 790 meters (2,600 ft). Associated species include laukahi kuahiwi (*Plantago princeps*).

The diverse habitats of the Waianae Mountains contain a large number of vulnerable native Hawaiian plant species. In October 1991 the Fish and Wildlife Service (FWS) listed *Silene perlmanii* and 25 other plant species from Oahu's Waianae Mountains as Endangered. This group listing was the result of the settlement of a 1989 lawsuit brought against the FWS by the Sierra Club Legal Defense Fund on behalf of a Hawaii conservation group. The terms of the settlement called for the proposed listing before October 1992 of 186 Hawaiian candidate plant species.

Historic Range

Silene perlmanii was discovered in 1987 in the Waianae Mountains of Oahu. It is known from a single population in the southern Waianae Mountains, between Palikea and Pohakea Pass.

Current Distribution

This recently discovered species is not known from any other location. The only known population is on private land and consists of between 10 and 20 plants.

Conservation and Recovery

The main threats to *Silene perlmanii* are competition from non-native plant species and the low number of known individuals. Almost all native Hawaiian flora are in competition with agressive alien species, and *Silene perlmanii* is threatened by several. Christmasberry (*Schinus terebinthifolius*) forms dense thickets and may also release chemicals that inhibit the growth of other species. Firetree (*Myrica faya*) was planted in the Waianae Mountains during a reforestation project. Besides forming a dense closed canopy that excludes other species, it produces its own nitrogen, enabling it to colonize areas to which native species have become adapted. Molasses grass (*Melinus minutiflora*) grows in dense mats that smother native vegetation.

In addition, with fewer than 20 plants known from a single population, *Silene perlmanii* is very vulnerable to extinction through unpredictable human or natural events.

Additional Sources

Cuddihy, L. W., and C. P. Stone. 1990. *Alteration of Native Hawaiian Vegetation: Effects of Humans, Their Activities and Introductions.* Cooperative National Park Resources Study Unit, University of Hawaii Press, Honolulu.

Culliney, J. L. 1988. *Islands in a Far Sea: Nature and Man in Hawaii.* Sierra Club Books, San Francisco.

Stone, C. P., and J. M. Scott, eds. 1985. *Hawai'i's Terrestrial Ecosystems: Preservation and Management.* Cooperative National Park Resources Study Unit, University of Hawaii Press, Honolulu.

Wagner, W. L., D. R. Herbst, and S. H. Sohmer. 1990. *Manual of the Flowering Plants of Hawai'i.* University of Hawaii Press and Bishop Museum Press, Honolulu.

Contacts

Regional Office of Endangered Species
U.S. Fish and Wildlife Service
Eastside Federal Complex
911 N.S. 11th Avenue
Portland, Oregon 97232-4181

Derral R. Herbst
U.S. Fish and Wildlife Service
300 Ala Moana Boulevard, Room 6307
P.O. Box 50167
Honolulu, Hawaii 96850

Fringed Campion
Silene polypetala

Jessie M. Harris   *Color Plate C-1*

Status	Endangered
Listed	January 18, 1991
Family	Caryophyllaceae (Pink)
Description	Perennial with opposite, obovate leaves and pink or white, fringed flowers.
Habitat	Moist hardwood forests.
Threats	Logging, residential development, competition from alien plant species.
Region 4	Florida, Georgia

Description

Fringed campion is a perennial belonging to the pink family. It spreads vegetatively by means of runner-like rhizomes (underground horizontal stems) and leafy off-shoots, both terminating in rosettes which persist through the winter. The opposite, obovate (ovals that taper toward the stem) leaves are 3 to 9 centimeters (1 to 4 in) long. Each rosette produces one or more flowering shoots up to 40 centimeters (16 in) tall. The pink or white flowers, which have leafy bracts, are arranged in groups of three to five in a terminal cluster. The flower consists of a hairy, tubular calyx and five separate petals, which are divided into a lower part equal in length to the calyx, and an upper part, extending about an inch from the calyx. this upper part is divided into slender segments giving it a fringed appearance. Flowers bloom from March to May. This species has also been known as *Cucubalus polypetalus* and *Silene baldwinii*.

Habitat

Fringed campion grows in moist hardwood forests in two separate geographic locations in Georgia and Florida. It is found both on steep ravine slopes and north-facing hillsides and on level bottomland. At one site in Talbot Country, Georgia, fringed campion occurs together with the Endangered relict trillium (*Trillium reliquum*); at another site it occurs with *Scutellaria ocmulgee*, which is a candidate for listing. Near the Georgia-Florida border, the species occurs along with the Endangered Florida torreya (*Torreya taxifolia*).

Historic Range

Fringed campion was first collected in central Georgia in 1788. It has been known only from two separate geographic areas: a four county area in central Georgia, west of Macon, and a three-county area near the confluence of the Flint and Apalachicola rivers on both sides of the Georgia-Florida border.

Current Distribution

The known population of fringed campion occurs on 15 sites within its historic range. The northern portion of that range is in central Georgia, from Macon in Bibb County, west through Crawford, Taylor, and Talbot counties. Ten sites are known in this area, with a population of over 610 rosette-clusters. The largest site contains over 225 rosette-clusters.

The southern portion of the range lies along the east side of the Flint and Apalachicola rivers at the boundary between Decatur Country, Georgia, and Gadsden County, Florida. There are two sites in Georgia, two in Gadsden County, Florida, (in and south of Chattahoochee) and one site west of the Apalachicola River in Jackson County, Florida. In 1988 there were about 250 plants in the two southwest Georgia sites, which are on public land administered by the Army Corps of Engineers. A 1980 survey counted about 250 plants at one of the Florida sites. There are no current estimates of the numbers at the other two Florida sites.

Conservation and Recovery

Principal threats to fringed campion are logging, invasion by Japanese honeysuckle (*Lonicera japonica*), and residential development. Two sites are threatened by nearby logging activities which may alter the water seepage pattern and summer shade, perhaps leading to the loss of some plants. Six more sites are vulnerable to direct clearcutting. At four of the sites vulnerable to logging, Japanese honeysuckle is present or encroaching. This weedy plant is known to destroy populations of forest herbs.

Three known sites are in residential areas. One of these is being conserved by the present homeowner, but another is likely to be lost to house construction or landscaping.

Fringed campion has been cultivated by a commercial garden since the 1950s. Cuttings collected from a wild population were propagated to create a nursery stock, and plants have been distributed to other nurseries. The species is easily propagated by tissue culture techniques as well as by cuttings. One botanist has created a hybrid between *Silene polypetala* and *Silene virginica* which has potential as a garden ornamental. This hybrid is sold commercially by a nursery in Aiken, South Carolina.

The Georgia Department of Natural Resources, in cooperation with the University of Georgia, is establishing new populations of fringed campion in two wildlife management areas in Monroe County and Troup/Heard counties.

Additional Sources

Allison, J. R. 1988. "Report on a Botanical Survey of North-facing Ravines and Bluffs along the Flint and Chattahoochee Rivers in Southwestern Georgia." U.S. Fish and Wildlife Service, Jacksonville, Florida.

Duncan, W. H., and L. E. Foote. 1975. *Wild-flowers of the Southeastern United States.* University of Georgia Press, Athens.

Faust, W. Z. 1980. "Status Survey for *Silene polypetala.*" U.S. Fish and Wildlife Service, Jacksonville, Florida.

Kral, R. 1983. *A Report on Some Rare, Threatened, or Endangered Forest-related Vascular Plants of the South.* USDA, Forest Service, Technical Publication R8-TP2.

McCollum, J. L., and D. R. Ettman. 1989. *Georgia's Protected Plants.* Georgia Department of Natural Resources and USDA Soil Conservation Service.

Contacts

Regional Office of Endangered Species
U. S. Fish and Wildlife Service
Richard B. Russell Federal Building
75 Spring Street, S.W.
Atlanta, Georgia 30303

David J. Wesley
U.S. Fish and Wildlife Service
3100 University Blvd. South, Suite 120
Jacksonville, Florida 32216

White Irisette
Sisyrinchium dichotomum

Nora Murdock

Status	Endangered
Listed	September 26, 1991
Family	Iridaceae (Iris)
Description	Perennial with forking stems, basal leaves, and clusters of tiny white flowers.
Habitat	Disturbed, thinly shaded, basic soils.
Threats	Natural succession, road construction, alien plants.
Region 4	North Carolina

Description

White irisette is a perennial in the iris family with forking stems that grow to a height of 11 to 20 centimeters (4.3 to 7.8 in). The pale green to bluish green basal leaves are from one-third to one-half the height of the stems. Very small white flowers (7.5 mm; 0.3 in) appear in clusters of four to six from late May through July. The fruit is a brown capsule containing three to six round or elliptical black seeds.

Habitat

This species occurs in thinly shaded, disturbed areas on rich, basic soils, probably derived from amphibolite. It has been found in clearings and at wood edges where water runoff has cleared the soil of leaf litter. Currently the species is confined to road right-of-way maintenance areas.

Historic Range

Since its discovery in 1899, white irisette has only been found in a small area of the Upper Piedmont of western North Carolina (Polk, Henderson, and Rutherford counties) bounded by Chimney Rock, White Oak Mountain, and Sugarloaf Mountain. Plant populations have steadily decreased over the last 50 years; in 1942 the species was described as locally "fairly common."

Current Distribution

Three populations of white irisette are known to survive. The Chimney Rock population contains fewer than 100 plants, and about 200 plants remain at the Sugarloaf Mountain location. The largest population, about 1,000 plants, is found at White Oak Mountain. All three populations are along roadside rights-of-way. One is on land maintained by the state Department of Transportation; the other two are along privately maintained roads.

Conservation and Recovery

The three remaining populations of white irisette are threatened by natural succession, road construction and maintenance, and invasive alien plant species. While the species requires some disturbance of its habitat to prevent natural succession from eventually shading out populations, bulldozing and other activities asssociated with road construction would destroy plants. Right-of-way maintenance that does not interfere with reproduction and that avoids the use of herbicides is essential to conserve remaining populations. All three populations are also vulnerable to competition from aggressive alien species such as kudzu (*Pueraria lobata*), Japanese honeysuckle (*Lonicera japonica*), and *Microstegium vimineum*. In addition, one population is particularly susceptible to human trampling since it occurs in a commercial recreation area that is visited by hundreds of thousands of tourists each year.

Additional Sources

Hornberger, K. 1987. "Systematics of the Genus *Sisyrinchium* (Iridaceae) in the Southeastern United States." Ph.D. diss. Fayetteville, University of Arkansas.

North Carolina Natural Heritage Program. 1990. "Element Occurrence Records for *Sisyrinchium dichotomum*." Raleigh, North Carolina.

Contacts

Regional Office of Endangered Species
U. S. Fish and Wildlife Service
Richard B. Russell Federal Building
75 Spring Street, S.W.
Atlanta, Georgia 30303

Nora Murdock
U.S. Fish and Wildlife Service
330 Ridgefield Court
Asheville, North Carolina

Gentian Pinkroot
Spigelia gentianoides

George Rogers   *Color Plate C-3*
Missouri Botanical Garden

Status	Endangered
Listed	November 26, 1990
Family	Loganiaceae (Logania)
Description	Perennial with opposite, stalkless leaves and tubular pink flowers.
Habitat	Upland pine and mixed pine-oak forests.
Threats	Limited distribution, timber cutting.
Region 4	Florida

Description

Gentian pinkroot is a perennial which has a single, erect, sharply ridged stem, 10 to 30 centimeters (4 to 12 in) tall. The opposite, sessile (stalkless) leaves are largest at the top of the stem. In May and June a few pale pink, upward-pointing, tubelike flowers form a cluster on a short, spikelike stem. The flowers, which usually stay nearly closed, have five slits, a fact that has led one botanist to suspect that the species is pollinated when a moth inserts its proboscis into the slits probing for nectar. The flowers resemble those of gentians, a fact reflected in its name.

The closest relative of *Spigelia gentianoides* is a plant that was widely used in folk medicine during the nineteenth century in the South. *S. marilandica* was a widespread species that grew in clumps and had red flowers. It was used as a popular cure for intestinal worms, although there are reports of it causing death. Collections for medicinal use substantially reduced its occurrence. The medicinal properties of gentian pinkroot have not been evaluated.

Habitat

Gentian pinkroot is found in both sunny and shaded areas of upland pine and mixed oak-pine forests. The plant is extremely rare and has seldom been collected. Little is known about its habitat requirements.

Historic Range

The species was first collected in 1837 near the Apalachicola River, probably in Jackson County, Florida. Other historical collections have been made from near Chattahoochee (Gadsden County), from Chipley (Washington County), and from near Wewahitchka (Calhoun County). The species was probably extirpated from much of its historic range during the nineteenth and early twentieth centuries when much of the upland forest in the area was cleared for cultivation or converted to pine plantations.

Current Distribution

At present, three populations of gentian pinkroot, all in northwestern Florida, are known to exist: two in Jackson County and one in Calhoun County. A recent survey of these populations found that one Jackson County site consisted of about 30 plants, a substantial decrease from the 150 plants surveyed 12 years earlier. The other site, which is on publicly owned land near the Jackson-Bay County line, consists of no more than 10 individuals. The Calhoun County population, located south of Blountstown, is the largest of the three. It occurs in a pineland which was cut in 1983 and replanted with pines in 1989.

Although a thorough search might uncover additional populations, the few historic collections and small number of sites discovered by field biologists strongly indicate that the plant was never widespread and is currently extremely rare.

Conservation and Recovery

The low numbers and limited range of gentian pinkroot make it vulnerable to extinction. One site is threatened by its proximity to recreational activities; the two others are vulnerable to habitat alteration by timber cutting and replanting. The smallest population occurs on land owned by the Army Corps of Engineers and is managed by the Florida Department of Natural Resources. It is easily accessible to the public and vulnerable to accidental damage or vandalism. The other two populations are on privately owned land that may be altered by timber cutting. The largest population appears to have survived one cutting and replanting. However, the landowner, aware of the presence of a rare plant, took special care with the timbering operation. The cutting was done with minimal habitat disturbance and the replanting was done by hand.

Another threat to this population is the possible use of herbicides to free the young pine trees from competition from herbs and grasses. The Fish and Wildlife Service expects to deal with this threat through direct contacts with the landowner.

Additional Source

Rogers, G. K. 1988. "*Spigelia gentianoides*—a Species on the Brink of Extinction. *Plant Conservation* 3(3):1, 8.

Contacts

Regional Office of Endangered Species
U. S. Fish and Wildlife Service
Richard B. Russell Federal Building
75 Spring Street, S.W.
Atlanta, Georgia 30303

David J. Wesley
U.S. Fish and Wildlife Service
3100 University Blvd. South, Suite 120
Jacksonville, Florida 32216

Virginia Spiraea
Spiraea virginiana

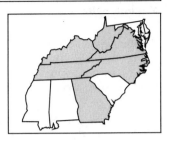

Paul Somers

Status . . . . Threatened
Listed . . . . June 15, 1990
Family . . . . Rosaceae (Rose)
Description . . . . . . Clump-forming shrub with clusters of cream-colored flowers.
Habitat . . . . Stream banks and flood plains.
Threats . . . . Hydroelectric projects; lack of reproduction.
Region 4 . . . . Georgia, Kentucky, North Carolina, Tennessee
Region 5 . . . . Virginia, West Virginia

Description

Virginia spiraea is a shrub in the rose family with upright, arching stems that grow between 0.6 to 3 meters (2 to 10 ft) high. New stems sprout from the base, forming dense clumps. Leaves are alternate and variable in size and shape. Plants bloom in June and July, producing branched, flat-topped clusters of small cream-colored flowers.

Habitat

This species is found almost exclusively along stream systems, either on the scoured banks of swiftly flowing mountain steams or in the open flood plains of the streams' lower reaches.

Historic Range

Widely scattered populations of Virginia spiraea have been found along stream systems in seven eastern states: Georgia, Kentucky, North Carolina, Pennsylvania, Tennessee, Virginia, and West Virginia. The species was first described from a specimen collected in 1890 from along the Monongahela River in Monongalia County, West Virginia.

Current Distribution

Virginia spiraea is currently known from 24 locations in six states. The species no longer occurs in Pennsylvania. Of the known populations, 13 are small (fewer than 10 clumps), eight are moderate in size (from 10 to 50 clumps), and three are large (more than 50 clumps).

In Georgia populations are found along Rock Creek (Walker County) and Bear Creek (Date County). Sites in North Carolina are on the South Fork of the New River (Ashe County), the Little Tennessee River (Macon County), the Nolichucky River (Mitchell and Yancey counties), and the South Toe and Cane Rivers (Yancey County).

Tennessee populations occur along Abrams Creek and the Little River (Blount County), Cane Creek (Van Buren County), White Oak Creek (Scott County), Clifty Creek (Roane County), Daddy's Creek (Cumberland County), and Clear Fork (Morgan and Scott counties).

Populations in Virginia are found on the Russell Fork and Pound River (Dickenson County), the New River (Grayson County), and the Guest River (Wise County). Sites in West Virginia are along the Bluestone River (Mercer County), the Buckhannon River (Upshur County), the Gauley and Meadow Rivers (Nicholas and Fayette counties), and in a wet meadow in Raleigh County. Kentucky sites are located along the Rockcastle River (Pulaski County) and Sinking Creek (Laurel County).

Extensive searches for additional populations were conducted by The Nature Conservancy in the late 1980s. No populations were found in Pennsylvania or Maryland. Because suitable habitat occurs in remote areas it is likely that some additional populations will eventually be found.

Conservation and Recovery

Virginia spiraea faces a combination of human and natural threats. Throughout its range human disturbance has been ob-

served, including cutting for right-of-way maintenance, stream access paths, and farm field clearing. One population in Monongalia County, West Virginia, was destroyed by the construction of a dam. Proposed hydroelectric projects at the Summersville Dam (Nicholas County, West Virginia) and the John Flannagan Dam (Dickenson County, Virginia) could affect nearby populations.

All known populations consist of mature plants; no seedlings have been found. Although plants flower profusely and attract a variety of pollinating insects, few seeds apparently mature. Unsuccessful seed germination tests and the lack of seedlings suggest that plants are not reproducing sexually, reducing the likelihood of the establishment of new colonies.

Virginia spiraea is found on a mixture of federal, state, and private lands. Those populations on federal and state lands receive protection under both the Endangered Species Act and various state acts. Protected populations include those in the Jefferson National Forest (Virginia), the Cherokee National Forest (Tennessee), Great Smoky Mountains National Park (Tennessee), and Big South Fork National River and Recreation Area (Tennessee).

Three populations in West Virginia are found in areas recently designated as a National Recreation Area and a National Scenic River (on the Gauley, Meadow, and Bluestone rivers). While these sites are currently in private hands, it is expected that they will eventually be acquired by the National Park Service. Four state parks—in Georgia, Tennessee, Virginia, and West Virginia—also support Virginia spiraea populations. And at least three sites on private land are being voluntarily protected by landowners contacted by The Nature Conservancy or state heritage programs.

Additional Sources

Bartgis, R. 1987. "Status Surveys in West Virginia for *Carex polymorpha, Spiraea virginiana,* and *Thalictrum steeleanum.*" West Virginia Field Office, The Nature Conservancy.

Clarkson, R. B. 1959. "The West Virginia Spiraea." *Castanea* 24:143-146.

Glencoe, J. F. 1961. *"Spiraea virginiana* Britton: A Rare Southern Appalachian Endemic." Master's thesis. University of West Virginia.

Ogle, D. 1987. "Contract Report to the Virginia Natural Heritage Program on *Spiraea virginiana.*" Virginia Highlands Community College.

Contact

Sharon W. Morgan
U.S. Fish and Wildlife Service
One Gateway Center, Suite 700
Newton Corner, MA 02158

Cóbana Negra
Stahlia monosperma

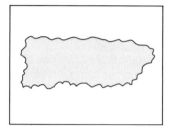

William M. Houghton/Fairchild Tropical Garden

Status	Threatened
Listed	April 5, 1990
Family	Fabaceae (Pea)
Description	Medium-sized, evergreen tree with pinnately compound, alternate leaves.
Habitat	Brackish, seasonally flooded wetlands.
Threats	Coastal development.
Region 4	Puerto Rico

Description

Cóbana negra is a medium-sized, evergreen tree that can attain a height of 7.6 to 15 meters (25 to 50 ft) and a diameter of 30 to 46 centimeters (12 to 18 in). Its leaves are pinnately compound, alternate, and bear from 6 to 12 opposite leaflets, which have scattered black glands beneath. Between March and May, depending on rainfall, it bears clusters of yellow flowers. The red, fleshy fruits, which have the odor of ripe apples, are about 2.5 centimeters (1 in) in diameter and contain a single, large seed.

Habitat

The species grows in brackish, seasonally flooded wetlands associated with black mangrove (*Avicennia germinans*) communities and at the edges of salt flats. Individual trees, apparently cultivated, have been planted in yards and along roadways.

Historic Range

Cóbana negra was first described in 1881. It was thought to be restricted to Puerto Rico and the island of Vieques but was later found in Hispaniola. Once fairly common on the margins of salt flats and shallow lagoons, coastal development has severely reduced its occurrence.

Current Distribution

The species survives in a few scattered populations on the islands of Puerto Rico and Vieques. The largest population, about 23 mature trees and 35 seedlings, occurs on the southwest coast of Puerto Rico near Boquerón at the edges of salt flats. Mature trees are also found on the northeast coast in Rio Grande near mangrove forests. Between 30 and 40 trees occur near mangrove forest on Vieques, a 52-square-mile island to the east of Puerto Rico, all on U.S. Navy property.

Conservation and Recovery

The main threat to cóbana negra is the elimination of coastal wetlands through tourist and residential development. Southwestern Puerto Rico is experiencing severe developmental pressures and cóbana negra trees are known to have been eliminated. Although many of the coastal mangrove forests in the area are included in the Commonwealth Forest system, cóbana negra sites often lie further inland, outside forest boundaries. On Vieques Island cóbana negra is found in Ensenada Honda and Laguna Kiani. The U.S. Navy has designated both places "special ecological zones" and prohibits the cutting of vegetation, development, or off-road maneuvers.

Remaining trees produce large quantities of viable seed and cultivation of the species has been successful. Besides scattered use as an ornamental, cultivated trees are found in the Vega Commonwealth Forest and on the Cayey Campus of the University of Puerto Rico. The commonwealth Department of Natural Resources has an ongoing propagation program for cóbana negra.

Additional Sources

Densmore, R. 1987. "Status Report on *Stahlia monosperma* (Cóbana Negra) in Southwestern Puerto Rico." U.S. Fish and Wildlife Service, Boquerón, Puerto Rico.

Department of Natural Resources, Natural Heritage Program. 1988. "Status Information on *Stahlia monosperma* in Puerto Rico and Adjacent Islands." San Juan, Puerto Rico.

Contacts

Regional Office of Endangered Species
U. S. Fish and Wildlife Service
Richard B. Russell Federal Building
75 Spring Street, S.W.
Atlanta, Georgia 30303

Susan Silander
U.S. Fish and Wildlife Service
P.O. Box 491
Boquerón, Puerto Rico 00622

Tetramolopium filiforme
No Common Name

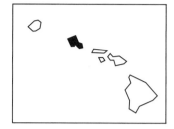

Yevonn Wilson-Ramsey from *Manual of the Flowering Plants of Hawai'i*

Status . . . . Endangered
Listed . . . . October 29, 1991
Family . . . . Asteraceae (Aster)
Description . . . . . . Dwarf shrub with narrowly linear leaves and flower heads with white ray florets and maroon disk florets.
Habitat . . . . Dry cliffs and ridges.
Threats . . . . Feral goats, alien plant species.
Region 1 . . . . Hawaii (Oahu)

Description

Tetramolopium filiforme is a branched dwarf shrub of the aster family that grows 5 to 15 centimeters (2 to 6 in) high. The leaves, which are bunched at the tops of the stems, are narrowly linear and un-toothed. The flower heads occur either singly or in clusters of two to four. Each head has 35 to 52 white to pale lavender ray florets and 18 to 30 maroon (occasionally yellow) disk florets. The ray florets are female flowers; the disk florets function as male flowers.

Some plants of the species have wider, toothed leaves and have been given the varietal status of *T. filiforme* var. *polyphyllum*. Both varieties have Endangered status.

Habitat

Tetramolopium filiforme is found only in the Waianae Mountain Range on the western side of the island of Oahu, Hawaii. This island is dominated by the remnants of two ancient volcanoes that have eroded into two "mountain ranges," which consist of long, narrow ridges. The Waianae Range lies on the western side of the island, while the Koolau Range traverses the eastern side. The Waianae Range, which runs northwest to southeast for about 40 miles, lies in the rain shadow of the Koolau Range, and, except for the summit of Mt. Kaala, the highest point on the island, receives much less rainfall.

A variety of plant habitats are found in

the Waianae Mountains, ranging from coastal dry shrubland to lowland dry forest to lowland wet forest. *Tetramolopium filiforme* grows on dry cliff faces and ridges at elevations between 340 and 900 meters (1,100 and 3,000 ft). Associated species include 'a'ali'i (*Dodonaea viscosa*), ahinahina (*Artemisia australis*), and *Schiedea manii*.

The diverse habitats of the Waianae Mountains contain a large number of vulnerable native Hawaiian plant species. In October 1991 the Fish and Wildlife Service (FWS) listed *Tetramolopium filiforme* and 25 other plant species from Oahu's Waianae Mountains as Endangered.

Historic Range

Tetramolopium filiforme was first collected in 1969. It has been found from the northern Waianae Mountains, from Ohikilolo Ridge, Keaau Valley, and Makaha Valley. The species is not known from any other island.

Current Distribution

The species survives at five sites on state land in Keaau Valley and on Ohikilolo Ridge. All populations occur in an area of less than one square mile and contain a total of fewer than 500 plants.

Conservation and Recovery

The main threats to *Tetramolopium filiforme* are habitat degradation by feral goats and competition from aggressive non-native plant species. Feral goats, which are managed by the state as game animals, have been on the island for 170 years. Because of their agility they are able to reach relatively inaccessible cliff areas. The disturbance of steep slopes promotes erosion which leads to a loss of plant life.

Tetramolopium filiforme, like most rare Hawaiian plant species, is threatened by several alien plant species. Christmasberry (*Schinus terebinthifolius*), an aggressive tree introduced to Hawaii before 1911, forms dense thickets and may also release chemicals that inhibit the growth of other species. Another tree, koa haole (*Leucaena leucocephala*), grows in dense stands, crowding out native flora. Daisy fleabane (*Erigeron karvinskianus*) and molasses grass (*Melinus minutiflora*) grow in dense mats that smother native vegetation. Molasses grass is also fire adapted and provides fuel for spreading wildfires.

Such wildfires are a threat to *Tetramolopium filiforme* populations which lie near the U.S. Army's Makua Military Reservation and Schofield Barracks. Within a 14-month period from 1989 to 1990, 10 fires resulted from weapons practice on the reservation. In order to minimize damage from fires, the army has constructed firebreaks between the target areas and the surrounding forest.

Additional Sources

Cuddihy, L. W., and C. P. Stone. 1990. *Alteration of Native Hawaiian Vegetation: Effects of Humans, Their Activities and Introductions*. Cooperative National Park Resources Study Unit, University of Hawaii Press, Honolulu.

Culliney, J. L. 1988. *Islands in a Far Sea: Nature and Man in Hawaii*. Sierra Club Books, San Francisco.

Contact

Derral R. Herbst
U.S. Fish and Wildlife Service
300 Ala Moana Boulevard, Room 6307
P.O. Box 50167
Honolulu, Hawaii 96850

Tetramolopium lepidotum ssp. lepidotum

No Common Name

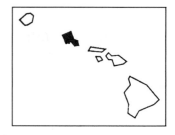

John Obata   Color Plate C-6

Status . . . . Endangered
Listed . . . . October 29, 1991
Family . . . . Asteraceae (Aster)
Description . . . . . . Shrub with lanceolate
                         leaves and flower heads
                         with white ray florets and
                         pale salmon disk florets.
Habitat . . . . Grassy ridgetops, slopes,
                         and west-facing cliffs.
Threats . . . . Alien plant species, low
                         numbers.
Region 1 . . . . Hawaii (Oahu)

Description

Tetramolopium lepidotum ssp. *lepidotum* is an erect shrub of the aster family. It grows from 12 to 36 centimeters (4.7 to 14 in) tall and branches toward the ends of the stems. The lanceolate leaves are 25 to 45 millimeters (1.0 to 1.8 in) long. The flower heads are in clusters of from 6 to 12. Each head contains 21 to 40 white to pinkish lavender ray florets which are female, and 4 to 11 pale salmon disk florets which are bisexual.

This subspecies has been known by several scientific names: *Erigeron lepidotus, E. pauciflorus, E. tennerrimus* var. *lepidotus, Tetramolopium chamissonis* var. *luxurians, T. lepidotum* var. *luxurians,* and *Vittadinia chamissonis.*

The other subspecies, *T. l.* ssp. *arbusculum,* is known from a single 1844 collection and is now considered extinct.

Habitat

Tetramolopium lepidotum ssp. *lepidotum* is found only in the Waianae Mountain Range on the western side of the island of Oahu, Hawaii. This island is dominated by the remnants of two ancient volcanoes that have eroded into two "mountain ranges," which consist of long, narrow ridges. The Waianae Range lies on the western side of the island, while the Koolau Range traverses the eastern side. The Waianae Range, which runs northwest to southeast for about 40 miles, lies in the rain shadow of the Koolau Range, and, except for the summit of Mt. Kaala, the highest point on the island, receives much less rainfall.

A variety of plant habitats are found in the Waianae Mountains, ranging from coastal dry shrubland to lowland dry forest to lowland wet forest. *Tetramolopium lepidotum* ssp. *lepidotum* occurs only on grassy slopes, ridgetops, and west-facing cliffs at elevations between 370 and 940 meters (1,200 and 3,100 ft).

The diverse habitats of the Waianae Mountains contain a large number of vulnerable native Hawaiian plant species. In October 1991 the Fish and Wildlife Service (FWS) listed *Tetramolopium lepidotum* ssp. *lepidotum* and 25 other plant species from Oahu's Waianae Mountains as Endangered.

Historic Range

Tetramolopium lepidotum ssp. *lepidotum* was first described in 1934. It has been known from nearly the entire range of the Waianae Mountains, from Makua Valley to Kaaikukae Ridge, and from the island of Lanai.

Current Distribution

Today three populations survive on federal and private land in the Waianae Mountains on Mauna Kapu and Puu Kaua. Fewer than 100 plants extend over an area of about 2.5 miles.

Conservation and Recovery

The main threat to *Tetramolopium lepidotum* ssp. *lepidotum* is competition from several non-native plant species. Christmasberry (*Schinus terebinthifolius*), an aggressive tree introduced to Hawaii before 1911, forms dense thickets and may also release chemicals that inhibit the growth of other species. Firetree (*Myrica faya*) was planted in the Waianae Mountains during a reforestation project. Besides forming a dense closed canopy that excludes other species, it produces its own nitrogen, enabling it to colonize areas to which native species have become adapted. Daisy fleabane (*Erigeron karvinskianus*) and molasses grass (*Melinus minutiflora*) grow in dense mats that smother native vegetation.

Fire is a threat to *Tetramolopium lepidotum* ssp. *lepidotum* populations that lie near the U.S. Army's Makua Military Reservation and Schofield Barracks. Within a 14-month period from 1989 to 1990, 10 fires resulted from weapons practice on the reservation.

Additional Sources

Cuddihy, L. W., and C. P. Stone. 1990. *Alteration of Native Hawaiian Vegetation: Effects of Humans, Their Activities and Introductions.* Cooperative National Park Resources Study Unit, University of Hawaii Press, Honolulu.

Culliney, J. L. 1988. *Islands in a Far Sea: Nature and Man in Hawaii.* Sierra Club Books, San Francisco.

Contacts

Regional Office of Endangered Species
U.S. Fish and Wildlife Service
Eastside Federal Complex
911 N.S. 11th Avenue
Portland, Oregon 97232-4181

Derral R. Herbst
U.S. Fish and Wildlife Service
300 Ala Moana Boulevard, Room 6307
P.O. Box 50167
Honolulu, Hawaii 96850

Tetramolopium remyi
No Common Name

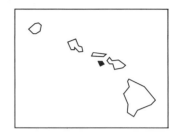

Robert Hobdy

Status	Endangered
Listed	September 20, 1991
Family	Asteraceae (Sunflower)
Description	Branched shrub with narrow leaves and yellow and white daisy-like flowers.
Habitat	Lowland dry scrub.
Threats	Alien plant species, low numbers.
Region 1	Hawaii (Lanai)

Description

Tetramolopium remyi is a branched shrub of the aster family, usually reclining but sometimes erect, that grows to a length of about 40 centimeters (16 in). The narrow leaves are curved inward; the stems and leaves are covered with sticky hairs. Each branch bears a single flower head, about 1.25 centimeters (0.5 in) in diameter. The flower head comprises 70 to 100 yellow disk flowers and 150 to 250 white ray flowers. The species has also been known by the names *Vittadinia remyi* and *Erigeron remyi*.

Habitat

This species grows on dry leeward slopes of the Lanaihale Ridge on the island of Lanai, Hawaii. A broad ridge runs northwest to southeast across this small island. The ridge is commonly known by the name of its highest peak, Lanaihale, which is 1,027 meters (3,370 ft) high. A lowland dry shubland plant community is found on the Lanaihale's leeward slopes and valleys. This stony, eroded land has an annual rainfall of only 25 to 64 centimeters (10 to 25 in), occurring mostly between November and April. Dominant members of the dry shrub plant community are lama (*Diospyros sandwicensis*), wiliwili (*Erythrina sandwicensis*), 'a'ali'i (*Dodonaea viscosa*), and nehe (*Lipochaeta* spp.). Another Endangered plant species, *Abutilon eremitopetalum*, is found in this community. A lowland wet forest is found on the summit and narrow valleys of Lanaihhale. This plant community supports four plant species listed as Endangered: *Cyanea macrostegia* var. *gibsonii*, *Gahnia lanaiensis*, *Phyllostegia glabra* var. *lanaiensis*, and *Viola lanaiensis*. All of these Endangered plant species are endemic to Lanaihale.

Historic Range

Tetramolopium remyi was first collected from the Lahaina area of western Maui between 1851 and 1855. It has not been found on that island since 1944 and is presumed extirpated. It was collected on Lanai and described in 1888.

Current Distribution

This species is now known from a single population of about 35 plants on private land on the Auala Ridge at an elevation of about 228 meters (750 ft). This population has been known for a little over a decade and has decreased slightly during that period.

Conservation and Recovery

The main threats to *Tetramolopium remyi* are browsing by axis deer and mouflon sheep, and competition from invasive alien plant species, such as broomsedge (*Andropogon virginicus*) and guinea grass (*Panicum maximum*). These aggressive species are more successful than native species in competing for water, space, and light.

Besides destroying plants directly, brows-ing by deer and mouflon promotes erosion and open up areas for the invasive species. With only a single extant population the species is vulnerable to extinction through an unpredictable event. Because this area is dry much of the year, fire is also a danger to the species.

Additional Sources

Cuddihy, L. W., and C. P. Stone. 1990. *Alteration of Native Hawaiian Vegetation: Effects of Humans, Their Activities and Introductions.* University of Hawaii Cooperative National Park Resources Study Unit, Honolulu.

Culliney, J. L. 1988. *Islands in a Far Sea: Nature and Man in Hawaii.* Sierra Club Books, San Francisco.

Lowrey, Timothy K. 1990. "Tetramolopium." In *Manual of the Flowering Plants of Hawai'i,* by W. L. Wagner, D. R. Herbst, and S. H. Sohmer. University of Hawaii Press and Bishop Museum Press, Honolulu.

Tomich, P. Q. 1986. *Mammals in Hawai'i.* 2d ed. Bishop Museum Special Publication 76. Bishop Museum Press, Honolulu.

Contacts

Regional Office of Endangered Species
U.S. Fish and Wildlife Service
Eastside Federal Complex
911 N.S. 11th Avenue
Portland, Oregon 97232-4181

Derral R. Herbst
U.S. Fish and Wildlife Service
300 Ala Moana Boulevard, Room 6307
P.O. Box 50167
Honolulu, Hawaii 96850

Urera kaalae
No Common Name

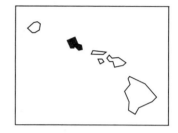

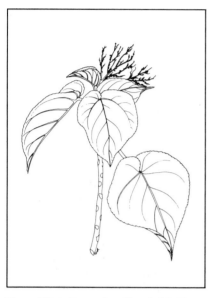

Yevonn Wilson-Ramsey from *Manual of the Flowering Plants of Hawai'i*

Status . . . . Endangered
Listed . . . . October 29, 1991
Family . . . . Urticaceae (Nettle)
Description . . . . . . Small tree with brown bark and heart-shaped, pale green leaves.
Habitat . . . . Slopes in moist forest.
Threats . . . . Feral pigs, alien plant species.
Region 1 . . . . Hawaii (Oahu)

Description

Urera kaalae is a shrub or small tree of the nettle family that grows 3 to 7 meters (10 to 23 ft) tall. On exposure to the air, the tree's sap turns greenish black. The branches are hollow, and the bark is pale brown. The heart-shaped leaves are pale green, thin and membranous, 10 to 27 centimeters (4 to 11 in) long. The flowers are male or female and can grow on the same or on different trees. The sepals of male flower are fused into a somewhat globe-shaped structure, about 1.5 millimeters (0.06 in) long.

Habitat

Urera kaalae is found only in the Waianae Mountain Range on the western side of the island of Oahu, Hawaii. This island is dominated by the remnants of two ancient volcanoes that have eroded into two "mountain ranges," which consist of long, narrow ridges. The Waianae Range lies on the western side of the island, while the Koolau Range traverses the eastern side. The Waianae Range, which runs northwest to southeast for about 40 miles, lies in the rain shadow of the Koolau Range, and, except for the summit of Mt. Kaala, the highest point on the island, receives much less rainfall.

A variety of plant habitats are found in the Waianae Mountains, ranging from coastal dry shrubland to lowland dry forest to lowland wet forest. *Urera kaalae* grows on slopes in moist forest dominated by papala kepau (*Pisonia umbellifera*) at elevations between 300 and 820 meters (980 and 2,700 ft).

The diverse habitats of the Waianae Mountains contain a large number of vulnerable native Hawaiian plant species. In October 1991 the Fish and Wildlife Service (FWS) listed *Urera kaalae* and 25 other plant species from Oahu's Waianae Mountains as Endangered.

Historic Range

Urera kaalae was first collected in the early 1800s. It was rediscovered and first described in 1874. The species has been found from the central to southern windward Waianae Mountains, from Waianae Uka to Kupehau Gulch. It is not known to occur on any other island.

Current Distribution

The species survives in Ekahanui and Kaluaa gulches, where three populations occur on private land. These populations are distributed over about one square mile and contain about 19 trees.

Conservation and Recovery

The main threats to *Urera kaalae* are disturbance of its habitat by feral pigs and competition from alien plant species. Feral pigs, which are managed by the state as game animals, have been in the Waianae Mountains for about 150 years and have had a major effect on the native flora. Their rooting destroys plants and opens the habitat to invasive species. They also help spread these alien plants by carrying seed on their bodies and in their feces.

Several non-native species are direct threats to *Urera kaalae*. Christmasberry (*Schinus terebinthifolius*), an aggressive tree

introduced to Hawaii before 1911, forms dense thickets and may also release chemicals that inhibit the growth of other species. Firetree (*Myrica faya*), planted in the Waianae Mountains during a reforestation project, and strawberry guava (*Psidium cattleianum*) form dense stands that exclude other species. Huehue haole (*Passiflora suberosa*) is a vine that smothers the subcanopy of dryland habitats. Molasses grass (*Melinus minutiflora*) and daisy fleabane (*Erigeron karvinskianus*) grow in dense mats that smother native vegetation.

Fire is a threat to *Urera kaalae* trees which lie near the U.S. Army's Makua Military Reservation and Schofield Barracks. Within a 14-month period from 1989 to 1990, 10 fires resulted from weapons practice on the reservation.

Additional Sources

Cuddihy, L. W., and C. P. Stone. 1990. *Alteration of Native Hawaiian Vegetation: Effects of Humans, Their Activities and Introductions*. Cooperative National Park Resources Study Unit, University of Hawaii Press, Honolulu.

Culliney, J. L. 1988. *Islands in a Far Sea: Nature and Man in Hawaii*. Sierra Club Books, San Francisco.

Contacts

Regional Office of Endangered Species
U.S. Fish and Wildlife Service
Eastside Federal Complex
911 N.S. 11th Avenue
Portland, Oregon 97232-4181

Derral R. Herbst
U.S. Fish and Wildlife Service
300 Ala Moana Boulevard, Room 6307
P.O. Box 50167
Honolulu, Hawaii 96850

Viola chamissoniana
ssp. chamissoniana
No Common Name

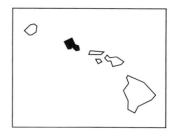

Status . . . . Endangered
Listed . . . . October 29, 1991
Family . . . . Violaceae (Violet)
Description . . . . . . Shrub with heart-shaped, toothed leaves and five-petaled, white and purple flowers.
Habitat . . . . Dry cliffs in moist shrubland.
Threats . . . . Feral pigs, alien plant species, low numbers.
Region 1 . . . . Hawaii (Oahu)

Description

Viola chamissoniana ssp. *chamissoniana* is a branched shrub of the violet family up to 90 centimeters (3 ft) tall. The toothed leaves, which are clustered at the branch tips, are triangular-oval to heart-shaped and measure about 2 to 4 centimeters (0.8 to 1.6 in) in length. Each flower stalk produces one or two five-petaled white flowers, which are tinged with purple. Fruits are capsules containing dark brown or black seeds. this subspecies has also been known as *Viola helioscopia*.

Habitat

Viola chamissoniana ssp. *chamissoniana* is found only in the Waianae Mountain Range on the western side of the island of Oahu, Hawaii. This island is dominated by the remnants of two ancient volcanoes that have eroded into two "mountain ranges," which consist of long, narrow ridges. The Waianae Range lies on the western side of the island, while the Koolau Range traverses the eastern side. The Waianae Range, which runs northwest to southeast for about 40 miles, lies in the rain shadow of the Koolau Range, and, except for the summit of Mt. Kaala, the highest point on the island, receives much less rainfall.

A variety of plant habitats are found in the Waianae Mountains, ranging from coastal dry shrubland to lowland dry forest to lowland wet forest. *Viola chamissoniana* ssp. *chamissoniana* grows on dry cliffs in moist shrubland at elevations between 700 and 1,000 meters (2,300 and 3,040 ft). Associated species include ahinahina (*Artemisia australis*), ko'oko'olau (*Bidens*), and ohia (*Metrosideros polymorpha*).

The diverse habitats of the Waianae Mountains contain a large number of vulnerable native Hawaiian plant species. In October 1991 the Fish and Wildlife Service (FWS) listed *Viola chamissoniana* ssp. *chamissoniana* and 25 other plant species from Oahu's Waianae Mountains as Endangered. This group listing was the result of the settlement of a 1989 lawsuit brought against the FWS by the Sierra Club Legal Defense Fund on behalf of a Hawaii conservation group. The terms of the settlement called for the proposed listing before October 1992 of 186 Hawaiian candidate plant species.

Historic Range

Viola chamissoniana ssp. *chamissoniana* has been known from the center and southern Waianae Mountains, from Makaleha Valley to Kaaikukai. It is not known to occur on any other island.

Current Distribution

Today this subspecies survives on Kamaileune Ridge, Puu Hapapa, and Puu Kumakalii in the Waianae Mountains. The three known populations, which are located on federal and state lands in an area of less than a square mile, contain about 15 plants.

Conservation and Recovery

The major threats to *Viola chamissoniana* ssp. *chamissoniana* are habitat degradation by feral pigs, competition from non-native

species, and the small number of surviving plants. Feral pigs, which are managed by the state as game animals, have been in the Waianae Mountains for about 150 years and have had a major effect on the native flora. Their rooting destroys plants and opens the habitat to invasive species. They also help spread these alien plants by carrying seed on their bodies and in their feces.

Several non-native species are a direct threat to *Viola chamissoniana* ssp. *chamissoniana*. Christmasberry (*Schinus terebinthifolius*), an aggressive tree introduced to Hawaii before 1911, forms dense thickets and may also release chemicals that inhibit the growth of other species. Molasses grass (*Melinus minutiflora*) grows in dense mats that smother native vegetation.

Additional Sources

Cuddihy, L. W., and C. P. Stone. 1990. *Alteration of Native Hawaiian Vegetation: Effects of Humans, Their Activities and Introductions.* Cooperative National Park Resources Study Unit, University of Hawaii Press, Honolulu.

Culliney, J. L. 1988. *Islands in a Far Sea: Nature and Man in Hawaii.* Sierra Club Books, San Francisco.

Contacts

Regional Office of Endangered Species
U.S. Fish and Wildlife Service
Eastside Federal Complex
911 N.S. 11th Avenue
Portland, Oregon 97232-4181

Derral R. Herbst
U.S. Fish and Wildlife Service
300 Ala Moana Boulevard, Room 6307
P.O. Box 50167
Honolulu, Hawaii 96850

Viola helenae
No Common Name

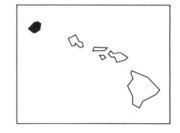

Derral Herbst

Status . . . . Endangered
Listed . . . . September 20, 1991
Family . . . . Violaceae (Violet)
Description . . . . . . Unbranched, small shrub
with lanceolate leaves
clustered at the stem end
and white or pale lavender
flowers.
Habitat . . . . Near streams in montane
wet forests.
Threats . . . . Low numbers, alien plant
species.
Region 1 . . . . Hawaii (Kauai)

Description

Viola helenae is an erect, unbranched, small shrub of the violet family that grows 30 to 80 centimeters (12 to 31 in) tall from a taproot. The lanceolate leaves are about 10 centimeters (4 in) long and are clustered near the upper part of the stem. One or two white or pale lavender flowers are borne in the upper leaf axils. The fruits are capsules containing pale olive-brown seeds.

Habitat

This species grows near stream banks in the Wahiawa drainage basin in the southern part of the island of Kauai, Hawaii.

Kauai has the largest number of endemic plants of all the islands, and the Wahiawa Mountain area is one of the oldest and most diverse montane wet forests in Hawaii. This area, which covers about 1,200 acres, is roughly triangular in shape, with Kapalaoa, Mt. Kahili, and Puuauuka forming the corners. Elevations range from 610 to 1,000 meters (2,000 to 3,300 ft).

In addition to *Viola helenae*, four other plant species endemic to the Wahiawa Stream drainage basin are listed as Endangered: *Cyanea undulata, Dubautia pauciflorula*, kamakahala (*Labordia lydgatei*), and *Hesperomannia lydgatei*. Eighteen other extremely rare plant species occur in this area.

Historic Range

Viola helenae was first collected in the Wahiawa Mountains in 1908. The species is unknown outside the Wahiawa Basin.

Current Distribution

Today *Viola helenae* is known from only two populations, one along each branch of Wahiawa Stream. The total number of plants is estimated at about 13. The land is owned by a corporation which manages it as an agricultural irrigation resource.

Conservation and Recovery

The main threats to *Viola helene* are the species' extremely small population, its limited distribution, and competition from invasive alien plant species. With only 13 remaining individuals at two sites, an unpredictable human or natural event could easily destroy all known plants. Although the Wahiawa drainage basin has been largely undisturbed, invasive plant species are now spreading upstream. Strawberry guava (*Psidium cattleianum*) and melastoma (*Melastoma candidum*) are aggressive plants that outcompete native species. They gained a foothold in the basin in 1982 when Typhoon Iwa opened sections of the forest canopy. This led to the disappearance of a small population (three or four plants) of *Viola helenae*. This invasion is assisted by feral pigs which transport seed and open additonal ground by rooting. Although there are only slight indications of pig activity in the basin, any increase could quickly help spread invading plants.

Additional Sources

Cuddihy, L. W., and C. P. Stone. 1990. *Alteration of Native Hawaiian Vegetation: Effects of Humans, Their Activities and Introductions.* Cooperative National Park Resources Study Unit, University of Hawaii Press, Honolulu.

Culliney, J. L. 1988. *Islands in a Far Sea: Nature and Man in Hawaii.* Sierra Club Books, San Francisco.

St. John, H. 1979. "Resurrection of *Viola helenae* Becker." Hawaiian Plant Studies 90. *Phytologia* 44:323-324.

_____. 1989. "Revision of the Hawaiian Species of *Viola* (Violaceae)." *Bot. Jahrb. Syst.* 111(2):165-204.

Stone, C. P., and J. M. Scott, eds. 1985. *Hawai'i's Terrestrial Ecosystems: Preservation and Management.* Cooperative National Park Resources Study Unit, University of Hawaii Press, Honolulu.

Wagner, W. L., D. R. Herbst, and S. H. Sohmer. 1990. *Manual of the Flowering Plants of Hawai'i.* University of Hawaii Press and Bishop Museum Press, Honolulu.

Contacts

Regional Office of Endangered Species
U.S. Fish and Wildlife Service
Eastside Federal Complex
911 N.S. 11th Avenue
Portland, Oregon 97232-4181

Derral R. Herbst
U.S. Fish and Wildlife Service
300 Ala Moana Boulevard, Room 6307
P.O. Box 50167
Honolulu, Hawaii 96850

Viola lanaiensis
No Common Name

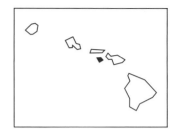

Derral Herbst

Status . . . . Endangered
Listed . . . . September 20, 1991
Family . . . . Violaceae (Violet)
Description . . . . . . Perennial with lance-
shaped leaves clustered
near the top and small
white flowers.
Habitat . . . . Lowland wet forest.
Threats . . . . Low numbers, tourist
development, alien plant
species.
Region 1 . . . . Hawaii (Lanai)

Description

Viola lanaiensis is a small, erect, un-branched (or few-branched) small shrub of the violet family that grows to a height of 10 to 40 centimeters (4 to 16 in). The lanceolate leaves are 6 to 11 centimeters (2.4 to 4.3 in) long and clustered near the top. Small white flowers, 1.0 to 1.5 centimeters (0.4 to 0.6 in) long, are tinged with purple or have purple veins. They appear singly or in small groups at the leaf axils.

Habitat

This species grows on the summit and upper slopes of the Lanaihale Ridge on the island of Lanai, Hawaii. A broad ridge runs northwest to southeast across this small is-land and is commonly known by the name of its highest peak, Lanaihale, which is 1,027 meters (3,370 ft) high. A lowland wet forest plant community is found on the Lanaihale summit and its narrow val-leys. Although annual rainfall is only about 94 centimeters (37 in), the area is usually cloud-covered in the afternoon and shrouded in fog at night. Dominant members of the plant community are ohia (*Metrosideros polymorpha*) and uluhe fern (*Dicranopteris linearis*). Three other Endan-gered plant species, *Cyanea macrostegia* var. *gibsonii, Phyllostegia glabra* var. *lanaiensis,* and *Gahnia lanaiensis,* occur in this low-land wet forest. A lowland dry shrubland plant community is found on the leeward slopes and valleys of Lanaihhale. This community supports two plant species listed as Endangered: *Abutilon eremitopetalum* and *Tetramolopium remyi*. All of these Endangered plant species are endemic to Lanaihale.

Historic Range

Viola lanaiensis was first collected between 1851 and 1855 on Lanai. It has been known from the upper slopes and summit of Lanaihale from near the head of Hookio Gulch to Haalelepaakai, a distance of about 2.5 miles.

Current Distribution

Two populations totalling less than 500 plants are known today. They are situated near the Munro Trail system which crosses Lanaihale.

Conservation and Recovery

The main threats to *Viola lanaiensis* are browsing axis deer and the encroachment of aggressive alien species into the rain forest. Deer, which are managed by the state as a game animal, browse native vegetation and disturb the habitat, which encourages the spread of invasive alien species.

Lanai is in the process of changing from an agricultural economy to a tourist economy, and plans to develop the island's tourist industry are a long-term threat to the species. The Munro Trail, which runs across Lanaihale, affords a scenic view of the island and is likely to be popular with tourists. This may have a harmful effect on *Viola lanaiensis* since most of the known plants grow along the trail.

Additional Sources

Cuddihy, L. W., and C. P. Stone. 1990. *Alteration of Native Hawaiian Vegetation: Effects of Humans, Their Activities and Introductions.* University of Hawaii Cooperative National Park Resources Study Unit, Honolulu.

Culliney, J. L. 1988. *Islands in a Far Sea: Nature and Man in Hawaii.* Sierra Club Books, San Francisco.

Wagner, W. L., D. R. Herbst, and S. H. Sohmer. 1990. *Manual of the Flowering Plants of Hawai'i.* University of Hawaii Press and Bishop Museum Press, Honolulu.

Contacts

Regional Office of Endangered Species
U.S. Fish and Wildlife Service
Eastside Federal Complex
911 N.S. 11th Avenue
Portland, Oregon 97232-4181

Derral R. Herbst
U.S. Fish and Wildlife Service
300 Ala Moana Boulevard, Room 6307
P.O. Box 50167
Honolulu, Hawaii 96850

Tennessee Yellow-Eyed Grass
Xyris tennesseensis

Robert Kral

Status	Endangered
Listed	July 26, 1991
Family	Xyridaceae
	(Yellow-eyed grass)
Description	Perennial grass with basal, linear leaves and stalks that bear small, yellow flowers.
Habitat	Seepages, wet meadows, stream banks and shallows.
Threats	Conversion of land to agriculture, logging, road maintenance.
Region 4	Alabama, Georgia, Tennessee

Description

Tennessee yellow-eyed grass is a perennial which grows in clumps from fleshy, bulbus bases to a height of 70 centimeters to 1 meter (2.3 to 3.3 ft). The deep green, linear leaves, 14 to 45 centimeters (5.5 to 17.7 in) long, arise at the base of the plant. Long stalks produce brown, conelike flower spikes at their ends. During August and September, small, pale yellow flowers open in the late morning and wither by mid-afternoon. Fruits are capsules containing numerous tiny seeds.

Habitat

This yellow-eyed grass occurs in open or thinly wooded areas with moist soils. It is found in seepages, wet meadows, and on the banks or shallows of small streams. While most yellow-eyed grasses prefer acidic soils, this species occurs on neutral to basic soils.

Historic Range

Tennessee yellow-eyed grass was first described in 1978 from a specimen collected in 1945 from Lewis County, Tennessee. It is known from three physiographic provinces: the Western Highland Rim of Tennessee (Lewis County), the Cumberland Plateau of Alabama (Franklin County), and the Valley and Ridge Province of Georgia (Bartow and Gordon counties).

Current Distribution

The species currently survives at seven sites: five in Lewis County, Tennessee, and one each in Franklin County, Alabama, and Bartow County, Georgia. Two of these sites have populations in the thousands, while another is limited to a few dozen plants. The others support populations of several hundred. Each site occupies less than an acre. Most populations are on private land, but plants extend onto a highway right-of-way in Alabama and onto National Park Service land—the Natchez Trace Parkway—in Tennessee.

Conservation and Recovery

The main threat to Tennessee yellow-eyed grass is disturbance of its habitat by conversion to agriculture, logging, and highway maintenance. Many of the larger stream bottoms and other moist habitat have been converted to pasture or row crops, or developed for housing. A historic site in Gordon County, Georgia, is now a soybean field. The population in Alabama has been disturbed by logging and gravel quarrying. Since 1982, the number of plants there has declined from several hundred to fewer than a hundred.

Highway construction and maintenance activities are also a threat to remaining sites. One population in Bartow County, Georgia, was destroyed by road construction. Three others are located near roads and are at risk from road work.

While most plants are on private land, the Tennessee Department of Conservation and The Nature Conservancy has several agreements with landowners to protect populations. The conservation department also has an agreement with the National Park Service to protect the plants that are found on federal land.

Additional Sources

Kral, R. 1978. "A New Species of *Xyris* (sec. *Xyris*) from Tennessee and Northwestern Georgia." *Rhodora* 80(823):444-447.

_____. 1983. *A Report on Some Rare, Threatened, or Endangered Forest-related Vascular Plants of the South.* USDA, Forest Service, Technical Publication R8-TP2.

_____. 1990. "A Status Report on *Xyris tennesseensis.*" U.S. Fish and Wildlife Service, Jackson, Mississippi.

Contacts

Regional Office of Endangered Species
U. S. Fish and Wildlife Service
Richard B. Russell Federal Building
75 Spring Street, S.W.
Atlanta, Georgia 30303

Cary Norquist
U.S. Fish and Wildlife Service
6578 Dogwood View Parkway, Suite A
Jackson, Mississippi 39213

Steller Sea Lion
Eumetopias jubatus

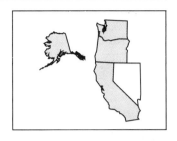

Status	Threatened
Listed	April 5, 1990
Family	Otariidae (Eared Seal)
Description	Large, brown sea lion; males may reach 2,400 pounds.
Habitat	Breeds on isolated North Pacific islands.
Food	Fishes and squid.
Reproduction	Pups born in May and June.
Threats	Depletion of food source, unknown factors.
Region 1	California, Oregon, Washington
Region 7	Alaska
Canada	British Columbia

Leonard Lee Rue III

Description

Steller sea lions are the largest of the eared seals, with males being considerably larger than females. The average length for male Stellers is 282 centimeters (9.2 ft) and the average weight is 566 kilograms (1,245 lbs), although some individuals may attain a weight of 1,120 kilograms (2,400 lbs). Females average 228 centimeters (7.6 ft) in length and 263 kilograms (578.6 lbs) in weight. The fur color is light buff to reddish brown and is slightly darker on the chest and abdomen. Adult males have large, muscular chests and necks, and long, coarse hair on their chest, shoulders, and backs. Vocalizations are long, steady roars.

Behavior

Between late May and early July, Steller sea lions inhabit rookeries where they pup and breed. Pregnant females arrive at the rookeries about three days before giving birth to pups, which are about one meter (3.3 ft) long. The pups stay on land for about two weeks, after which they begin swimming close to shore. About two weeks after the pups are born, the females mate, usually with only one male. Implantation of the embryo takes place after a delay of three to four months, usually in late September after the sea lions have left the rookeries. Females, which attain sexual maturity at about three years, may live for 30 years; males live about 20 years.

Steller sea lions feed on a variety of fishes and vertebrates, including walleye pollock, hake, herring, octopus, squid, Pacific cod, rockfish, salmon, and lamprey. They have also been known to prey on other seal species as well as sea otters. During the breeding season males remain on land and do not feed, while females feed mostly at night. After the breeding season Steller sea lions disperse widely, generally returning year after year to the rookeries where they were born.

Habitat

The Steller sea lion breeds on isolated, unpopulated islands in the North Pacific Ocean. Rookery beaches may extend across low-lying reefs and islands, or may be restricted to a narrow strip of beach bounded by steep cliffs. When not on land, the sea lions inhabit coastal waters out to the edge of the continental shelf. After the breeding season Stellers rest at a variety of sites, including rocks, reefs, beaches, jetties, breakwaters, and floating docks. They also rest on the water's surface in large tightly packed groups.

Historic Range

This sea lion species is known from Hokkaido, Japan, through the Kuril Islands and Okhotsk Sea, the Aleutian Islands and central Bering Sea, Gulf of Alaska, southeast Alaska, and south to central California. Breeding colonies have been found from the Kuril Island to Año Nuevo Island, California. During the 1970s estimates of the total population ranged from 245,000 to 290,000.

Current Distribution

Today, the Steller sea lion survives in rapidly diminishing numbers throughout its range. The center of abundance for the species is the Gulf of Alaska and the Aleutian Islands, where more than 50 rookeries have been identified. In Alaska between the Kenai Peninsula and Kiska Island the Steller sea lion population has fallen from 140,000 in the late 1950s, to 68,000 in 1985, and to 25,000 in 1989.

Conservation and Recovery

The causes of the swift decline in the Steller sea lion population are not currently known. Some studies have indicated that a reduction in the availability of walleye pollock, the sea lion's most important food fish, is a major factor in the population crash. Increased commercial fishing for pollock has been blamed for this loss of fish stock.

Between 1963 and 1972 over 45,000 Steller sea lion pups were killed for their pelts. And between 1973 and 1988 an estimated 14,000 were drowned in commercial fishing nets. These losses, while contributing to the overall population loss, are not large enough to account for the dramatic decline in recent years.

As protective measures for the Steller sea lion, the National Marine Fisheries Service (NMFS) established a recovery team which produced a draft recovery plan in February 1991. The NMFS is also lowering the number of sea lions it allows to be killed in commercial fishing operations. In addition, buffer zones have been established around important rookeries. No vessels are allowed within three miles of the rookeries, and on land human approach closer than a half mile is forbidden.

Additional Sources

Hoover, A. A. 1988. "Steller Sea Lion (*Eumetopias jubatus*)." In *Selected Marine Mammals of Alaska: Species Accounts and Management Recommendations*, edited by J. W. Lentfer. U.S. Marine Mammal Commission.

National Marine Fisheries Service. 1991. "Recovery Plan for the Steller Sea Lion (*Eumetopias jubatus*)—Technical Draft." National Marine Fisheries Service, Washington, D.C.

Proceedings of the International Symposium on the Biology and Management of Walleye Pollock, November 14-16, 1988, Anchorage, AK. University of Alaska Sea Grant Report AK-SG-89-01.

Contacts

Charles Karnella
Protected Species Management Division
National Marine Fisheries Service
1335 East-West Highway
Silver Spring, Maryland 20910

Howard Braham, Director
National Marine Mammal Laboratory
7600 Sand Point Way, N.E.
BIN C15700
Seattle, Washington 98115

Florida Salt Marsh Vole
Microtus pennsylvanicus dukecampbelli

Charles A. Woods   *Color Plate C-6*

Status	Endangered
Listed	January 14, 1991
Family	Muridae (Mouse and Rat)
Description	Short-tailed rodent with a blunt head and short ears.
Habitat	Salt marshes.
Food	Plant matter.
Reproduction	Unknown.
Threats	Limited range and low numbers.
Region 4	Florida

Description

The Florida salt marsh vole, a subspecies of the widespread meadow vole or field mouse (*Microtus p. pennsylvanicus*), is a short-tailed rodent about 17 to 19 centimeters (6.5 to 7.5 in) in total length. It is brownish black above and gray below, with a blunt head and short, rounded ears. It is distinguished from the meadow vole by its larger size, darker color, smaller ears, and certain skull characteristics.

Behavior

Because of its recent discovery and rarity, the life history and reproductive behavior of the Florida salt marsh vole have not been well studied. Typically, voles are active both day and night and are good swimmers. They feed on a great variety of plant matter, including grass, bark, seeds, and roots. The meadow vole is the the most fecund mammal in North America. It reproduces throughout the year over much of its range and is capable of producing up to 17 litters of four to six young each year. After a gestation period of about 20 days, newborn voles grow rapidly and are weaned at about 14 days. They are an important prey for snakes, foxes, hawks, and owls.

Habitat

The Florida salt marsh vole inhabits a single salt marsh on the Gulf Coast of Florida. Vegetation in the marsh consists of smooth cordgrass (*Spartina alterniflora*), black rush (*Juncus roemerianus*), and saltgrass (*Distichlis spicata*).

Historic Range

This subspecies was described in 1982 from specimens taken along the Waccasassa Bay in Levy County, Florida. It is thought to be a relict of a population dating from a period of the Pleistocene Era 8,000 to 30,000 years ago. In the past, lower sea levels exposed areas along the west coast of Florida that are now submerged. This coastal prairie and savanna provided habitat for voles. Meadow vole fossils have been found in Alachua, Citrus, and Levy counties. Today the closest meadow vole population is in Georgia, about 500 kilometers (310 mi) to the north.

Current Distribution

The Florida salt marsh vole has not been found outside the single salt marsh on Waccasassa Bay. The marsh is privately owned, and at this time there are no plans for its development. Searches to discover additional populations in the coastal marshes of Levy and Citrus counties have proven unsuccessful. During the field work that discovered the subspecies, only 31 voles were taken. In a 1989 survey, only a single male vole was captured.

Conservation and Recovery

With its extremely limited range and small species population, the Florida salt marsh vole is extremely vulnerable to extinction. Its decline appears to have been caused by naturally occurring climatic changes that have gradually turned coastal prairie habitat into woodland unsuitable for voles. This isolated subspecies is the last remnant of a much larger and wide-ranging population.

It is likely that the drop in the Florida salt marsh vole population over the last decade was caused by Hurricane Elena in August 1985. That storm remained stationary off the coast near Waccasassa Bay for 24 hours. The Florida salt marsh vole could be rendered extinct by another such hurricane.

Because of its designation as an Endangered species, the Army Corps of Engineers must consider the conservation of the Florida salt marsh vole when evaluating any permit request to alter the animal's salt marsh habitat.

Additional Sources

Bentzien, M. M. 1989. "Florida Saltmarsh Vole Survey." U.S. Fish and Wildlife Service, Jacksonvile, Florida.

Woods, C. A., et al. 1982. "*Microtus pennsylvanicus* (Rodentia: Muridae) in Florida: a Pleistocene Relict in a Coastal Saltmarsh." *Bulletin of the Florida State Museum of Biological Science* 28(2):25-52.

Contacts

Regional Office of Endangered Species
U. S. Fish and Wildlife Service
Richard B. Russell Federal Building
75 Spring Street, S.W.
Atlanta, Georgia 30303

David J. Wesley
U.S. Fish and Wildlife Service
3100 University Boulevard, South, Suite 120
Jacksonville, Florida 32216

Silver Rice Rat
Oryzomys palustris natator

Numi Goodyear   *Color Plate C-6*

Status	Endangered
Listed	April 30, 1991
Family	Muridae (Mouse and Rat)
Description	Rat with silvery fur on back.
Habitat	Wetlands.
Food	Plants and insects.
Reproduction	One to five young.
Threats	Limited numbers, development.
Region 4	Florida

Description

The rice rat is found from the southeastern United States and Mexico through Central America to northern South America. One subspecies of the rice rat, *Oryzomys palustris natator*, occurs in peninsular Florida. The southernmost population of this subspecies, known as the silver rice rat, occurs only on Florida's Lower Keys.

The silver rice rat is about 25 centimeters (10 in) long, has a generalized rat-like appearance, coarse fur, and a long, sparsely haired tail about 12.5 centimeters (5 in) long. It is distinguised from other rice rat populations by the silver-gray coloration on its back.

Disagreement exits on the taxonomic sta-

tus of the silver rice rat. It was described as a separate species, *Oryzomys argentatus*, in 1978 on the basis of certain skull measurements and characteristics, as well as the difference in fur color. Some mammologists challenged this classification and argued against its status as either a separate species or subspecies. They consider the silver rice rat to be members of *O. palustris natator*. Fish and Wildlife Service (FWS) scientists have indicated that on the basis of current scientific information they incline toward viewing the silver rice rat as a separate subspecies. However, in listing the silver rice rat, FWS acknowledges the taxonomic uncertainty and for the time being officially considers it a separate geo-

graphical populaton of *O. palustris natator.*
Under the Endangered Species Act such
separate vertebrate populations can be
considered a "species" for listing purposes.
The silver rice rat receives full protection
under the Endangered Species Act, regardless of its eventual taxonomic fate.

Behavior

The silver rice rat nests in grassy areas
near wetlands. It forages for plant matter
and insects over a home range of about 50
acres, an unusually large range for a small
rodent. Little is known of the natural history of this recently discovered species, but
it is likely to be similar to that of the mainland rice rat. Studies of rice rats in Louisiana and the Carolinas indicate that one to
five young are produced during the spring
and summer after a gestation period of
about 25 days. The young develop rapidly.
Their eyes open after six days, and they are
weaned at 11 days. Rice rats feed on the
seeds and succulent parts of a variety of
plants and are known to eat insects and
small crabs. They, in turn, are a favored
prey of owls, northern harriers and other
raptors, carnivorous mammals such as
foxes and skunks, and large snakes.

Habitat

Home ranges of silver rice rats usually include flooded intertidal areas, saltmarsh
flats, and drier elevated areas, which are
used mainly for nesting. This nesting area
is vegetated with abundant grasses (*Distichlis* and *Sporobolus*), sea oxeye (*Borrichia
frutescens*), and buttonwood (*Conocarpus
erectus*).

Historic Range

It is believed that the ancestor of the silver rice rat colonized the area that is now
Florida's Lower Keys during the late Pleistocene, when lower sea levels exposed
more land and supported larger mangrove
forests and salt marshes. Several thousand
years ago rising sea levels created the current geography of the Florida Keys, isolat-
ing silver rice rat populations.

The precise historic range of the silver
rice rat is not precisely known, but it is believed to have inhabited suitable habitat
west of the Seven Mile Bridge. A known
population was recently extirpated from
Cudjoe Key, and researchers believe that
silver rice rats were once found on Big Pine
and Boca Chica keys.

Current Distribution

The silver rice rat is now found on eight
of the Lower Keys: Big Torch, Johnston,
Middle Torch, Raccoon, Saddlebunch, Little Pine, Summerland, and Water keys. In
addition, researchers indicate that a population has recently been found at the U.S.
Naval Air Station on Boca Chica Key. It occurs in very low population densities, except on Johnston and Raccoon keys where
it is more common. A portion of the silver
rice rat's range is within the Great White
Heron National Wildlife Refuge and the
Key Deer Refuge. There are no current
population estimates.

Conservation and Recovery

The taxonomic controversy over the silver
rice rat resulted in a complicated listing
process. Following its description as a new
species, FWS determined that the silver
rice rat was entitled to listing. However,
when its taxonomic status was challenged,

FWS changed its evaluation and announced that it would not propose the silver rice rat for listing because it did not fit the law's definition of a species. This prompted a lawsuit in December 1989 by the Sierra Club Legal Defense Fund, which claimed that FWS failed to evaluate the silver rice rat as a distinct vertebrate population, a process specifically allowed under the Endangered Species Act. In May 1990, the lawsuit was settled after FWS announced that it was reconsidering its listing decision for the silver rice rat.

The main threat to the silver rice rat is the loss of wetland habitat to commercial and residential development. Although habitat on the keys included in the two national wildlife refuges is secure, those keys crossed by U.S. Highway 1 continue to be developed.

There is also some evidence that the silver rice rat is suffering from predation by native raccoons, which are increasing because of the availability of human garbage as food. Another species associated with human habitation, the Old World black rat (*Rattus rattus*) is also increasing in the Lower Keys and may be displacing silver rice rat populations. These introduced rats are abundant on Big Pine and Boca Chica keys and may have contributed to the disappearance of the silver rice rat from them.

Additional Sources

Barbour, D. B., and S. R. Humphrey. 1982. "Status of the Silver Rice Rat (*Oryzomys argentatus*)." *Florida Sci.* 45(2):112-116.

Goodyear, N. C. 1984. "Final Report on the Distribution, Habitat, and Status of the Silver Rice Rat *Oryzomys argentatus*." U.S. Fish and Wildlife Service, Jacksonville, Florida.

_____. 1991. "Taxonomic Status of the Silver Rice Rat, *Oryzomys argentatus*." *Journal of Mammology* 72(4):723-730.

Goodyear, N. C., and J. D. Lazell, Jr. 1986. "Relationships of the Silver Rice Rat *Oryzomys argentatus* (Rodentia: Muridae)." *Postilla* 198:1-7.

Humphrey, S. R., ed. 1992. *Rare and Endangered Biota of Florida: Mammals.* 2d ed. University of Florida Press, Gainesville.

Humphrey, S. R., and H. W. Setzer. 1989. "Geographic Variation and Taxonomic Revision of Rice Rats (*Oryzomys paulstris* and *O. argentatus*) of the United States." *Journal of Mammology* 70(3):557-570

Spitzer, N. C., and J. D. Lazell, Jr. 1978. "A New Rice Rat (Genus *Orzomys*) from Florida's Lower Keys." *Journal of Mammology* 59:789-792.

Contacts

Regional Office of Endangered Species
U. S. Fish and Wildlife Service
Richard B. Russell Federal Building
75 Spring Street, S.W.
Atlanta, Georgia 30303

David J. Wesley
Jacksonville Field Office
U.S. Fish and Wildlife Service
3100 University Boulevard, South, Suite 120
Jacksonville, Florida 32216

Lower Keys Rabbit
Sylvilagus palustris hefneri

Alan S. Maltz   *Color Plate C-6*

Status	Endangered
Listed	June 21, 1990
Family	Leporidae (Rabbit)
Description	Short-eared rabbit, brown above and grey below.
Habitat	Fresh and saltwater marshes.
Food	Plant material.
Reproduction	Probably 5 to 6 litters of 2 to 3 young per year.
Threats	Residential and comercial development.
Region 4	Florida

Description

The Lower Keys rabbit, a subspecies of the widespread marsh rabbit of the southeastern coastal plain, is about 40 centimeters (16 in) in length. It is dark brown to a dark, rusty red above, with a gray to buffy belly and abdomen. The tail is small, rusty brown above and a dingy brown below. It differs from the mainland marsh rabbit in details of its skull characteristics.

Behavior

Although the Lower Keys marsh rabbit has not been widely studied, researchers assume that its life history is similar to that of the mainland marsh rabbit. Marsh rabbits are generally noctornal and feed on a variety of plant material. Unlike most other rabbit species they seem to enjoy swimming.

Marsh rabbits reproduce throughout the year and have a gestation period of from 30 to 37 days. Each litter consists of two or three young. Adult male marsh rabbits are sexually active year round, while juveniles are most active from December through May. Marsh rabbits do not excavate burrows but construct nests of grass and fur among vegetation near water.

Habitat

The Lower Keys rabbit occurs in both fresh and salt water marshes. Inhabited salt marshes are vegetated with fringerush (*Fimbrystylis* sp.), buttonwood (*Conocarpus erectus*), cordgrass (*Spartina alterniflora*), saltwort (*Batis maritima*), glasswort (*Salicornia virginica*), sawgrass (*Cladium jamaicense*), and sea oxeye (*Borrichia frutescens*). Freshwater marsh vegetation consists of sawgrass, cattail (*Typha latifolia*), and sedges (*Cyperus* sp.). Mangroves occupy most of the coastal areas of the Lower Keys and marsh habitat is not abundant. Recent studies suggest that the rabbit is more abundant in saltwater marshes than freshwater marshes.

Historic Range

This rabbit once probably occurred in marshes throughout Florida's Lower Keys. It no longer is found on Key West, Cudjoe, Ramrod, Middle Torch, and Big Torch keys. According to long-time residents, the rabbit was locally common as recently as the 1950s.

Current Distribution

Today, the Lower Keys rabbit survives on Sugarloaf, Welles, Annette, Boca Chica, Hopkins, and Big Pine keys in small, scattered populations. A few individuals may also survive on Saddlehill Key. Rabbits on Saddlebunch and Geiger keys, which were observed as recently as 1984, are believed extirpated.

This rabbit occurs on federal land at the National Key Deer Refuge and the Key West Naval Air Station, on state land administered by the Florida Department of Transportation, and on private land. It is estimated that the entire subspecies numbers only 300 to 400 rabbits, with over 100 occurring on navy land on Boca Chica Key.

Conservation and Recovery

The principal cause of the decline of the Lower Keys rabbit is the loss of wetland habitat to residential and commercial development. Only six of 13 known sites are secure from development.

The navy is not planning any activities at the Key West Naval Air Station that would adversely affect the rabbit and has indicated a willingness to cooperate in conservation efforts. The Army Corps of Engineers has authority over permits to modify wetlands and must now consider the potential effects on the Lower Keys rabbit.

Additional Sources

Howe, S. E. 1988. "Lower Keys Rabbit Status Survey." U.S. Fish and Wildlife Service, Jacksonville, Florida.

Humphrey, S. R., ed. 1992. *Rare and Endangered Biota of Florida: Mammals.* 2d ed. University of Florida Press, Gainesville.

Lazell, J. D. 1984. "A New Marsh Rabbit (*Sylvilagus palustris*) from Florida's Lower Keys." *Journal of Mammology* 65(1):26-33.

Contacts

Regional Office of Endangered Species
U. S. Fish and Wildlife Service
Richard B. Russell Federal Building
75 Spring Street, S.W.
Atlanta, Georgia 30303

David J. Wesley
U.S. Fish and Wildlife Service
Jacksonville Field Office
3100 University Boulevard, South, Suite 120
Jacksonville, Florida 32216

Golden-Cheeked Warbler
Dendroica chrysoparia

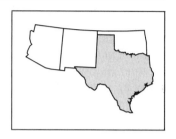

G. Lasley/VIREO   *Color Plate C-7*

Status	Endangered
Listed	May 4, 1990
Family	Emberizidae; Subfamily: Parulinae (Wood Warbler)
Description	Small songbird, black above, with bright yellow cheeks and a black eyestripe.
Habitat	Mature, mixed Ashe juniper/oak woods.
Food	Insects
Reproduction	Clutch of 3 to 5 eggs.
Threats	Habitat destruction.
Region 2	Texas

Description

The golden-cheeked warbler is a small insectivorous songbird, about 14 centimeters (5.5 in) long. In breeding plumage, the male has bright yellow cheeks, outlined in black, and a black stripe running through the eye. The crown, throat, upperparts, and upper breast are black. The lower parts are white with black streaks along the sides. The female has yellowish olive upperparts, grayish wings and tail, and a duller yellow cheek patch.

Behavior

After wintering in Central America, the golden-cheeked warbler migrates north in early spring, arriving at its Texas breeding range in mid-March. Individuals return to the same nesting location year after year. Nests are located about 15 feet from the ground in Ashe juniper (*Juniperus ashei*) trees. They are constructed of strips of Ashe juniper bark, bound together by cobwebs to form a small cup, which is then lined with feathers and fur. The female lays 3 to 5 creamy white eggs which she incubates for 12 days. Both male and female feed and care for the young, which fledge in about nine days, remaining nearby and forming a loose family group.

Golden-cheeked warblers feed on available insects or spiders, including caterpillars, green lacewings, moths, small butterflies, katydids, walkingsticks, and small cicadas.

Habitat

The golden-cheeked warbler requires a mixed woods of mature Ashe juniper and various species of oak for nesting. It relies on Ashe juniper for nesting material and forages for insects in the oak canopies. The presence of Ashe juniper is an important habitat requirement, since even nests found in other types of trees are made of juniper bark. In addition, the junipers must be mature, since only trees over 20 years old shed their bark.

Historic Range

The golden-cheeked warbler was discovered in Guatemala in 1859. It winters in Guatemala, Honduras, Nicaragua, Mexico, and possibly Belize. In spring the entire population migrates north to its breeding grounds which lie entirely within the state of Texas.

Current Distribution

The breeding range of the golden-cheeked warbler is in central Texas, from Palo Pinto and Bosque counties, south through the eastern and south-central portions of the Edwards Plateau. One researcher has identified 31 counties in cental Texas as the nesting range of the species. In 1976 the total adult population was estimated at between 15,000 and 17,000 birds. Recent studies have found that the median population density was 15 pairs per 100 hectares (247 acres). The remaining suitable Ashe juniper/oak habitat has been only roughly estimated. At present it would have a carrying capacity of between 4,800 and 16,000 pairs.

Conservation and Recovery

The major threat to the golden-cheeked warbler is destruction of its breeding habitat for urban development and removal of junipers as a range management practice. As habitat areas are lost, remaining Ashe juniper/oak woods often become more fragmented, putting the golden-cheeked warbler at greater risk from predators and nest parasitism by brown-headed cowbirds.

During the late 1940s a juniper eradication program (including Ashe juniper) was begun in Texas in order to clear land for pasture improvement and urbanization. By 1970 about 50 percent of juniper acreage had been cleared.

Over the last two decades destruction of Ashe juniper/oak habitat has continued, particularly in expanding urban areas. A 1990 study indicated that over the last ten years sample areas suffered losses of warbler habitat ranging from 15 to 45 percent. Western Travis County, immediately west of Austin, and the Austin-San Antonio corridor experienced yearly losses of habitat of about 4 percent. In the northern portion of the breeding range, 15 percent of available habitat was lost over an eight year interval. In rural areas habitat loss has been holding steady at about 2 percent a year for the last 20 years. At the present rate of loss, however, the estimated carrying capacity of the habitat will be reduced by more than 50 percent by the year 2000.

When areas of golden-cheeked warbler habitat are lost, adjacent areas become more fragmented. This results in an increase in the amount of "edge" habitat, in turn allowing predators, such as scrub jays, grackles, feral cats, and rat snakes, easier access to warbler nests. Increased edge also leads to more brood parasitism by brown-headed cowbirds, which lay their own eggs in the nests of smaller birds. The larger cowbird chicks are raised by the foster parents and outcompete the smaller chicks for food.

The loss of golden-cheeked warbler habitat was occurring so rapidly in the urban areas around Austin that the Fish and Wildlife Service (FWS) used its power to list the species as Endangered on an emergency basis. FWS hoped that this action would allow time for the development of a conservation plan for the Austin region that would protect the golden-cheeked warbler and other Endangered species occurring in the area, including the black-capped vireo and five rare cave species.

Additional Sources

Kroll, J. C. 1980. "Habitat Requirements of the Golden-cheeked Warbler: Management Implications." *Journal of Range Management* 33:60-65.

Pease, C. M. and L. G. Gingerich. 1989. "Habitat Requirements of the Black-capped Vireo and Golden-cheeked Warbler Populations Near Austin, Texas." Report Prepared for Austin Regional Habitat Conservation Plan, Biological Advisory Team, Austin, Texas.

Pulich, W. M. 1976. "The Golden-cheeked Warbler, a Bioecological Study." Texas Parks and Wildlife Department, Austin.

Wahl, R., D. D. Diamond, and D. Shaw. 1990. "The Golden-cheeked Warbler: a Status Review." U.S. Fish and Wildlife Service, Fort Worth, Texas.

Contacts

Regional Office of Endangered Species
U.S. Fish and Wildlife Service
P.O. Box 1306
Albuquerque, New Mexico 87103

Robert Short
U.S Fish and Wildlife Service
9A33 Fritz Lanham Building
819 Taylor Street
Fort Worth, Texas 76102

Northern Spotted Owl

Strix occidentalis caurina

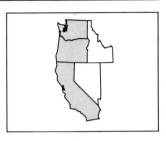

B. "Moose" Peterson   *Color Plate C-6*

Status	Threatened
Listed	June 26, 1990
Family	Strigidae (Owl)
Description	Medium-sized, dark brown owl with dark eyes, white spots on head and neck, and white mottling on breast.
Habitat	Old-growth and mixed old-growth/mature forest.
Food	Small reptiles and vertebrates.
Reproduction	Clutch of 2 eggs.
Threats	Logging of habitat.
Region 1	Washington, Oregon, California
Canada	British Columbia

Description

The northern spotted owl, one of three spotted owl subspecies, is a medium-sized owl with a round head, dark brown plumage, and dark eyes. It has white spots on the head and neck and white mottling on the breast and abdomen. The female is slightly larger than the male and has a higher-pitched call. Juveniles go through a series of downy plumages in their first summer; afterwards they are distinguishable from adults only by ragged white downy tips on their tail feathers.

The northern spotted owl is distinguished from the two other subspecies—the California spotted owl (*Strix o. occidentalis*) and the Mexican spotted owl (*S. o. lucida*) by slight differences in plumage and their respective geographic ranges. The Mexican spotted owl was proposed for listing as Threatened in November 1991.

Behavior

The northern spotted owl inhabits a relatively large home range, which it uses for nesting, foraging, and roosting. It usually spends the entire year on its territory.

Like most other owls, it is primarily nocturnal, swooping down from perches to take prey. It's diet consists mostly of small mammals, but also includes birds, reptiles, and insects. The most important prey are flying squirrels (*Glaucomys sabrinus*), red tree voles (*Arborimus longicaudus*), and dusky-footed woodrats (*Neotoma fuscipes*).

Owl pairs do not nest every year, and not all nesting attempts are successful. It is believed that nesting patterns may be related to local prey availability. Nesting behavior begins in February and March, and nests are located almost exclusively in tree cavities or platforms. Pairs do not build their own nest but use cavities at the broken tops of old-growth conifers, nests built by other birds or mammals, and naturally occurring platforms. Females lay a clutch of two eggs in March or early April, and incubate them for about 32 days. The male feeds the female and young during incubation and brooding. The young leave the nest after about a month and remain near the nest where they are fed by the adults until early fall. The young disperse in September or October.

Young northern spotted owls have a much higher mortality rate than adult birds. Recent studies have found that only about 19 percent survived their first year. The principal causes of juvenile death appeared to be starvation and predation by great horned owls.

Habitat

The northern spotted owl inhabits old-growth forests or mixed stands of old-growth and mature trees. Pairs establish extensive territories, which are used for nesting, foraging, and roosting. The species is occasionally found in younger forests that have remnant patches of large trees or scattered individual large trees. Old-growth forests possess a combination of characteristics required by the owl: a high, multistory canopy dominated by large trees, numerous trees with cavities or broken tops, woody debris or fallen trees,

and open space beneath the canopy for flying.

The size of a pair's home range varies across the subspecies' geographical distribution. The median size of a pair's home range is about 10,000 acres for the Olympic Peninsula, 6,300 acres for the Washington Cascades, 3,000 acres for the Oregon Cascades, 4,800 acres for the Oregon Coast Range, and 3,300 acres for the Klamath Provence.

Historic Range

The precise historic range of the northern spotted owl cannot be known with certainty. Early European settlers began cutting the old-growth forests, particularly in coastal and foothill areas, before the owl's range was determined. Researchers generally believe that the owl inhabited all suitable habitat from southern British Columbia to northern California. There are no historic population estimates.

Current Distribution

Northern spotted owls are found in what old-growth forest remains throughout the species' historic range. Today most privately owned old-growth forest has been cut; approximately 90 percent of the remaining old-growth is on federal land managed by the Forest Service, Bureau of Land Management (BLM), and the National Park Service. The current range is from southwestern British Columbia, south through western Washington, western Oregon, and northern California to near San Francisco Bay. The southern boundary that separates the northern spotted owl from the California spotted owl is the Pit River area of Shasta County, California.

Northern spotted owls are not uniformly

distributed throughout this range. Most inhabit the Cascades in Oregon and the Klamath Mountains of southwestern Oregon and northwestern California. Densities are lowest in northern Washington, southern British Columbia, and northeastern California. Approximately 2,000 breeding pairs are known, and the total population is estimated to number between 3,000 and 5,000 pairs.

Conservation and Recovery

The principal threat to the northern spotted owl is the ongoing reduction of its old-growth forest habitat through logging. Nearly all privately owned old-growth forest has already been cut in the Pacific Northwest, and suitable spotted owl habitat is almost completely confined to federal land. Conflict about forest management practices to conserve the spotted owl date at least to the mid-1970s when wildlife officials in Oregon, in concert with federal scientists, attempted to establish a state management plan for the species.

The decision to list the northern spotted owl and institute a conservation plan has generated more controversy than any other action taken under the Endangered Species Act in several decades. Citing a threat to the regional economy, companies, organizations, and localities dependent on the timber industry vigorously opposed any action that would reduce the timber cut on federal land in the Pacific Northwest. A coalition of environmental organizations and independent and government scientists has been equally vigorous in pressing for additional protection for the region's old-growth forests that serve as the owl's habitat.

Following a January 1987 petition from a private conservation organization to list the owl, the Fish and Wildlife Service (FWS) determined in December 1987 that listing the owl was not warranted. The Sierra Club Legal Defense Fund then filed a lawsuit against FWS in the U.S. District Court for the Western District of Washington (*Northern Spotted Owl* v. *Hodel*, No. C88-573Z) challenging that decision. On November 17, 1988, the court found that FWS's failure to list the northern spotted owl was "arbitrary and capricious or contrary to law" and directed the service to reconsider its decision.

Following this judicial rebuke, FWS organized a special listing review team to evaluate the scientific evidence concerning the threat to the owl. In June 1989, FWS proposed that the northern spotted owl be listed as Threatened. The listing was made final on June 26, 1990. Meanwhile the controversy between timber interests and enviromentalists had escalated into a major political debate over the health of the local economy versus conservation of the owl and its old-growth forest habitat.

In 1989, while the listing proposal was under consideration, an interagency scientific committee was established to develop a conservation plan for the owl. On April 2, 1990, it issued a report, "A Conservation Strategy for the Northern Spotted Owl" (popularly known as the "Jack Ward Thomas Report" after the committee's chairman). This report recommended the establishment of habitat conservation areas on nearly eight million acres of federal land throughout the owl's range. The conservation plan called for a network of individual reserves, each large enough to support a minimum of 20 pairs of owls. No logging would be allowed on these reserves, and a strict timber management policy would apply on federal land connecting the conservation areas.

In February 1991, FWS was ordered by the U.S district court presiding over *North-*

ern Spotted Owl v. *Hodel* to designate critical habitat for the owl. On May 6, FWS
proposed a network of critical habitat areas
totaling over 11 million acres of federal,
state, and private land in Washington, Oregon, and California. These areas were
largely based on the habitat conservation
areas mapped in the Jack Ward Thomas
Report. On August 13, 1991, FWS revised
its proposal to include only federal and
state land. It proposed that approximately
8.2 million acres be designated as critical
habitat. The final determination was made
on January 9, 1992, when FWS announced
that critical habitat for the owl would en-
compass approximately 6.9 million acres of
federal land.

The listing of the northern spotted owl as
Threatened and the determination of its
critical habitat has hardly ended the political or legal struggle. On May 23, 1991, a
U.S. district judge ordered the suspension
of timber sales in the national forests of the
Pacific Northwest until the Forest Service
produces an effective protection plan for
the northern spotted owl.

And on September 30, 1991, Secretary of
the Interior Manuel Lujan decided to con-
vene the Endangered Species Committee,
sometimes known as the "God Committee," to consider a BLM request for an exemption from the Endangered Species Act.
BLM is seeking permission to sell timber
from about 4,000 acres of northern spotted
owl habitat. While this is only a small portion of the owl's critical habitat, propo-
nents of protecting the owl regard this as
the first step in a campaign to weaken the
provisions of the Endangered Species Act.
The committee will announce its decision
on the exemption in early 1992.

Additional Sources

Forsman, E., and E. C. Meslow. 1986. "The
Spotted Owl." In *Audubon Wildlife Report
1986*. Academic Press, San Diego, California.

Thomas, J. W., et al. 1990. "A Conservation
Strategy for the Northern Spotted Owl."
U.S Department of Agriculture, Forest
Service, and U.S. Department of the Inte-
rior, Fish and Wildlife Service, Bureau of
Land Management, and National Park
Service, Portland, Oregon.

U.S. Fish and Wildlife Service. 1992. "Determination of Critical Habitat for the Northern Spotted Owl." *Federal Register* (January
9, 1992).

Contacts

Regional Office of Endangered Species
U.S. Fish and Wildlife Service
Eastside Federal Complex
911 N.S. 11th Avenue
Portland, Oregon 97232-4181

Yellow-Blotched Map Turtle
Graptemys flavimaculata

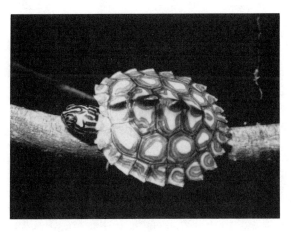

Terry L. Vanderventer   *Color Plate C-7*

Status . . . . Threatened
Listed . . . . January 14, 1991
Family . . . . Emydidae (Turtle)
Description . . . . . . Aquatic turtle with bright yellow or orange blotches.
Habitat . . . . Unshaded rivers with sandy banks and numerous snags.
Food . . . . Snails and insect larvae.
Reproduction . . . . Clutch of about 6 eggs.
Threats . . . . Alteration of river habitat, shooting, collecting.
Region 4 . . . . Mississippi

Description

The yellow-blotched map turtle is an aquatic turtle with an olive to light brown upper shell (carapace) and a bright yellow or orange blotch on each plate shield. Females attain a carapace size of about 8 centimeters (3 in), while males are about 5 centimeters (2 in) long. Males and juveniles (and occasionally females) have four sawtooth-shaped, black spines on the top of their shells.

The species is also known as the yellow-blotched sawback turtle and is closely related to the Endangered ringed-sawback turtle (*Graptemys oculifera*) found in Mississippi and Louisiana.

Behavior

The yellow-blotched map turtle spends a great deal of time basking in the sun. Juveniles grow rapidly, with males maturing in about two years. Females probably achieve sexual maturity at about seven years of age. Reproductive behavior has not been well-studied, but it is known that females construct nests on sandy riverbanks, where they probably produce three or four clutches annually, each consisting of about six eggs. Egg mortality from predation is high—probably around 90 percent. Like other river turtle species, the yellow-blotched map turtle feeds primarily on snails and insects.

Habitat

This turtle inhabits river stretches that receive several hours of sunshine per day. It prefers river areas that have a moderate current, a sand or clay bottom, sand bars or sandy banks for nesting, and numerous basking logs.

Historic Range

The yellow-blotched map turtle was first described in 1954 from specimens taken from the Pascagoula River in George County, Mississippi. It has been known from the Pascagoula River system, including the Leaf, Chickasawhay, and Escatawpa rivers, as well as smaller tributaries. In 1971 the species was documented from the Red, Black, and Tallahala creeks, but a 1980 survey failed to locate any in those waters.

Current Distribution

This turtle is primarily limited to the Pascagoula, Leaf, and Chickasawhay rivers in southeastern Mississippi. Recent surveys have counted about three or four turtles per mile in the Leaf, Chickasawhay, and upper Pascagoula rivers. It is most abundant in the Pascagoula River between Wade and Vancleave, Mississippi. Mark and recapture surveys indicate a population estimate of 336 turtles per mile in the lower Pascagoula River.

Most of the Pascagoula River basin is privately owned agricultural land. However the Forest Service manages considerable acreage in the DeSoto National Forest and the state of Mississippi has several wildlife management areas in the basin.

Conservation and Recovery

The main threat to this turtle is human modification of its river habitat. The species relies on snags for basking and sandbars or sandy banks for nesting. Its food sources, insect larvae and snails, are extremely sensitive to water pollution.

The Army Corps of Engineers has proposed or begun a number of flood control and navigation projects throughout the Pascagoula River system. These projects often involve dredging channels and removing snags and other debris from the river, thereby altering the turtle's preferred habitat. The Fish and Wildlife Service and the Corps will consult on a project-by-project basis to ensure that projects allow for the conservation of the yellow-blotched map turtle.

This turtle species faces additional threats from wanton shooting, collecting, and high egg mortality. Basking turtles are often the victims of target shooters. The species is attractive to collectors, and specimens are often advertised for sale. These factors make the high natural egg mortality of the spcies a more serious threat to the turtle's survival.

Additional Source

McCoy, C. J., and R. C. Vogt. 1980. "Distribution and Population Status of the Yellow-blotched Sawback, *Graptemys flavimaculata* Cagle in Mississippi." U.S. Fish and Wildlife Service.

Contact

Ren Lohoefener
Jackson Field Office
U.S. Fish and Wildlife Service
6578 Dogwood View Parkway, Suite A
Jackson, Mississippi 39213

Cheat Mountain Salamander
Plethedon nettingi

Ray E. Ashton, Jr.   *Color Plate C-7*

Status	Threatened
Listed	August 18, 1989
Family	Plethodontidae (Lungless Salamander)
Description	Gray to black with silver or gold flecks on its back.
Habitat	Moist, highland woods.
Food	Insects.
Reproduction	Egg masses laid May to August.
Threats	Habitat alteration by timbering, mining, and recreational development.
Region 5	West Virginia

Description

The Cheat Mountain salamander is one of the lungless salamanders, also known as woodland salamanders. These salamanders lack lungs and must rely on respiratory exchange directly through their skin. This species, which grows to a length of about 12 centimeters (4.6 in), has a dark back, marked with silver or gold flecks, and a dark gray to black belly. It generally has 18 vertical grooves on its sides that show the position of the ribs. Once considered a subspecies of *Plethodon richmondi*, it was reclassified as a full species in 1971.

Behavior

This salamander generally spends the day under rocks and logs or in rock crevices. At night, particularly in wet weather, it forages on the forest floor for mites, springtails, beetles, flies, and other insects. Although mating has not been observed, it is assumed to be similar to other woodland salamanders. The eggs are fertilized internally and undergo complete development. Unlike most other salamanders there is no aquatic larval stage. Masses of from four to 17 eggs are deposited on logs or moss from May to June.

Habitat

The Cheat Mountain salamander is found in moist West Virginia forests at elevations above about 915 meters (3,000 ft), typically where red spruce (*Picea rubens*) and yellow birch (*Betula alleghaniensis*) are the dominant species.

Historic Range

The precise historic range of the species is unknown because almost all of its preferred habitat was stripped of trees before the species was discovered. Researchers believe that the species was much more widespread in West Virginia prior to deforestation in the late nineteenth and early twentieth centuries.

Current Distribution

Today the Cheat Mountain salamander survives in the Allegheny Mountains of eastern West Virginia in Pendleton, Pocahontas, Randolph, and Tucker counties. Its range consists of an area of approximately 700 square miles, almost entirely within the Monongahela National Forest. A total of 68 populations are known; 60 are on Forest Service land, three are in West Virginia state parks, and five are on private land. Detailed population studies of the known sites are now in progress. During the initial surveys made during the 1980s fewer than 10 salamanders were observed at three-quarters of the sites.

Conservation and Recovery

The chief threat to the Cheat Mountain salamander is alteration of its habitat by logging and other activities that remove the forest canopy. Loss of forest cover exposes the salamander to hot, dry condi-

tions in which it cannot survive. Between 1880 and 1920 virtually all of the old-growth timber in eastern West Virginia was cut. The Cheat Mountain salamander managed to survive in pockets of marginal high-elevation habitat. One of the healthiest populations is found near a 200-acre tract of the only virgin red spruce remaining. In recent decades some forest regeneration has taken place. Today mixed spruce-hardwood forests cover an estimated 27,000 to 67,000 acres, and timber sales are again taking place. One population has been extirpated by clear-cutting and seven others are likely to die out because of timbering activity.

In addition, some high-elevation forest is being cut for the constuction of ski resorts. Within the species' range four resorts are operating and another is being developed.

High-elevation coal mining has also had a negative effect on the species. At least five salamander populations have been severely affected by mining activities.

Additional Source

U.S. Fish and Wildlife Service. 1991. "Cheat Mountain Salamander (*Plethedon nettingi*) Recovery Plan." U.S. Fish and Wildlife Service, Newton Corner, Massachusetts.

Contacts

Regional Office of Endangered Species
U.S. Fish and Wildlife Service
One Gateway Center, Suite 700
Newton Corner, MA 02158

Judy Jacobs
U.S. Fish and Wildlife Service
1825 Virginia Street
Annapolis, Maryland 21401

Shenandoah Salamander

Plethedon shenandoah

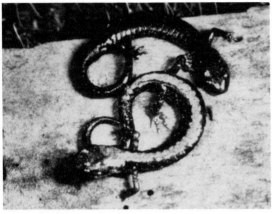

David Liebman   *Color Plate C-7*

Status	Endangered
Listed	August 18, 1989
Family	Plethodontidae (Lungless Salamander)
Description	Two color phases; dark-backed with a few gold flecks or with a narrow red stripe on the back.
Habitat	North-facing talus slopes.
Food	Insects.
Reproduction	Egg masses laid from May to August.
Threats	Competition from abundant salamander species.
Region 5	Virginia

Description

The Shenandoah salamander is one of the lungless salamanders, also known as woodland salamanders. These salamanders lack lungs and must rely on respiratory exchange directly through their skin. Two color phases of this species are known. Individuals of the unstriped phase have dark backs, marked with a few gold or silver flecks, and dark gray to black bellies. Striped phase individuals have a narrow red stripe down their backs. This salamander grows to a length of about 12 centimeters (4.6 in). It generally has 18 vertical grooves on its sides that mark the position of the ribs.

This species was first described as a sub-species of *Plethodon richmondi* in 1967 and later considered a subspecies of the Cheat Mountain salamander (*P. nettingi*). It was recognized as a distinct species in 1979.

Behavior

The Shenandoah salamander generally spends the day under rocks and logs or in rock crevices. At night, particularly in wet weather, it forages for mites, springtails, beetles, flies, and other insects. Although mating has not been observed, it is assumed to be similar to other woodland salamanders. The eggs are fertilized internally and undergo complete development. Unlike most other salamanders there is no aquatic larval stage. Masses of from 4 to 17 eggs are deposited on logs or moss from May to August.

Habitat

The Shenandoah salamander is found on north-facing talus slopes at elevations above 915 meters (3,000 ft). It is limited to areas where the moisture conditions are favorable, but can survive in drier areas than other *Plethodon* species.

Historic Range

Because of its recent discovery and limited range, the actual historic range of the Shenandoah salamander is unknown. Because of the species' narrow ecological niche, it is surmised that it was never numerous.

Current Distribution

Today the Shenadoah salamander survives on talus slopes on three mountains in Madison and Page counties, Virginia. All three sites are within the boundaries of Shenandoah National Park. There are no current population estimates.

Conservation and Recovery

The main threat to the continued existence of the Shenendoah salamander is competition from the abundant red-backed salamander (*Plethodon cinereus*). The Shenandoah salamander can survive in dryer conditions than the red-backed salamander. However, as the talus slopes disintegrate and organic debris decomposes, moister conditions develop. As this process develops, the red-backed salamander is likely to invade the Shenandoah

salamander's habitat, pushing it towards extinction.

Additional Sources

Jaeger, R. G. 1970. "Potential Extinction through Competition Between Two Species of Terrestrial Salamanders." *Evolution* 24: 632-642.

_____. 1974. "Competitive Exclusion: Comments on Survival and Extinction of Species." *Bioscience* 24:33-39.

_____. 1980. "Density-dependent and Density-independent Causes of Extinction of a Salamander Population." *Evolution* 34(4):617-621.

Contacts

Regional Office of Endangered Species
U.S. Fish and Wildlife Service
One Gateway Center, Suite 700
Newton Corner, MA 02158

Judy Jacobs
U.S. Fish and Wildlife Service
1825 Virginia Street
Annapolis, Maryland 21401

Gulf Sturgeon
Acipenser oxyrhynchus desotoi

Status	Threatened
Listed	September 30, 1991
Family	Acipenseridae (Sturgeon)
Description	Large fish, brown above and white below, with a cylindrical body, extended snout, ventral mouth, and chin barbels.
Habitat	Spawns in rivers, winters in the Gulf of Mexico and its estuaries.
Food	Crustaceans, worms, mollusks, brachiopods, insect larvae.
Reproduction	Spawns February to May.
Threats	Dam construction, channel maintenance.
Region 4	Alabama, Florida, Louisiana, Mississippi

John Moran   *Color Plate C-8*

Description

The Gulf sturgeon, a subspecies of the Atlantic sturgeon (*Acipenser oxyrhynchus*), is a large, long-lived, slow maturing fish, which is brown above and white below. Adults usually range from 1.8 to 2.4 meters (6 to 8 ft) in length, with females being larger than males. It is nearly cylindrical in overall shape, with an extended snout and chin barbels. The upper lobe of its tail is longer than the lower. It lacks scales, but has five rows of bony plates. In external appearance it is virtually identical to the Atlantic sturgeon and is differentiated by the size of its head, pectoral fins, and spleen. It is also known as the Gulf of Mexico sturgeon.

Behavior

The Gulf sturgeon is a bottom feeder, primarily eating invertebrates, including crustaceans, brachiopods, mollusks, worms, and insect larvae. Females reach sexual maturity at 8 to 12 years, males at 7 to 10 years. Fish winter in the Gulf of Mexico and its estuaries, entering river systems in February to breed. They are believed to ascend the same river in which they hatched. The sticky eggs adhere to rocks and snags. Adults remain in fresh water until November.

Habitat

Although found in the Gulf of Mexico as far west as Louisiana, the Gulf sturgeon prefers the hard, sandy bottoms of the eastern Gulf, which is more suitable for its feeding habits. For spawning, the sturgeon seeks deep river channels with clear sand, rock, or gravel bottoms.

Historic Range

The Gulf sturgeon has been known from the Gulf of Mexico from the Mississippi River in Louisiana to Florida's Tampa Bay. While its center of abundance was along the Florida panhandle and peninsula, it spawned in almost all the region's rivers. Commercial fishing for Gulf sturgeon took place from Florida to Alabama.

Current Distribution

Although in recent years Gulf sturgeons have been collected from all Gulf states east of Texas, it is still found primarily along the Florida coast. The Suwannee River is believed to support the largest population. In a tagging program sponsored by the Caribbean Conservation Foundation, 300 Gulf sturgeon were caught and released in 1988, 500 in 1989. Fewer than 300 sturgeon are estimated to breed in the Apalachicola River. Populations in the other states are undoubtedly small, although some researchers believe that a potentially healthy population inhabits the Pearl River and its tributaries in Mississippi. In addition, sturgeon have been taken in recent years from the Mobile River in Alabama; the Pascagoula River and its tributary, the Chickasawhay River, in Mississippi; and Lake Pontchartrain and the Pearl River in Louisiana.

Conservation and Recovery

The Gulf sturgeon population has declined because of overfishing and the dam-

ming of rivers that fish use for spawning. Three major rivers, the Pearl in Mississippi, the Alabama in Alabama, and the Apalachicola in Florida, have been dammed. The Jim Woodruff Lock and Dam was constructed on the Apalachicola River in the 1950s. This restricted the sturgeon to 107 miles of the river. Previously it had used over 600 miles of the Apalachicola River and its tributaries. Spawning habitat has also been dredged to maintain navigation channels. In Mississippi, Gulf sturgeon are restricted to the lower 150 miles of the Pearl River by the Ross Barnett Dam near Jackson.

A short-lived commercial fishery for Gulf sturgeon apparently severely depleted the population near the turn of the last century. Currently, taking Gulf sturgeon is illegal in all four Gulf states.

Additional Sources

Barkuloo, J. M. 1988. "Report on the Conservation of the Gulf Sturgeon." U.S. Fish and Wildlife Service, Panama City, Florida.

Huff, J. S. 1975. "Life History of the Gulf of Mexico Sturgeon, *Acipenser oxyrhynchus desotoi*, in the Suwanee River, Florida." Marine Resources Publication No. 32.

Contacts

Regional Office of Endangered Species
U. S. Fish and Wildlife Service
Richard B. Russell Federal Building
75 Spring Street, S.W.
Atlanta, Georgia 30303

David J. Wesley
Jacksonville Field Office
U.S. Fish and Wildlife Service
3100 University Boulevard, South, Suite 120
Jacksonville, Florida 32216

Pygmy Sculpin
Cottus pygmaeus

Richard Wallace

Status	Threatened
Listed	September 28, 1989
Family	Cottidae (Sculpin)
Description	Small fish, grayish black to black, with 2 to 3 saddle markings.
Habitat	Spring and spring run.
Food	Insects.
Reproduction	Spawns year-round.
Threats	Groundwater contamination, highway construction, limited range.
Region 4	Alabama

Description

The pygmy sculpin is a small freshwater fish about 45 millimeters (1.8 in) in length. Its coloration varies by maturity, sex, and breeding condition. Patterning consists of up to three dorsal saddles and spotted fins. Juveniles have a black head and a grayish black body with three light saddles. Mature fish have white heads and lighter bodies, with the grayish black color remaining in the form of two saddles. Breeding males become almost entirely black; spots in the dorsal fin enlarge and the margin becomes reddish orange. Breeding females are slightly darker than nonbreeding females.

Behavior

The pygmy sculpin feeds on a variety of insects and small aquatic crustaceans, with isopods being the most important food. The species spawns throughout the year, with a peak occurring in spring and summer. Usually more than one female deposits eggs in batches on the underside of rocks. These nests are probably guarded by the male.

Habitat

This species inhabits a single spring and spring run in Alabama. The spring flow averages 32 million gallons per day, with a water temperature between 61° and 64° F. The bottom of the spring pool and run is gravel and sand; large mats of vegetation occur in both the pool and the run.

Historic Range

The pygmy sculpin was discovered in 1968 at Coldwater Spring and the spring run near Anniston, Alabama. The spring has been impounded and forms a one-acre pool, 2 to 4 feet deep. The run is up to 60 feet wide and flows for about 500 feet where it is joined by Dry Creek. Below this point it is known as Coldwater Creek which flows into Choccolocco Creek. The pygmy sculpin is restricted to the spring and the spring run; it has not been found elsewhere.

Current Distribution

The pygmy sculpin survives at Coldwater Spring, which is owned by the City of Anniston. The city uses the spring as its primary water supply, drawing about 16 million gallons a day.

Conservation and Recovery

The main threats to the pygmy sculpin are groundwater contamination, the adverse impacts of highway construction on the source aquifer, and the species' restricted range.

Both the surface water and the underground aquifer have shown some degree of toxic contamination. The Anniston Army Depot is nearby and studies have indicated that toxic chemicals, including chlorinated hydrocarbons, phenols, and hexavalent chromium, have been found in groundwater at the depot. Although migration of these compounds is not an immediate threat, they may sink into the aquifer and have a future impact on the water quality of Coldwater Spring. The spring water itself contains high levels of trichloroethylene.

The Alabama Highway Department plans to construct a highway bypass from Interstate 20 to Anniston. Three alternative routes for the bypass have been proposed. The preferred route would run along the side of Coldwater Mountain, just above and to the east of Coldwater Spring. The use of explosives in cutting a mountain road might change the system of cracks and fissures that route water to and from the underground aquifer, thus affecting Coldwater Spring. The two other proposed routes present less risk to the spring.

Since only a single population of the pygmy sculpin is known to exist, the species is vulnerable to an unpredictable human or natural event. A toxic spill that would contaminate the spring's source aquifer is perhaps the most dangerous potential threat of this type.

Additional Sources

Mount, R. H. 1986. "Vertebrate Animals of Alabama in Need of Special Attention." Alabama Agricultural Experiment Station.

Williams, J. D. 1968. "A New Species of Sculpin, *Cottus pygmaeus*, from a Spring in the Alabama River Basin." *Copeia* 1968: 334-342.

Contacts

Regional Office of Endangered Species
U. S. Fish and Wildlife Service
Richard B. Russell Federal Building
75 Spring Street, S.W.
Atlanta, Georgia 30303

James Stewart
Jackson Field Office
U.S. Fish and Wildlife Service
6578 Dogwood View Parkway, Suite A
Jackson, Mississippi 39213

Virgin River Chub
Gila robusta seminuda

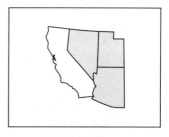

Status	Endangered
Listed	August 24, 1989
Family	Cyprinidae (Minnow)
Description	Medium-sized, silvery minnow with a narrow tail and deeply cleft caudal fin.
Habitat	Deep, swift currents over sand or gravel bottoms.
Food	Algae, insects, crustaceans, organic detritus.
Reproduction	Little known.
Threats	Impoundments, water diversion, predation by introduced species.
Region 1	Nevada
Region 2	Arizona
Region 6	Utah

John N. Rinne

Description

The Virgin River chub is a silvery fish in the minnow family that usually grows to about 20 centimeters (8 in). but has been known to attain a length of 45 centimeters (18 in). It has an elongated body with a narrow tail and deeply cleft caudal fin. It is distinguished from other subspecies of *Gila robusta* by the number of rays in the dorsal, anal, and pelvic fins (9 to 10) and the number of gill rakers (24 to 31). It has small, embedded scales on its back, breast, and belly that are difficult to see, which accounts for the subspecific name *seminuda*.

Behavior

The Virgin River chub is omniverous, feeding on algae, aquatic and terrestrial insects, crustaceans, and organic detritus. Little is known about its spawning behavior.

Habitat

This chub prefers deep, swift-flowing water, where there are boulders or other cover. It is tolerant of high salinity and turbidity and occurs over sand and gravel bottoms in water less than 30°C (90°F).

Historic Range

It is believed that the Virgin River chub once inhabited about 134 miles of the Virgin River, from its confluence with the Colorado River upstream to La Verkin Creek, near Hurricane, Utah. In the late nineteenth century it was considered common.

Current Distribution

Today this subspecies is restricted to a 50-mile portion of the Virgin River, between Mesquite, Nevada, and La Verkin Creek, near Hurricane, Utah. The land bordering this stretch of the river is both public and privately owned. In Arizona the federal Bureau of Land Management (BLM) administers about 80 to 90 percent of the river frontage; privately owned land is concentrated in the vicinity of Littlefield. In Utah, about 13 miles are managed by BLM; the state owns four small parcels and the rest is privately owned. In Nevada, land north of the town of Mesquite is in private hands.

Conservation and Recovery

The original range of the Virgin River chub was reduced almost 60 percent by nineteenth-century water diversions and the construction of Hoover Dam and Lake Mead. The chub is currently threatened by further water removal and impoundments, reduced reproduction, and competition from introduced fish species.

Although the Virgin River chub has survived a major reduction of its habitat caused by dams and water diversions, additional impoundments or diversions may drive the subspecies toward extinction. Federal listing as an Endangered species will require the Washington County Conservancy District, which has identified four potential reservoir sites, and the federal Soil Conservation Service, an agency of the Department of Agriculture which is planning flood control and irrigation projects, to make provisions for the conservation of the chub and its habitat.

The population of many river species often fluctuates because of changing environmental conditions, many of which are poorly known. However, it is clear that the species' survival is heavily dependent on the frequency of successful reproductive years. Recent studies have indicated that between 1984 and 1988 the Virgin River chub had only one good reproductive year.

Several other recent events have had a negative effect on Virgin River chub populations. In 1988, an attempt was made to eradicate the exotic red shiner (*Notropis lutrensis*) from the Virgin River from the Washington Fields diversion downstream to the Virgin River Gorge. This introduced species is a major threat to native species. In 1985 it became established in the St. George area and within a year became the dominant fish species. After first salvaging 1,200 Virgin River chub, all remaining fish in that 21-mile stretch of the river were eradicated and a barrier dam was installed at the head of the Virgin River Gorge to prevent return of the shiner.

Another 1988 event had a major impact on Virgin River fish populations. A dike at the Quail Creek Reservoir failed, releasing 25,000 acre-feet of water into the river. This scouring flood is believed to have had a devastating effect on the entire fish population of the Virgin River.

Also found in the Virgin River is the federally Endangered woundfin, *Plagopterus argentissimus*. In planning for recovery of both species, the Woundfin Recovery Team of the Fish and Wildlife Service, which developed much of the data relating to the Virgin River chub, will be renamed

▲ **Michigan Monkey-Flower** *(p. 1300)*

Walker's Manioc *(p. 1298)* ▼

Roan Mountain Bluet *(p. 1261)* ▼

Fringed Campion *(p. 1356)* ▼

▲ Western Prairie Fringed Orchid *(p. 1560)*

▲ Leafy Prairie Clover *(p. 1232)*

Barneby Ridge-Cress *(p. 1282)* ▼

▲ Northeastern Bulrush *(p. 1351)*

Gentian Pinkroot *(p. 1361)* ▲

▼ Garett's Mint *(p. 1235)*

Dudley Bluffs Bladderpod *(p. 1284)* ▲

▼ Sebastopol Meadowfoam *(p. 1288)*

▼ Baker's Sticky Seed *(p. 1201)*

▲ Sacramento Prickly-Poppy *(p. 1193)*

San Joaquin Wooly-Threads *(p. 1278)* ▼

▲ Terlinga Creek Cat's Eye *(p. 1222)*

Texas Trailing Phlox *(p. 1312)* ▼

▼ Dudley Bluffs Twinpod *(p. 1318)*

▲ California Jewelflower *(p. 1210)*

Kern Mallow *(p. 1245)* ▲

▼ *Diella falcata (p. 1237)*

Bakersfield Cactus *(p. 1308)* ▼

▲ *Chamaesyce celastroides* var. *kaenana (p. 1214)*

Alsinidendron trinerve (p. 1188) ▼

▲ Lower Keys Rabbit *(p. 1392)*

Northern Spotted Owl *(p. 1397)* ▼

▲ Silver Rice Rat *(p. 1389)*

Florida Salt Marsh Vole *(p. 1387)* ▼

Golden-Cheeked Warbler *(p. 1394)* ▲

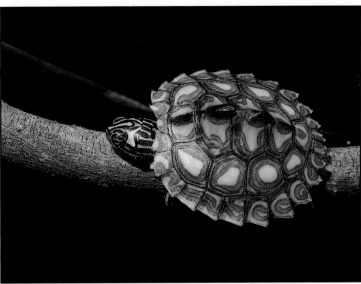

Yellow-Blotched Map Turtle *(p. 1401)* ▲

▼ Shenendoah Salamander *(p. 1405)*

▼ Cheat Mountain Salamander *(p. 1403)*

Roanoke Logperch *(p. 1426)* ▼

▲ Tulotoma Snail *(p. 1467)*

Puritan Tiger Beetle *(p. 1475)* ▼

Gulf Sturgeon *(p. 1407)* ▲

▼ Cracking Pearly Mussel *(p. 1447)*

▼ Northeastern Beach Tiger Beetle *(p. 1472)*

▼ Winged Mapleleaf Mussel *(p. 1457)*

▼ Mitchell's Satyr Butterfly *(p. 1478)*

the Virgin River Fishes Recovery Team, and will explore ways to enhance the populations of both species. As part of the recovery process, a captive population of Virgin River chub is held at the Dexter National Fish Hatchery as insurance against extinction and as a source of fish for ongoing restocking efforts.

Additional Sources

Cross, J. N. 1975. "Ecological Distribution of the Fishes of the Virgin River (Utah, Arizona, Nevada)." Master's thesis. University of Nevada, Las Vegas.

Heckman, R. A., J. E. Deacon, and P. D. Gregor. 1966. "Parasites of the Woundfin Minnow, *Plagopterus argentissimus,* and Other Endemic Fishes from the Virgin River, Utah." *Great Basin Naturalist* 46(4): 663-676.

Hickman, T. J. 1988. "Study of Fishes in the Virgin River (Utah)." Annual Report for 1987. Western Ecosystems, St. George, Utah.

Rinne, John N., and W. L. Minckley. 1991. *Native Fishes and Arid Lands: Dwindling Resource of the Desert Southwest.* USDA Forest Service, Fort Collins, Colorado.

Contacts

Regional Office of Endangered Species
U.S. Fish and Wildlife Service
P.O. Box 25486
Denver Federal Center
Denver, Colorado 80225

Donald L. Archer
U.S. Fish and Wildlife Service
1745 West, 1700 South
Salt Lake City, Utah 84104

Cahaba Shiner
Notropis cahabae

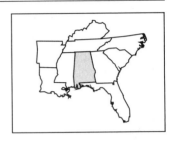

Status	Endangered
Listed	October 25, 1990
Family	Cyprinidae (Minnow)
Description	Small, silvery minnow with a dark lateral stripe below a narrow, peach-colored stripe.
Habitat	Shoal areas of main river channel.
Food	Small crustaceans, insect larvae, and algae.
Reproduction	Spawns late May through June.
Threats	Water pollution.
Region 4	Alabama

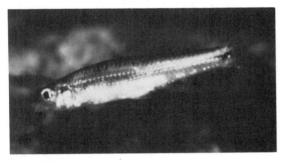

Robert A. Stiles

Description

The Cahaba shiner is a small, silvery fish that reaches a length of about 6.4 centimeters (2.5 in). On its side it has a dark stripe below a narrow peach-colored stripe. It is distinguished from the closely related mimic shiner (*Notropis volucellus*) by details of its markings and characteristics of its scales.

Behavior

This shiner feeds on small crustaceans, insect larvae, and algae. Like others in the mimic shiner group, the Cahaba shiner spawns later than other North American minnows, typically from late May through June.

Habitat

The Cahaba shiner is found in large shoal areas of the main river channel, below swift riffle areas. It prefers quiet waters less than 2 feet deep, with sandy bottoms near gravel beds.

Historic Range

This shiner is endemic to the Cahaba River in the central Alabama counties of Bibb, Perry, and Shelby. Collections have been made over about 76 miles of the river, from 3 miles northeast of Heiberger in Perry County to the Highway 52 bridge near Helena in Shelby County.

Current Distribution

Today the Cahaba shiner is found over about 60 miles of the Cahaba River, from 3 miles northeast of Heiberger to 3.8 miles above Booth Ford. The stronghold of the species is now limited to about 15 miles between the fall line and Piper Bridge.

Conservation and Recovery

Deteriorating water quality is the main threat to the Cahaba shiner and other fishes in the Cahaba River. Discharges from sewage treatment plants, limestone quarries, and mining operations, as well as increased siltation have led to the extirpation the blue shiner (*Notropis caeruleus*) and reduced the range of the Cahaba shiner by over 20 percent. Collections made during the most recent status survey have documented striking declines. In the shiner's stronghold area the ratio of Cahaba shiners to mimic shiners declined from about equal numbers to 1 to 16.

Many sections of the river show an increase in blue-green algae, indicating a degradation in water quality. At one location in Shelby County the algae has displaced riverweed, resulting in the extirpation of the Cahaba shiner, goldline darter, and blue shiner from the area.

In 1979 there were four municipal and 13 private wastewater treatment systems in the area. An environmental impact statement by the Environmental Protection Agency called attention to high levels of nitrogen and phosphorus. Some improvement has taken place in the last decade but degradation of the water quality continues to adversely affect the Cahaba shiner.

Additional Sources

Howell, W. M., et al. 1982. "Status Survey of the Cahaba Shiner (*Notropis* D.) and Goldline Darter (*Percina aurolineata*) in the Cahaba River from Trussville to Booth Ford, Alabama." U.S. Fish and Wildlife Service.

Mayden, R. L., and B. R. Kuhajda. 1989. "Systematics of *Notropis cahabae*, a New Cyprinid Fish Endemic to the Cahaba River of the Mobile Basin." *Bulletin of the Alabama Museum of Natural History* No. 9.

Pierson, J. M., et al. 1989. "Fishes of the Cahaba River System in Alabama." Geological Survey of Alabama.

Ramsey, J. S. 1982. "Habitat and Distribution of the Cahaba Shiner and Appraisal of Methods for its Capture." Alabama Cooperative Fishery Research Unit, U. S. Fish and Wildlife Service.

_____. 1986. "Cabaha Shiner, *Notropis* D. cf. *volucellus*." In *Vertebrate Animals of Alabama in Need of Special Attention*, edited by R. H. Mount. Alabama Agricultural Experiment Station, Auburn University, Alabama.

Contacts

Regional Office of Endangered Species
U. S. Fish and Wildlife Service
Richard B. Russell Federal Building
75 Spring Street, S.W.
Atlanta, Georgia 30303

James Stewart
Jackson Field Office
U.S. Fish and Wildlife Service
6578 Dogwood View Parkway, Suite A
Jackson, Mississippi 39213

Neosho Madtom
Noturus placidus

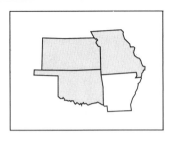

Status . . . . Threatened
Listed . . . . May 22, 1990
Family . . . . Ictaluridae (Catfish)
Description . . . . . . Mottled catfish, up to 3 inches long.
Habitat . . . . Shallow riffles over gravel bottoms.
Food . . . . Aquatic insects.
Reproduction . . . . Spawns in late June and July.
Threats . . . . Impoundments, water pollution.
Region 2 . . . . Oklahoma
Region 3 . . . . Missouri
Region 6 . . . . Kansas

Suzanne L. Collins & Joseph T. Collins/University of Kansas

Description

The Neosho madtom is a small catfish, with an average length of less than 7.5 centimeters (3 in). It has a midstripe of dark brown and is distinguished from similar catfish by its mottled skin.

Behavior

Little is known about the natural history of the Neosho madtom. Researchers have surmised that the fish spawns in late June and July and that it feeds primarily on aquatic insects.

Habitat

The Neosho madtom shows a strong habitat preference for stream riffles over small-sized gravel bottoms. The species is only abundant where the bottom consists of loosely packed gravel about half an inch in diameter. Adults prefer swift currents and depths of less than 0.3 meters (12 in), while juveniles inhabit slower currents at depths up to 1 meter (39 in).

Historic Range

The first collection of a Neosho madtom was in 1886 from the Neosho River near

Emporia, Kansas. Since then specimens have been taken from the Neosho River in Kansas and Oklahoma, the Cottonwood River in Kansas, the Spring River in Kansas and Missouri, and the lower Illinois River in Oklahoma.

Current Distribution

The Neosho madtom survives only in the northern section of its historic range in the Neosho River drainage. It has been extirpated from the lower Illinois River. The Neosho River (Grand River) in Oklahoma has largely been converted into a series of impoundments. This has flooded the riffle habitat of the fish and it is no longer found in those portions of the river.

This madtom survives in three distinct populations in the Neosho River drainage upstream from Miami, Oklahoma, into central Kansas. One population inhabits the Neosho River up to the John Redmond Reservoir at Burlington, Kansas. This portion of the range encompasses two counties in Oklahoma (Craig and Ottawa) and six counties in Kansas (Cherokee, Labette, Neosho, Allen, Woodson, and Coffey).

The second population inhabits the Neosho River and its tributary, the Cottonwood River, north of the reservoir to Elmdale (Lyon and Chase counties).

A third population survives on a stretch of the Spring River on either side of the Kansas/Missouri line (Cherokee County, Kansas, and Jasper County, Missouri).

Conservation and Recovery

The main threat to the Neosho madtom has been the destruction and modification of its habitat through the construction of impoundments. The conversion of the lower section of the Neosho River into a series of impoundments has eliminated up to a third of the species' original habitat.

Other known threats include changes in water quality downstream of dams; sand and gravel dredging; decline in stream flow; and pollution from livestock feedlots, wastewater discharges, and mining activities.

The extirpation of the species from the lower Illinois River has been attributed to cold water discharges from the Tenkiller Ferry Dam. The fish was not able to grow and reproduce in the colder water.

Sand and gravel dredging destroy the habitat and have dramatic short-term negative effects on madtom populations. However, once the disturbance ceases, natural deposition reestablishes the habitat and the species can recolonize the area.

Pollution from livestock feedlots caused a number of fish kills in the late 1960s. While state water pollution laws passed at the time have somewhat lessened this threat, this type of pollution remains a danger.

A number of proposed federal activities have the potential to affect Neosho madtom habitat. The Soil Conservation Service of the Department of Agriculture and the Army Corps of Engineers are considering the construction of over 100 small dams in the upper Neosho and Cottonwood watersheds.

In addition, the Corps of Engineers in considering increasing the water supply to the Wolf Creek Nuclear Generating Station, which draws water from the John Redmond Reservoir. If this is done, it may decrease the downstream flow of the Neosho River. The federal agencies responsible for these projects will be consulting with the Fish and Wildlife Service to evaluate the effects on Neosho madtom habitat.

Additional Sources

Deacon, J. E. 1961. "Fish Populations, Following a Drought, in the Neosho and Marais des Cygnes Rivers of Kansas." *University of Kansas Publications, Museum of Natural History* 13:359-427.

Moss, R. "Life History Information for the Neosho Madtom (*Noturus placidus*)." Kansas Nongame Wildlife Improvement Program, Contract No. 38.

Wagner, B., A. A. Echelle, and O. E. Maughan. "Status of Three Oklahoma Fishes (*Notropis perpallidus, Noturus placidus, Percina nasuta*)." Contract No. 14-16-0009-1513-W02-MI. Final report to U.S. Fish and Wildlife Service from Oklahoma Cooperative Fishery Research Unit, Stillwater, Oklahoma.

Contacts

Regional Office of Endangered Species
U.S. Fish and Wildlife Service
P.O. Box 25486
Denver Federal Center
Denver, Colorado 80225

Daniel Mulhern
U.S. Fish and Wildlife Service
315 Houston Street, Suite E
Manhattan, Kansas 66502

Sockeye Salmon
(Snake River)
Oncorhynchus nerka

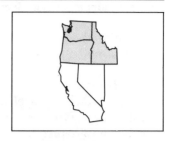

Status	Endangered
Listed	November 14, 1991
Family	Salmondiae (Trout)
Description	Unspotted, silvery salmon; in spawning season fish develop reddish orange coloration, males develop hooked jaws.
Habitat	Spawns on gravel near shore of alpine lake, migrates to ocean.
Food	Plankton, aquatic invertebrates, insects, smaller fish.
Reproduction	Female lays about 2,000 eggs in October.
Threats	Hydroelectric dams, water diversions.
Region 1	Idaho, Oregon, Washington

Chris van Dyck

Description

The sockeye is a smaller, unspotted, silvery Pacific salmon that averages about five or six pounds. During the breeding season both sexes develop a brilliant reddish orange coloration and males develop sharply hooked jaws.

The Snake River sockeye salmon shares its spawning habitat, Redfish Lake, Idaho, with kokanee, which are non-migrating sockeye salmon which spend their entire lifespan in the lake. Recent studies have indicated that kokanee and the sockeye do not interbreed. And although the National Marine Fisheries Service acknowledges that it cannot know with certainty, it is assuming that the original sockeye salmon gene pool still exists in Redfish Lake. This qualifies the population for listing as a distinct "species."

Behavior

Adult Snake River sockeye salmon enter the Columbia River in June and July and ascend the river system at the rate of about 13 miles per day. Fish do not feed once they enter fresh water, but live off their accumulated body flesh.

Those fish that complete their spawning journey usually arrive at Redfish Lake, Idaho, in August, and take four to eight weeks preparing to spawn. During this period the fish develop a reddish orange body color, the females swell with maturing eggs, and the males develop hooked jaws.

In October, females construct nests, known as redds, in gravel areas of the eastern shoreline of the lake. Using her tail, the female digs a depression in the gravel and deposits between 50 and 100 eggs, which are then fertilized by sperm released by the male. The process continues until the female has deposited about 2,000 eggs. The adults die within a few weeks of spawning.

The eggs incubate in the redds until April or May, when the young sockeye emerge. They remain in the gravel and feed from attached yolk sacs. After exhausting this food source the young fry swim up from the gravel and begin to feed on plankton.

In late April or early May, after spending one or two years in Redfish Lake, the juvenile sockeye, now known as smolt, begin their migration to the Pacific. While migrating, fish undergo chemical changes that will allow them to survive in a salt water environment. Those that successfully reach the Pacific disperse widely for one to three years before attempting the return journey to spawn.

Habitat

Sockeye salmon inhabit both salt and fresh water at different stages of their life histories. Successful reproduction requires loose gravel that can serve for the construction of redds. Juvenile sockeye require unobstructed passage to the ocean and a water flow strong enough to bring them to salt water in time to coincide with their physiological changes.

Historic Range

Historically, Idaho's sockeye salmon are known from lakes in the Stanley Basin of the Salmon River and the Snake River Basin. In the Stanley Basin they were produced in at least five lakes: Redfish, Alturas, Stanley, Yellow Belly, and Petit. They also spawned in Big Payette Lake on the North Fork Payette River and in Wallowa Lake on the Wallowa River.

For centuries sockeye salmon were a staple food resource of the Shoshone and Bannock Indian Tribes. In the late 1800s miners and other settlers arrived in the area and began taking sockeye for food. Between 1870 and 1880 several commercial sockeye fisheries operated at Payette Lake, and plans made to establish a cannery at Redfish Lake. In the early twentieth century construction of dams on the Salmon and Payette rivers sharply reduced sockeye salmon in the Snake River Basin.

Current Distribution

Today the Snake River sockeye salmon is almost extinct in the wild. Only Redfish Lake has supported a spawing sockeye population and the number of fish returning in recent years has steadily approached zero. Access to other lakes in the Stanley Basin which have supported the sockeye in the past have been blocked by irrigation diversions and fish barriers. The Sunbeam Dam, which initially blocked access to the Stanley Basin lakes in 1913, was partially removed in 1934 and sockeye populations began to recover. By 1942, 200 sockeye spawned in Redfish Lake. The population increased yearly and reached a peak of almost 4,500 in 1955.

However, the construction of a series of hydropower dams on the lower Snake River in the 1960s created additional obstacles to migration and the population began a steady decline. By 1989 only two fish returned to Redfish Lake. None were seen the following year and in 1991 only four fish returned.

Conservation and Recovery

While many factors have contributed to the decline in the Snake River sockeye salmon, including predation, drought, and overharvesting, the overwhelming threat to this race of salmon, as for all Pacific Northwest salmon, is the network of hydroelectric dams and irrigation projects that has obstructed the fishes' passage and disrupted the historic pattern of spring water flows. Outmigrating juveniles must deal with eight hydropower dams along the lower Snake and Columbia rivers. Studies have found that from 77 to 96 percent of migrating juveniles die on their voyage to the ocean. Upstream-migrating adults also face high mortality because of the dams; between 34 and 57 percent of adults never reach their spawing ground.

Although there have been a number of attempts to institute a program to conserve Pacific Coast salmon and steelhead, the most comprehensive was mandated by the Pacific Northwest Electric Power Planning and Conservation Act of 1980. This federal law established the Northwest Power Planning Council, which in turn developed a Fish and Wildlife Program with provisions to conserve the Snake River sockeye and other salmon runs. Conservation methods which involved increased spring water releases from the dams have met with only limited success, mainly because the timing and amount of releases are not mandated and have been resisted by hydropower producers, who would have to forgo some electrical generation. Attempts to capture juvenile sockeye and transport them around the dams have failed because most have died from the

stresses of handling, transport, and overcrowding.

Most experts believe that the only way to promote the recovery of the Snake River sockeye and other threatened salmon runs is to greatly speed up water flow during the spring migration. This would require the drawing down of reservoirs behind the four lower Snake River dams: Lower Granite, Little Goose, Lower Monumental, and Ice Harbor. Water dedicated to salmon conservation would then be used to replenish the reservoirs. This long-term solution would involve the modification of existing fish passage facilities and, since it would also require changes in irrigation practices, river transportation, and patterns of recreational use such as boating and fishing, would encounter significant political opposition and require a lengthy phase-in period. And perhaps more importantly, any change in operation of the hydroelectric dams could effect the production and pricing of electricity in the region.

In the short term, while these issues are being debated, efforts to conserve the Snake River salmon will involve the production of hatchery-spawned fish and strategies to increase the spring flow from available sources. The Idaho Department of Fish and Game and the Shoshone-Bannock Indian Tribes, with funding from the Bonneville Power Administration, has begun a hatchery program to increase sockeye production. Young sockeye from Redfish Lake have been trapped and placed in a hatchery. The only female in the group of four fish that returned to the lake in 1991 was captured to conserve the genetic traits of the wild sockeye in hatchery-raised fish.

While the extremely low number of Snake River sockeye have led many researchers to conclude that the run is functionally extinct already, they hope that conservation policies and methods developed for this species will help preserve other imperiled Pacific salmon runs in the future. Researchers have recently identified 101 Pacific salmon runs that they regard as at "high risk of extinction" and another 58 runs that are at "moderate risk."

Additional Sources

Bjornn, T. C., D. R. Craddock, and D. R. Corley. 1968. "Migration and Survival of Redfish Lake, Idaho, Sockeye Salmon, *Oncorhynchus nerka." Transactions of the American Fisheries Society* 37:360-373.

Chapman, D. W., et al. 1990. "Status of Snake River Sockeye Salmon." Final Report for Pacific Northwest Utilites Conference Committee. 101 SW Main Street, Suite 810, Portland, Oregon 97204.

Nehlson, W., Williams, J. E., and Lichatowich, J. A. 1991. "Pacific Salon at the Crossroads: Stocks at Risk from California, Oregon, Idaho, and Washington." *Fisheries* 16(2):4-21.

Oregon Department of Fish and Wildlife and National Marine Fisheries Service. 1990. "Past and Present Abundance of Snake River Sockeye, Snake River Chinook, and Lower Columbia River Coho Salmon." Report Prepared at the Request of Honorable Senator Hatfield."

Waples, R. S. 1991. "Definition of 'Species' Under the Endangered Species Act: Application to Pacific Salmon." U.S. Department of Commerce, NOAA Technical Memorandum NMFS F/NWC-194.

Waples, R. S., O. W. Johnson, and R. P. Jones, Jr. 1991. "Status Review Report for Sanke River Sockeye Salmon." U.S. Department of Commerce. NOAA Technical Memorandum NMFS F/NWC-195.

Contact

Tracey Vriens
Environmental and Technical Services Division
National Marine Fisheries Service
911 NE. 11th Avenue, Suite 620
Portland, Oregon 97232

Chinook Salmon (Sacramento River Winter-Run)

Oncorhynchus tschawytscha

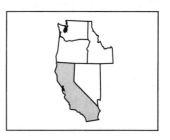

Status .... Threatened
Listed .... August 4, 1989
Family .... Salmonidae (Trout)
Description ...... Large, silvery fish with black spots.
Habitat .... Lives in ocean, ascends rivers to spawn on gravel bottoms.
Food .... Aquatic invertebrates, insects, smaller fishes.
Reproduction .... Spawns during the spring and summer.
Threats .... Loss or degredation of spawning habitat, predation.
Region 1 .... California

David Vogel

Description

Chinook salmon, also known as king salmon, are large, silvery fish that can grow to a weight of about 10 kilograms (22 lbs). During the breeding season, fish develop a reddish coloration and the jaws of males become hooked. Chinook salmon mature in the ocean, but ascend rivers to spawn. Separate races of chinook salmon are distinguished by the particular river they enter, the time of year of their entry, and their final spawning grounds. Since the Sacramento River winter run constitutes a distinct geographical population that does not interbreed with other chinook salmon races it qualifies as a "species" under the Endangered Species Act. It is the sole remaining winter run chinook salmon in California.

Behavior

Winter-run chinook salmon that spawn on the Sacramento River ascend the river between December and May. The run consists of mostly three-year-old fish along with smaller numbers of two- and four-year-old fish. In the late spring and summer females build gravel nests, known as redds, in water from 9 to 42 inches deep. The female excavates a foot-deep depression in the gravel by turning on its side and rapidly flexing its tail. This dislodges gravel which settles slightly downstream.

The female then extrudes eggs into the depression which are fertilized by attending males. The female then moves slightly upstream and excavates another depression, with the dislodged gravel covering the eggs in the first depression. This process continues until all the female's eggs, usually numbering between four and five thousand, have been deposited and fertilized. Both males and females die after spawning; the females usually remain on the redd, while the males move off downstream.

Newly hatched fish, called alevins, emerge from the eggs after about four months. They remain buried in the gravel for another one to four months, nourished by their yolk sacks. The new salmon fry spend only a short time in their rearing areas before beginning their outmigration to the ocean, passing through the river's delta between December and April.

Habitat

For reproduction to be successful chinook salmon need clean gravel bottoms with an adequate flow of oxygenated water to aerate the eggs. Water temperatures must be below 56°F for eggs to hatch.

Historic Range

Before construction of the Shasta and Keswick dams in the 1940s, the winter-run chinook salmon ascended the Sacramento River to spawn in the cold, spring-fed waters of the McCloud, Pitt, Sacramento, and Little Sacramento rivers in northern California. Disagreement exists on the size of the historic run. Some researchers claim that it was relatively small and confined to the McCloud River. However, recent archival research indicates that in the 1870s the winter run numbered over 200,000 fish

and took place throughout the Sacramento River system.

Current Distribution

The Shasta and Keswick dams cut off the salmon from their traditional spawning grounds. In 1966 construction of the Red Bluff Diversion Dam created another barrier to upstream migrating salmon. Estimates of the winter run, made each year since 1967 by the California Department of Fish and Game at the Red Bluff Dam, document a steady decline in the size of the winter run. When the dam was built the average run was about 84,000 fish. In the early 1980s the run had declined to an average of 2,000 fish. In the winter of 1988-1989 the run unaccountably fell to just over 500, about 75 percent of the expected size, and has not rebounded in subsequent years. The most recent count listed the size of the population at 200 fish.

Conservation and Recovery

The disruption of the winter-run of chinook salmon in the Sacramento River was caused by the construction of the Shasta and Keswick dams during the 1940s and the Red Bluff Diversion Dam in the 1960s. Although the Shasta Dam blocked the salmon from reaching traditional spawning habitat, cold water releases from the dam created new spawning habitat downstream. But in dry years the level of Lake Shasta falls too low for normal cold water releases to take place. Consequently, downstream water temperatures become too warm for successful spawning. Recent drought years have created water temperature conditions which make salmon reproduction impossible. Since 1987, emergency cold water discharges have been made from Shasta Dam to promote a successful spawn. In order to do this, the water must bypass the dam's electrical generating equipment, at the cost of electrical power generation. The Bureau of Reclamation is planning to modify the dam to enable water discharges from all levels of the lake to be used to generate electrical power.

The construction of the Red Bluff Diversion Dam in the 1960s was another barrier to winter-run chinook spawning. The fish ladders that were constructed proved inadequate. Studies determined that up to 40 percent of migrating chinook failed to make it above the dam. Below the dam water temperatures were too warm for successful spawning. In an attempt to reverse the decline in the winter run, since 1986 the gates at Red Bluff Dam have been opened between December and April to allow unobstructed passage to fish. In those years between 85 and 97 percent of the salmon spawned above the dam.

Juvenile salmon encounter their own difficulties when they descend the river to the Pacific. Many are eaten by predators such as squawfish and striped bass, others are diverted into the numerous irrigation projects that draw water from the river. In order to minimize this threat, new fish screens have been fashioned at many of the diversion intake points.

In 1985 the California Department of Fish and Game began restoring degraded spawning riffles below Shasta Dam. Current plans are to add up to a million cubic yards of gravel to the upper Sacramento River over the next decade.

Despite the measures taken to restore the winter run during the 1980s, the steep 1988 decline prompted both the California Department of Fish and Game to grant the winter run state endangered status and the Fish and Wildlife Service to list it as a Threatened species.

Additional Sources

California Department of Fish and Game. 1990. "Report to the California Fish and Game Commission on the Status of the Winter-run." August 1990.

Garcia, A. 1989. "The Impacts of Squawfish Predation on Juvenile Chinook Salmon at Red Bluff Diversion Dam and Other Locations in the Sacramento River." U.S. Fish and Wildlife Service Report No. AFF/FAO-89-05.

Hallock, R. J., and F. W. Fisher. 1985. "Status of the Winter-run Chinook Salmon, (*Oncorhynchus tschawytscha*), in the Sacramento River." California Department of Fish and Game Anadromous Fish Branch Office Report.

Vogel, D. A., K. R. Marine, and J. G. Smith. 1988. "Fish Passage Action Program for Red Bluff Diversion Dam: Final Report on Fishery Investigations." U.S. Fish and Wildlife Service Report No. FR1/FAO-83-19.

Williams, J. W., and C. D. Williams. 1991. "The Sacramento River Winter Chinook Salmon: Threatened with Extinction." In *California's Salmon and Steelhead Trout: The Struggle to Restore an Imperiled Resource*, edited by A. Lufkin. University of California Press, Berkeley.

Contacts

Margaret Lorenz
National Marine Fisheries Service
Office of Protected Resources
1335 East West Highway
Silver Spring, Maryland 20910

James H. Lecky
National Marine Fisheries Service
Southwest Region
Protected Species Management Branch
300 S. Ferry Street
Terminal Island, California 90731

Roanoke Logperch
Percina rex

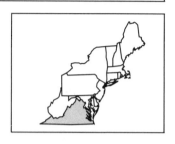

Status	Endangered
Listed	August 18, 1989
Family	Percidae (Perch)
Description	Large darter, green above, yellowish white below; marked with dark patches, small saddles, and oval side markings.
Habitat	Pools and riffles with clear bottoms.
Food	Aquatic insect larvae.
Reproduction	Spawns in April and May.
Threats	Water pollution, low stream flow.
Region 5	Virginia

Noel Burkhead and Robert Jenkins   *Color Plate C-7*

Description

The Roanoke logperch is a large darter that reaches a length of about 14 centimeters (5.5 in). It has an elongated cylindrical or slab-sided body with a complete lateral line. It has a dark green back, greenish yellow sides, and a white to yellowish belly. The sides and back are marked with numerous dark patches and distinct small saddles. It has oval markings on its side that are usually separated from the upper markings.

Behavior

The usual food of the Roanoke logperch is aquatic insect larvae. Individuals live for five to six years and become sexually mature at age four. Spawning occurs in April or May in deep runs over gravel.

Habitat

During the winter the Roanoke logperch inhabits deep pools where it usually finds shelter under boulders. In spring and summer, adults occupy gravel runs and riffles, while juveniles gather in slower runs and shallow pools with clean sand bottoms.

Historic Range

The Roanoke logperch was discovered in 1888 in the Roanoke River, near Roanoke,

Virginia. It has been found only in the Roanoke River drainage (including tributaries) in south central Virginia and the Notoway River drainage in southeast Virginia.

Current Distribution

Today, small populations of the Roanoke logperch inhabit rivers and streams in the two drainages of its historic range. In the Roanoke drainage, the largest and healthiest population occurs in the upper Roanoke River (Roanoke and Montgomery counties) from within the city of Roanoke upstream into the North and South Forks and Tinker Creek. A scattered population occurs in the Pigg River in Pittsylvania and Franklin counties and in Big Chestnut Creek, a tributary of the Pigg, in Franklin County. An extremely small population inhabits a 2.5-mile section of the Smith River in Patrick County, upstream of Philpott Reservoir, and Town Creek, a tributary of the Smith River in Henry County.

In the Nottoway River drainage, the Roanoke logperch is found in a 32-mile reach of the river in Sussex County and in Stony Creek, a tributary in Dinwiddie and Sussex counties. The population in this drainage is believed to be lower than that in the Pigg River.

Conservation and Recovery

The main threat to the Roanoke logperch is degradation of the water quality. Expanding urban and industrial development around Roanoke has a growing impact on the largest remaining population. Urban runoff and a variety of nonpoint-source pollutants, such as silt, oil, fertilizer, and toxic chemicals, are a growing threat to the species.

In addition, several proposed projects could have an adverse effect on this fish. The West Roanoke County Water Supply Project is intended to provide for the future needs of the county by taking water from the river. This could result in a low water flow for a seven-mile section of the river which is excellent logperch habitat. Low-flow periods could possibly expose riffles, increase the water temperature during the summer and fall, and increase the concentration of pollutants while decreasing the amount of dissolved oxygen. Modifications to the original proposal may lessen some of the impacts to logperch habitat.

The Army Corps of Engineers has proposed the Upper Roanoke Flood Control Project which would modify the river's channel within the city limits. Even if efforts are made to avoid damage to logperch habitat, some adverse effects are expected.

The National Park Service has proposed construction of a Roanoke River Parkway. While this project is still in an early planning stage and its impact on the logperch cannot yet be evaluated, any road construction adjacent to the river is a cause for concern.

The Fish and Wildlife Service will monitor all three of these projects to ensure that conservation of the Roanoke logperch is considered.

Additional Sources

Burkhead, N. M. 1983. "Ecological Studies of Two Potentially Threatened Fishes (the Orangefin Madtom, *Noturus gilberti*, and the Roanoke Logperch, *Percina rex*) Endemic to the Roanoke River Drainage." Report to Wilmington District Corps of Engineers, Wilmington, North Carolina.

_____. 1986. "Potential Impact of the West County Reservoir Project on Two Endemic

Rare Fish and the Aquatic Biota of the Upper Roanoke River, Roanoake County, Virginia." Report to Roanoke County Public Facilities Department, Roanoke, Virginia.

Jenkins, R. E. 1979. "Freshwater and Marine Fishes." In *Endangered and Threatened Plants and Animals of Virginia,* edited by D. W. Linzey. Virginia Polytechnic Institute and State University, Blacksburg, Virginia.

Simonson, T. D., and R. J. Neves. 1986. "A Status Survey of the Orangefin Madtom (*Noturus gilberti*) and Roanoke Logperch (*Percina rex*)." Virginia Commission of Game and Inland Fisheries, Richmond, Virginia.

Contacts

Regional Office of Endangered Species
U. S. Fish and Wildlife Service
Richard B. Russell Federal Building
75 Spring Street, S.W.
Atlanta, Georgia 30303

G. Andrew Moser
Annapolis Field Office
U.S. Fish and Wildlife Service
Annapolis, Maryland 21401

Independence Valley Speckled Dace

Rhinichthys osculus lethoporus

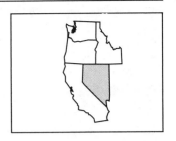

Status	Endangered
Listed	October 10, 1989
Family	Cyprinidae (Minnow)
Description	Small minnow with olive green back, silvery belly, and black spots.
Habitat	Spring and outflow.
Food	Insects.
Reproduction	Presumably spawns in mid-summer.
Threats	Limited distribution, low numbers, water diversion, introduced fish species.
Region 1	Nevada

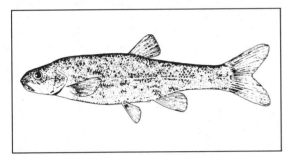

Speckled Dace

Description

The Independence Valley speckled dace, a subspecies of the speckled dace, is a small minnow that seldom exceeds 10 centimeters (4 in). Speckled dace typically have olive green backs, silver/gold abdomens, and a random pattern of black spots. Most have a distinct dark lateral stripe.

This subspecies is distinguished from other speckled dace by a more laterally compressed body. It differs from the Endangered Clover Valley speckled dace, found in nearby springs, by a less developed lateral line, fewer number of pectoral fin rays, and a straighter and more oblique mouth.

Behavior

The speckled dace is an adaptable species, able to occupy a variety of habitats, from cold streams and rivers with rocky bottoms to thermal springs with silt bottoms. This adaptability has enabled it to survive in environments too harsh for other species. The isolation of populations has led to a large number of forms that are recognized as subspecies. They feed primarily on insects, and are presumed to spawn in mid-summer.

Habitat

The Independence Valley speckled dace inhabits a single spring and its outflow in northeastern Nevada. The spring has been impounded for agricultural irrigation and only very limited numbers of the fish have been observed.

Historic Range

This subspecies was first collected in 1965, but not described until 1972. It is known from a single spring in Independence Valley, Elko County, Nevada. Although this subspecies was not known the springs were modified, scientists believe that it once occupied a larger aquatic system supported by the spring.

Current Distribution

The Independence Valley speckled dace has not been found outside the Elko County spring system, which is located on private ranch land. Population figures are not available, but very few fish have been collected. Its discoverer had a difficult time securing enough specimens for taxonomic classification.

Conservation and Recovery

This dace is threatened by its limited distribution and low numbers, diversion of the spring water, and predation by introduced fish species. The spring has long been impounded for irrigation purposes, limiting the dace to the outflow and certain sections of the reservoir. Spring reservoirs are often stocked with sport fish, such as rainbow trout (*Salmo gairdneri*), largemouth bass (*Micropterus salmoides*), and bluegill (*Lepomis machrochirus*), which feed on the dace, forcing it to retreat to areas safe from the predatory species. The Independence Valley tui chub (*Gila bicolor isolata*), which once inhabited the same

spring, is now believed to be extinct because of predation by introduced species.

The Fish and Wildlife Service hopes to obtain a conservation easement on the spring habitat and institute a management program that will protect the dace.

Additional Sources

Hubbs, C. L., R. R. Miller, and L. C. Hubbs. 1974. *Hydrographic History and Relict Fishes of the North Central Great Basin.* Memoirs of the California Academy of Sciences. Volume 7.

McNatt, R. M. 1988. "Field Trip Report on Investigation of Three Speckled Dace Sites in Clover Valley, Nevada." U.S. Fish and Wildlife Service, Great Basin Complex, Reno, Nevada.

Vinyard, G. L. 1984. "A Status Report about the Independence Valley Speckled Dace (*Rhinichthys osculus lethoporus*), Independence Valley Tui Chub (*Gila bicolor isolata*), and Clover Valley Speckled Dace (*Rhinichthys osculus oligoparus*); Three Fishes Restricted to the Northeastern Portion of Nevada." U.S. Fish and Wildlife Service, Reno, Nevada.

Contacts

Regional Office of Endangered Species
U.S. Fish and Wildlife Service
Eastside Federal Complex
911 N.S. 11th Avenue
Portland, Oregon 97232-4181

Richard J. Navarre
U.S. Fish and Wildlife Service
4600 Kietzke Lane, Building C
Reno, Nevada 89502

Clover Valley Speckled Dace

Rhinichthys osculus oligoporus

Status	Endangered
Listed	October 10, 1989
Family	Cyprinidae (Minnow)
Description	Small minnow with olive green back, silvery belly, and black spots.
Habitat	Springs and outflows.
Food	Insects.
Reproduction	Presumably spawns in mid-summer.
Threats	Limited distribution, water diversion, introduced fish species.
Region 1	Nevada

Gary Vinyard

Description

The Clover Valley speckled dace is a small minnow that seldom exceeds 10 centimeters (4 in). Speckled dace typically have olive green backs, silver or gold abdomens, and a random pattern of black spots. Most have a distinct dark lateral stripe.

The Clover Valley speckled dace is distinguished from other speckled dace by its less developed lateral stripe, the location of its pectoral fins, and the number of pectoral fin rays.

Behavior

The speckled dace is an adaptable species, able to occupy a variety of habitats, from cold streams and rivers with rocky bottoms to thermal springs with silt bottoms. This adaptability has enabled it to survive in environments too harsh for other species. The isolation of populations has led to a large number of forms that are recognized as subspecies. They feed primarily on insects and are presumed to spawn in mid-summer.

Habitat

The Clover Valley speckled dace inhabits a few springs and their outflows in northeastern Nevada. The springs have been impounded for agricultural irrigation and the dace inhabits the springs, outflows, impoundments, and irrigation ditches.

Historic Range

This dace subspecies was first collected in 1934, but not described until 1972. It is only known from three springs in Clover Valley, Elko County, Nevada. Although this subspecies was not known before the springs were modified, scientists believe that it once occupied the system of streams and wetlands that were supported by the springs.

Current Distribution

The Clover Valley speckled dace has not been found outside these three Elko County spring systems, all of which are on private ranch land. It is estimated that there are several hundred dace surviving in each spring system.

Conservation and Recovery

This dace is threatened by its limited distribution, diversion of the spring water, and predation by introduced fish species. These springs have long been impounded for irrigation purposes, limiting the dace to the outflow and certain sections of the reservoir. Often the reservoirs are stocked with sport fish, such as rainbow trout (*Salmo gairdneri*), largemouth bass (*Micropterus salmoides*), and bluegill (*Lepomis machrochirus*), which feed on the dace, forcing it to retreat to areas safe from the predatory species.

So far the owners of the springs have not been willing to sign agreements to conserve the species. One has indicated an intention to increase the use of a spring for irrigation, while another plans to intoduce game fish into a reservoir, despite the danger to the Clover Valley speckled dace. The Fish and Wildlife Service hopes that it will be able to obtain conservation easements and manage the spings to protect the dace.

Additional Sources

Hubbs, C. L., R. R. Miller, and L. C. Hubbs. 1974. *Hydrographic History and Relict Fishes of the North Central Great Basin.* Memoirs of the California Academy of Sciences. Volume 7.

McNatt, R. M. 1988. "Field Trip Report on Investigation of Three Speckled Dace Sites in Clover Valley, Nevada." U.S. Fish and Wildlife Service, Great Basin Complex, Reno, Nevada.

Minckley, W. L., and J. E. Deacon. 1968. "Southwestern Fishes and the Enigma of 'Endangered Species.' "*Science* 159: 1424-1432.

Vinyard, G. L. 1984. "A Status Report about the Independence Valley Speckled Dace (*Rhinichthys osculus lethoporus*), Independence Valley Tui Chub (*Gila bicolor isolata*), and Clover Valley Speckled Dace (*Rhinichthys osculus oligoparus*); Three Fishes Restricted to the Northeastern Portion of Nevada." U.S. Fish and Wildlife Service, Reno, Nevada.

Contacts

Regional Office of Endangered Species
U.S. Fish and Wildlife Service
Eastside Federal Complex
911 N.S. 11th Avenue
Portland, Oregon 97232-4181

Richard J. Navarre
U.S. Fish and Wildlife Service
4600 Kietzke Lane, Building C
Reno, Nevada 89502

Pallid Sturgeon
Scaphirhynchus albus

Status	Endangered
Listed	September 6, 1990
Family	Acipenseridae (Sturgeon)
Description	Large, bony-plated fish with flattened head.
Habitat	Large, turbid, free-flowing rivers with rock or gravel bottoms.
Food	Crustaceans, worms, insect larvae, other fish.
Reproduction	Spawns in swift water over gravel or rocky bottoms.
Threats	Impoundments, lack of reproduction.
Region 3	Illinois, Iowa, Missouri
Region 4	Arkansas, Kentucky, Louisiana, Mississippi, Tennessee
Region 6	Kansas, Montana, Nebraska, North Dakota, South Dakota

Kent Keenlyne

Description

The pallid sturgeon is a large, slow-maturing, long-lived freshwater fish. It has a flattened, shovel-like head, five rows of bony plates, and an unequally lobed tail. There is a row of sensory barbels in front of its ventral, toothless mouth.

This sturgeon is distinguished from the more common shovelnose sturgeon (*Scaphirhynchus platorhynchus*) by a number of characteristics. The pallid is lighter in color and attains a larger size. It appears smoother overall and has a longer nose. The most notable difference is the length and placement of the barbels. The pallid sturgeon's barbels are situated about a third of the distance from the mouth to the nose; those of the shovelnose sturgeon are at the midpoint between the two. The inner barbels of the pallid sturgeon are about half the length of the outer barbels; all the shovelnose sturgeon's barbels are about the same length. The species has also been known as *Parascaphirhynchus albus*, and by the common name of white sturgeon.

Behavior

Like other sturgeon species, the pallid is an opportunistic bottom feeder, consuming mollusks, crustaceans, worms, aquatic insects, and other fish. The barbels are sensory organs, and are important in the fish's feeding process.

The reproductive cycle of this sturgeon is not well known, although it is probably similar to other North American sturgeon species. Fish reach sexual maturity at about five years of age and spawn every few years thereafter. When spawning, small batches of sticky eggs are periodically released over a period of about 12 hours.

Habitat

The pallid sturgeon is found in large, turbid, free-flowing rivers with rocky or sandy bottoms. It inhabits swifter flowing waters than the related shovelnose sturgeon.

Historic Range

The pallid sturgeon has been reported from the mouth of the Mississippi River to the mouth of the Missouri River; from the Missouri River as far as Fort Benton, Montana; and from the lower reaches of the Yellowstone River. The total length of the species' historic range was over 3,500 miles and involved river habitat in 13 states: Louisiana, Mississippi, Arkansas, Tennessee, Kentucky, Missouri, Illinois, Iowa, Kansas, Nebraska, South Dakota, North Dakota, and Montana. While it appears that the pallid sturgeon was never abundant, it was once considered fairly common. As late as 1967 researchers were able to capture several fish in a single net set, and fishermen reported taking hundreds of pallid sturgeon as the reservoirs on the Missouri River filled.

Current Distribution

The species still occurs, but in dramatically reduced numbers, throughout much of its historic range. This decline is graphi-

cally illustrated by the number of pallid sturgeon sightings over the last three decades. In the 1960s about 500 observations were made; in the 1970s, there were 209 sightings. In the 1980s the number of observations fell to 65. The decline has been especially notable from the impounded sections of the Missouri River above the Gavins Point Dam along the South Dakota/Nebraska border.

Remnant populations probably exist in the Missouri River near the mouth of the Yellowstone River below Fort Peck, Montana; in the upper end of Lake Sharpe near Pierre, South Dakota, and between the mouth of the Platte River in Nebraska and Gavins Point Dam. Scattered sightings in the Mississippi River in the 1980s indicate that a small number of pallids may survive there.

Conservation and Recovery

The decline in pallid sturgeon populations has been caused by the alteration of virtually its entire river habitat by channelization and impoundment. About 51 percent has been channelized, 28 percent impounded, and the remaining 21 percent affected by the upstream impoundments.

The Mississippi and Missouri rivers have had an important role in the development of the nation's commerce, and since the early 1800s they have been modified for commercial navigation. In the 1950s and 1960s a series of dams were constructed on the Missouri River in North and South Dakota, in effect turning the free-flowing river into a series of long narrow impoundments. This has led to a number of habitat changes which have apparently interfered with pallid sturgeon reproduction. Studies of the fish populations of the impoundments have consistently failed to document any young pallid sturgeon. There has been no documeted reproduction in a decade, and the aging remnant population seems headed for extinction.

The dams block the normal movement of the sturgeon to historic spawning or feeding areas and have destroyed some spawning and nursery areas. They have produced changes to the water quality, temperature, and flow rates, which may affect reproduction and food sources.

Studies are underway, using the shortnose sturgeon as a surrogate species, to determine the feasibility of propagating the pallid sturgeon in captivity. During recent years researchers have been developing new techniques to locate and caputure pallid sturgeon in preparation for a captive propagation program.

Since the federal government is heavily involved with the river habitats of the pallid sturgeon, agencies involved in dam operations and river channel maintanence will be consulting with the Fish and Wildlife Service on the recovery of the species.

Additional Sources

Carlson, D. M., et al. 1985. "Distribution, Biology, and Hybridization of *Scaphirhynchus albus* and *S. platorynchus* in the Missouri and Mississippi Rivers." *Environmental Biology of Fishes* 14:51-59

Deacon, J. E., G. Kobetich, J. D. Williams, and S. Contreras. 1979. "Fishes of North America, Endangered, Threatened, or of Special Concern, 1979." *Fisheries* 4(2):29-44.

Gilbraith, D. M., M. J. Schwalbach, and C. R. Berry. 1988. "Preliminary Report on the Status of the Pallid Sturgeon, *Scaphirhynchus albus*, a Candidate Endangered Species." South Dakota State University, Brookings, South Dakota.

Hesse, L. W. 1987. "Taming the Wildlife Missouri River: What Has It Cost?" *Fisheries* 12(2):2-9.

Hallemeyn, L. W. 1983. "Status of the Pallid Sturgeon (*Scaphirhynchus albus*)." *Fisheries* 8(1):3-9.

Keenlyne, K. D. 1989. "A Report on the Pallid Sturgeon." U.S. Fish and Wildlife Service, Pierre, South Dakota.

Whitley, J. R., and R. S. Campbell. 1974. "Some Aspects of Water Quality and Biology of the Missouri River." *Transactions of the Missouri Academy of Science* 7-8:60-670.

Contacts

Regional Office of Endangered Species
U.S. Fish and Wildlife Service
P.O. Box 25486
Denver Federal Center
Denver, Colorado 80225

Kent D. Keenlyne
U.S. Fish and Wildlife Service
P.O. Box 986
Pierre, South Dakota 57501

Razorback Sucker
Xyrauchen texanus

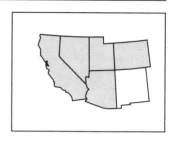

Status	Endangered
Listed	October 23, 1991
Family	Catostomidae (Sucker)
Description	Robust fish with a sharp, dorsal ridge behind the head.
Habitat	River channels, gravel bars.
Food	Algae, plankton, insects.
Reproduction	Spawns in the spring.
Threats	Lack of recruitment of young, loss of habitat.
Region 1	California, Nevada
Region 2	Arizona
Region 6	Colorado, Utah

John N. Rinne

Description

The razorback sucker is a large freshwater fish, often exceeding 3 kilograms (6 lbs) in weight and 60 centimeters (24 in) in length. Adults have an abrupt, sharp-edged dorsal ridge behind the head and a fleshy mouth situated on the underside the head. Younger fish, less than 15 centimeters (6 in) long, lack the distinctive keel. This species was originally placed in the genus *Catostomus*. It has also been known by the common name, humpback sucker.

Behavior

In the lower Colorado River basin, razorback suckers spawn from late January through April; in the upper basin spawning takes place mostly in May and June.

After migrating considerable distances to spawning areas, females are accompanied by several males over clean gravel bars. The collection of fertilized eggs and young larvae indicates that the species is reproducing successfully. However, almost no larvae over about one-half inch in length have been found, indicating that the species is not successfully recruiting young to the population. Adult razorback suckers feed primarily on algae, but also eat plankton, insects, and decaying organic matter.

Habitat

The razorback sucker shows different habitat preferences depending on the season. During the spring spawning season it is found mostly over sand, gravel, and cobble runs; flooded bottomlands; and the eddies formed at the flooded mouths of tributary streams.

In winter the fish take up a relatively sedentary position in deeper water or the main stream channel. Studies with radio-tagged fish indicate that during the winter fish travel only about 5 kilometers (3 miles) over the course of several months. Because they have not been seen by researchers, the habitat requirements of larvae and young fish are largely unknown.

Historic Range

First described in 1861, the razorback sucker was once an abundant species throught the 3,500-mile Colorado River basin. It is believed to have occurred in Arizona, California, Colorado, Nevada, New Mexico, Utah, Wyoming, and in the Mexican states of Baja California Norte and Sonoma. A significant commercial fishery for the species existed in southern Arizona during the early 1900s, and in Colorado thousands were observed during spring runoffs during the 1930s and early 1940s.

Current Distribution

In recent decades the razorback sucker has undergone a steady decline in both range and numbers. It now occurs in about 750 miles of the upper Colorado River basin and in about 200 miles of the lower basin. The largest population of adult fish—an estimated 60,000—survives in Lake Mohave, on the Arizona-Nevada border. Small numbers of the species are also found in Lake Mead and Senator Wash Reservoir. In the upper Colorado basin an estimated 750-1,200 individuals inhabit the upper Green River and some of its tributaries in Utah and Colorado. Razorbacks are also found in the upper Green River,

Utah; lower Yampa River, Colorado; and the Colorado River, near Grand Junction, Colorado. The species is present but very rare in the San Juan, Dirty Devil, and Colorado arms of Lake Powell.

Conservation and Recovery

Since the early 1900s construction of dams on the Colorado River and its major tributaries have radically altered the river system, impounding nearly the entire lower basin and greatly decreasing water flows. The once abundant razorback sucker has progressively declined as the natural flow of the river has been disrupted. The changes in flow caused by dams has reduced available spawning areas and rendered other parts of the river too cold to support the species. However, of most concern to researchers is the fact that despite successful reproduction, the young are not surviving. It is believed that the present population consists almost entirely of adults. If this situation continues, the extinction of the species in the near future is a certainty.

It appears that the main causes of the death of razorback sucker larvae are predation by nonnative fish species and a lack of food availability. A number of predatory species, including carp, channel catfish, flathead catfish, largemouth bass, smallmouth bass, and bluegill, feed on razorback sucker eggs and larvae. In addition, recent studies in Lake Mohave have suggested that there is not sufficient zooplankton in the lake to support the growing larvae.

The conservation and recovery of federally listed fish species in the Colorado River basin—the Colorado squawfish (*Ptychocheilus lucius*), humpback chub (*Gila cypha*), and bonytail chub (*Gila elegans*)—has been coordinated by the Colorado

River Endangered Fishes Recovery Implementation Committee, which consists of representatives from a number of federal agencies. Protective measures for the razorback sucker will now be included in the committee's work. As part of the recovery process a captive population of razorback suckers is held at the Dexter National Fish Hatchery as insurance against extinction and a population source for an ongoing restocking effort. Unfortunately, this effort does not appear to be succeeding. Over the last ten years, over 13 million razorback sucker fry have been stocked in over 50 sites in Arizona. It is believed that these juveniles were heavily preyed upon by introduced nonnative fishes.

Alteration of the Colorado River system is continuing and the Fish and Wildlife Service has been in consultation with over 100 federally funded or regulated projects in the upper Colorado basin over the last decade. Among the more prominent projects are the Central Utah Project, which will divert water from the Green River, and the Two Forks Project, which will divert water from the Colorado River. These will affect listed fish species by decreasing the flow in most of the remaining riverine habitat.

Additional Sources

Bozek, M. A., L. J. Paulson, and J. E. Deacon. 1984. "Factors Affecting Reproductive Success of Bonytail Chubs and Razorback Suckers in Lake Mohave." Final report, 14-16-0002-81-251. Bureau of Reclamation, Boulder City, Nevada.

Loudermilk, W. E. 1985. "Aspects of Razorback Sucker (*Xyrauchen texanus*, Abbott) Life History which Help Expain Their Decline." *Proceedings of the Desert Fishes Council* 13(1981):67-72.

Marsh, P. C., and W. L. Minckley. 1989. Observations on Recruitment and Ecology of Razorback Sucker: Lower Colorado River, Arizona- California." *Great Basin Naturalist* 49(1):71-78.

Minckley, W. L., et al. 1991. "Management Toward Recovery of Razorback Sucker (*Xyrauchen texanus*)." In *Battle Against Extinction*, edited by W. L. Minckley and J. E. Deacon. University of Arizona Press, Tucson.

Papoulis, D. 1986. "The Effect of Food Availability on Growth and Mortality of Larval Razorback Sucker, *Xyrauchen texanus*." U.S. Fish and Wildlife Service, Albuquerque, New Mexico.

Rinne, John N., and W. L. Minckley. 1991. *Native Fishes and Arid Lands: Dwindling Resource of the Desert Southwest*. USDA Forest Service, Fort Collins, Colorado.

Tyus, H. M. 1987. "Distribution, Reproduction, and Habitat Use of the Razorback Sucker in the Green River, Utah, 1979-1986." *Transactions of the American Fisheries Society* 116:111-116.

Tyus, H. M., and C. A. Karp. 1989. "Habitat Use and Streamflow Needs of Rare and Endangered Fishes, Yampa River, Colorado." U.S. Fish and Wildlife Service, *Biological Report* 89(14).

Contacts

U.S. Fish and Wildlife Service
2078 Administration Building
1745 West, 1700 South
Salt Lake City, Utah 84104-5110

Patricia A. Schrader
U.S. Fish and Wildlife Service
529 25½ Road, Suite B-113
Grand Junction, Colorado 81505-6199

Dwarf Wedge Mussel
Alasmidonta heterodon

A. E. Spreitzer/OSU Museum of Zoology

Status	Endangered
Listed	March 14, 1990
Family	Unionidae (Freshwater Mussel)
Description	Small mussel with two lateral teeth on the right valve and a single tooth on the left valve.
Habitat	Mud, sand, and gravel stream bottoms.
Threats	Water pollution, dam and bridge construction.
Region 4	North Carolina
Region 5	Maryland, New Hampshire, Vermont

Description

The dwarf wedge mussel is a small mussel, rarely over 3.8 centimeters (1.5 in) long. It is the only North American freshwater mussel that has two lateral teeth on the right valve, but only one tooth on the left. It has also been known by the name *Unio heterodon*.

Habitat

This mussel inhabits mud, sand, and gravel stream bottoms in areas of slow to moderate current and little silt. Like all freshwater mussels, this species feeds by filtering food particles from the water. Its reproductive life cycle involves a stage when the mussel larvae attach to the gills of host fish species. For a general discus-

sion of the freshwater mussel life cycle see the species account of the birdwing pearly mussel (*Conradilla caelata*) on page 955 of volume two of this guide.

Historic Range

The dwarf wedge mussel was once widely distributed in Atlantic Coast river systems from New Brunswick, Canada, to the Neuse River system in North Carolina. Known from 15 drainages in 11 states and one Canadian province, it has been collected from the following river systems: the Peticodiac River system in New Brunswick; the Taunton, Agawam, Merrimac, Connecticut, and Quinnipac river systems in New England; the Hackensack, Delaware, and Susquehanna river systems in the Middle

Atlantic states; and the Choptank, Rappahannock, James, Tar, and Neuse river systems in the Southeast.

Current Distribution

Today the distribution of the dwarf wedge mussel is vastly reduced. A recent survey of the species' range by The Nature Conservancy found it surviving at only at 10 sites in five river drainages in four states. Populations exist in the Ashuelot River in Cheshire County, New Hampshire, and two reaches of the Connecticut River in Sullivan County, New Hampshire, and Windsor County, Vermont. In Maryland the mussel occurs in McIntosh Run in St. Mary's County and two tributaries of Tuckahoe Creek in Talbot, Queen Annes, and Caroline counties. North Carolina populations survive in the Little River in Johnston County, the Tar River in Granville County, and two of that river's tributaries in Franklin County.

Conservation and Recovery

The decline of the dwarf wedge mussel is attributed to the damming and channelizing of rivers throughout the species' range, resulting in the loss of large amounts of the mussel's habitat. Water upstream from dams generally experience siltation and low oxygen levels, while downstream areas suffer from fluctuating temperatures and water levels.

The dwarf wedge mussel has been further depleted by water pollution from agricultural, domestic, and industrial sources. Several undammed sections of the Connecticut River no longer contain mussels, attesting to the harmful effects of water pollution. One of the largest remaining populations occurs in a section of the Ashuelot River that passes through a golf course. In recent years this population has experienced a rapid decline, most likely from the effects of chemicals applied to the course.

The construction of roads and bridges often threatens nearby dwarf wedge mussel populations. In Massachusetts, for example, one population was decimated when bridge construction resulted in sedimentation and erosion which buried and killed many of the mussels.

Only one federal project is known that may possibly effect this mussel species. A new bridge is planned on Maryland Route 404 over a tributary of Tuckahoe Creek. In accordance with the Endangered Species Act, the Fish and Wildlife Service has conferred with the Maryland highway authorities on ways to avoid damage to known dwarf wedge mussel populations.

Additional Sources

Havik, M. E., and L. L. Marking. 1987. *Effects of Contaminants on Naiad Mollusks (Unionidae): A Review*. Department of the Interior, Fish and Wildlife Service, Resource Publication 164. Washington, D.C.

Master, L. 1980. "*Alasmidonta heterodon*; Results of a Global Status Survey and Proposal to List as an Endangered Species." U.S. Fish and Wildlife Service, Newton Corner, Massachusetts.

Contacts

Regional Office of Endangered Species
U.S. Fish and Wildlife Service
One Gateway Center, Suite 700
Newton Corner, MA 02158

G. Andrew Moser
Annapolis Field Office
U.S. Fish and Wildlife Service
1825 Virginia Street
Annapolis, MD 21401

Ouachita Rock-Pocketbook
Arkansia wheeleri

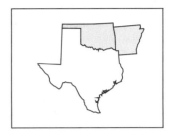

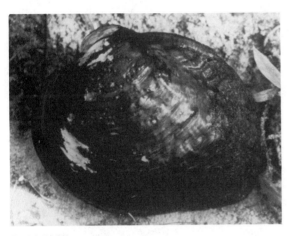

Patricia Mehlhop

Status	Endangered
Listed	October 23, 1991
Family	Unionidae
	(Freshwater Mussel)
Description	Medium-sized, silky textured, chestnut brown to black shell.
Habitat	Slow-moving side channels and pools with muddy or rocky bottoms.
Threats	Impoundments, water pollution.
Region 2	Oklahoma
Region 4	Arkansas

Description

The Ouachita rock-pocketbook is a medium-sized freshwater mussel up to 10 centimeters (3.9 in) long. The shell exterior is chestnut brown to black and has a silky texture. This species is also known as *Arcidens wheeleri* and by the alternate common name Wheeler's pearly mussel.

Habitat

This mussel species is usually found on muddy or rocky bottoms in side channels and backwaters where there is little or no current. Freshwater mussels feed by filtering food particles from the water. Their reproductive life cycle involves a stage when the mussel larvae attach to host fish species. For a general discussion of the freshwater mussel life cycle see the species account of the birdwing pearly mussel (*Conradilla caelata*) on page 955 of volume two of this guide.

Historic Range

The Ouachita rock-pocketbook is known from the Kiamichi River in southeastern Oklahoma and the Little River near the Oklahoma-Arkansas border. It was first described in 1912 from specimens taken from the "Old River," at Arkadelphia, Arkansas, a reference to a series of connected oxbow lakes. The Ouachita River was mentioned as another collection site. It has been recorded in the Kiamichi River near Antlers, Tuskahoma, Clayton, and Spencerville Crossing, all in Pushmataha County. The site near Spencerville Crossing has been flooded by the Hugo Reservoir. In the Little River in Arkansas, historic collections include White Cliffs, Little River County, and at the border of Little River and Sevier counties.

Current Distribution

This mussel survives in the Kiamichi River in Oklahoma and the Little River in Arkansas. The Kiamichi River holds an estimated 1,000 individuals in a section of the river between the southwestern corner of LeFlore County and Antlers in Pushmataha County. Fewer than 100 individuals are estimated to survive in a five-mile section of the Little River that flows from the Oklahoma border between Little River and Sevier counties, Arkansas. In all, the Ouachita rock-pocketbook occurs in low densities over an estimated range of 85 river miles.

Conservation and Recovery

The main factors in the decline of the Ouachita rock-pocketbook have been water pollution and the construction of reservoirs. The Ouachita River near Arkadelphia has been altered by a number of reservoirs and is now so polluted that it is unlikely that any mussel species could exist there. In the Little River, cold water discharges from Pine Creek Dam and pollution of the Rolling Fork Creek tributary has eliminated many mussel species. East of the five-mile stretch of the Little River where the mussel still occurs, the water

quality is too poor to allow the Ouachita rock-pocketbook to survive.

The main threat to many Kiamichi River Ouachita rock-pocketbook populations is the planned construction of the Tuskahoma Reservoir in Pushmataha County, Oklahoma. This would flood mussel populations and affect habitat downstream. In addition, the proposed addition of hydropower to the Sardis Reservoir on Jackfork Creek, a tributary of the Kiamichi River, would disturb the current water regime, most likely stressing downstream mussels.

Along with other native mussels, the Ouachita rock-pocketbook face a threat from the introduced Asiatic clam (*Corbicula fluminea*). This introduced species now occurs in Hugo Reservoir and is slowly moving upstream.

Additional Sources

Harris, J. L., and M. E. Gordon. 1987. *Distribution and Status of Rare and Endangered Mussels (Mollusca: Margaritiferidae, Unionidae) in Arkansas*. Arkansas Game and Fish Commission, Little Rock, Arkansas.

Mehlhop-Cifelli, P., and E. K. Miller. 1989. "Status and Distribution of *Arkansia wheeleri* Ortmann & Walker, 1912 (Syn. *Arcidens wheeleri*) in the Kiamichi River, Oklahoma." U.S. Fish and Wildlife Service, Tulsa, Oklahoma.

Contacts

Regional Office of Endangered Species
U.S. Fish and Wildlife Service
P.O. Box 1306
Albuquerque, New Mexico 87103

David Martinez
U.S. Fish and Wildlife Service
222 South Houston, Suite A
Tulsa, Oklahoma 74127

Fanshell
Cyprogenia stegaria

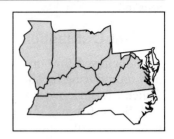

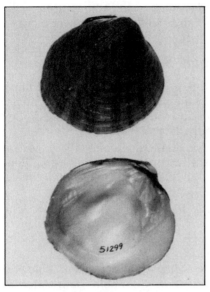

A. E. Spreitzer/OSU Museum of Zoology

Status	Endangered
Listed	June 21, 1990
Family	Unionidae (Freshwater Mussels)
Description	Mottled yellow shell with green rays and a silvery white interior.
Habitat	Gravel riffles in streams.
Threats	Impoundments, sand and gravel mining, water pollution.
Region 3	Illinois, Indiana, Ohio
Region 4	Kentucky, Tennessee
Region 5	Virginia, West Virginia

Description

The fanshell is a medium-sized freshwater mussel up to 8 centimeters (3.2 in) long. The outside of the shell has green rays on a light green or yellow surface, mottled with green; the inside is silvery white. The species is also known as *Cyprogenia irrorata*.

Habitat

The fanshell inhabits streams where it buries itself in gravel riffles. Freshwater mussels feed by filtering food particles from the water. Their reproductive life cycle involves a stage when the mussel larvae attach to the gills of host fish species. For a general discussion of the freshwater mussel life cycle see the species account of the birdwing pearly mussel (*Conradilla caelata*) on page 955 of volume two of this guide.

Historic Range

Historically the fanshell was widely distributed in the Ohio, Wabash, Cumberland, and Tennessee rivers and their larger tributaries. In all, the fanshell has been known from 26 rivers. The species has been found in Pennsylvania, Ohio, West Virginia, Illinois, Indiana, Kentucky, Tennessee, Alabama, and Virginia. The fanshell no longer occurs in Pennsylvania and Alabama.

Current Distribution

It is believed that only three rivers support reproducing fanshell populations: the Clinch River, Hancock County, Tennessee, and Scott County, Virginia; the Green River, Edminson and Hart counties, Kentucky; and the Licking River, Campbell, Kenton, and Pendleton counties, Kentucky. Researchers believe that the Green River population is the healthiest. In recent years newly dead mussels of all ages have been found at muskrat feeding places along the river.

Besides the three reproducing populations, several small populations are apparently not reproducing. Older individuals have been found in the Muskingum River in Morgan and Washington counties, Ohio; the Wabash River in White and Wabash counties, Illinois, and Posey County, Indiana; the East Fork White River, Martin County, Indiana; and the Tippecanoe River, Tippecanoe County, Indiana. In addition, the Kanawha River, Fayette County, West Virginia; Tygarts Creek, Greenup and Carter counties, Kentucky; the Cumberland River, Smith County, Tennessee; and the Tennessee River, Rhea, Meigs, and Hadin counties, Tennessee, all support small, nonreproducing populations.

Conservation and Recovery

The main factors causing the decline in the fanshell, as for all of the region's freshwater mussels, have been the alteration of stream habitat by impoundments, the direct destruction of habitat by sand and gravel mining, and the degradation of water quality caused by water pollution.

Even though it lies partly within the boundaries of Mammoth Cave National Park, the Green River has suffered from pollution runoff from oil and gas exploration and production sites. The Clinch River has been somewhat polluted by coal mining activities and in recent years suffered two widespread fish and mussel kills caused by toxic spills from a power plant.

Additional Sources

Ahlstedt, S. A. 1986. "Cumberland Mollusk Conservation Program Activity 1: Mussel Distribution Surveys." Tennessee Valley Authority, Norris, Tennessee.

Bates, J. M., and S. D. Dennis. 1985. "Mussel Resource Survey—State of Tennessee." Tennessee Wildlife Resources Agency Technical Report No. 85-3.

Starnes, L. B., and A. E. Bogan. 1988. "The Mussels (Mollusca: Bivalvia: Unionidae) of Tennessee." *American Malacological Bulletin* 5(1):19-37.

Tennessee Valley Authority. 1988. "Biological Assessment of Columbia Dam Alternatives, Duck River, Tennessee." Tennessee Valley Authority, Knoxville, Tennessee.

Warren, M. L., Jr., et al. 1986. "Endangered, Threatened and Rare Plants and Animals of Kentucky." *Transactions of the Kentucky Academy of Science* 47(3-4):83-98.

Contacts

Regional Office of Endangered Species
U. S. Fish and Wildlife Service
Richard B. Russell Federal Building
75 Spring Street, S.W.
Atlanta, Georgia 30303

Richard G. Biggins
Asheville Field Office
U.S. Fish and Wildlife Service
330 Ridgefield Court
Asheville, North Carolina 28806

Purple Cat's Paw
Pearly Mussel
Epioblasma obliquata

A. E. Spreitzer/OSU Museum of Zoology

Status	Endangered
Listed	July 10, 1990
Family	Unionidae
	(Freshwater Mussel)
Description	Medium-sized, greenish yellow shell, marked by wavy green lines; purple interior.
Habitat	Gravel or sand river bottoms.
Threats	Lack of reproduction, water pollution, dredging.
Region 4	Kentucky, Tennessee

Description

The purple cat's paw pearly mussel has a medium-sized shell with a smooth, shiny, greenish yellow surface and faint, wavy, green lines. The interior is purple. The species is also known as *Dysnomia obliquata obliquata* and *Epioblasma sulcata sulcata*.

The northern subspecies, the white cat's paw pearly mussel (*Epioblasma sulcata delicata* or *Dysnomia sulcata delicata*), was federally listed as Endangered on June 14, 1976.

Habitat

This species inhabits silt-free, gravelly river bottoms. Freshwater mussels feed by filtering food particles from the water. Their reproductive life cycle involves a stage when the mussel larvae attach to the gills of host fish species.

For a general discussion of the freshwater mussel life cycle see the species account of the birdwing pearly mussel (*Conradilla caelata*) on page 955 of volume two of this guide.

Historic Range

The purple cat's paw pearly mussel was once found throughout the Ohio, Cumberland, and Tennessee river systems in Ohio, Illinois, Indiana, Kentucky, Tennessee, and Alabama.

Current Distribution

Today, small and apparently nonreproducing populations of the purple cat's paw pearly mussel occur in the Cumberland River, Smith County, Tennessee, and the Green River, Warren and Butler counties, Kentucky. In the Green River a single, freshly dead purple cat's paw was found in 1988. Prior to that, the species was last collected there in 1971.

Conservation and Recovery

The decline of the purple cat's paw pearly mussel is attributed to the conversion of large sections of its river habitat to a series of large impoundments. This vastly reduced the gravel and sand habitat and most likely affected the distribution of the mussel's fish host.

Since it is probable that all individuals in the known populations are beyond reproductive age, the species will soon be extinct, unless unknown reproducing populations exist. Surviving purple cat's paw pearly mussels in the Green River are threatened by water pollution from oil and gas production. In the Cumberland River the species is threatened by gravel dredging and channel maintenance.

Additional Sources

Bates, J. M., and S. D. Dennis. 1985. "Mussel Resource Survey—State of Tennessee." Ten-nessee Wildlife Resources Agency Technical Report No. 85-3.

Parmalee, P. W., W. E. Klippel, and A. E. Bogan. 1980. "Notes on the Prehistoric and Present Status of Naiad Fauna of the Middle Cumberland River, Smith County, Tennessee." *The Nautilus* 94(3):93-105.

Sickel, James B. 1985. "Biological Assessment of the Freshwater Mussels in the Kentucky Dam Tailwaters of the Tennessee River." Kentucky Division of Water, Frankfort, Kentucky.

Contacts

Regional Office of Endangered Species
U. S. Fish and Wildlife Service
Richard B. Russell Federal Building
75 Spring Street, S.W.
Atlanta, Georgia 30303

Richard G. Biggins
Asheville Field Office
U.S. Fish and Wildlife Service
330 Ridgefield Court
Asheville, North Carolina 28806

Cracking Pearly Mussel
Hemistena lata

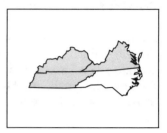

A. E. Spreitzer/OSU Museum of Zoology   *Color Plate C-8*

Status	Endangered
Listed	September 23, 1989
Family	Unionidae (Freshwater Mussel)
Description	Greenish brown to brown elongated shell, with dark green rays and a pale blue to purple interior.
Habitat	Riffles on medium-sized streams.
Threats	Dam construction, water pollution.
Region 4	Kentucky, Tennessee
Region 5	Virginia

Description

The cracking pearly mussel is medium-sized, with a thin, elongated shell. The outer surface is greenish brown to brown, usually with broken, dark green rays. The interior is pale blue to purple. The species has also been known as *Lastena lata*.

Habitat

The cracking pearly mussel inhabits medium-sized streams where it buries itself in gravel riffles. Freshwater mussels feed by filtering food particles from the water. Their reproductive life cycle involves a stage when the mussel larvae attach to the gills of host fish species. For a general discussion of the freshwater mussel life cycle see the species account of the birdwing pearly mussel (*Conradilla caelata*) on page 955 of volume two of this guide.

Historic Range

The cracking pearly mussel was once widely distributed in the Ohio, Cumberland, and Tennessee river systems. In the Ohio River Basin it was found from Ohio downstream to Illinois. In Indiana and Illinois it was known from the White, Wabash, and Tippecanoe rivers. In Kentucky the species inhabited the upper Cumberland, Big South Fork, Green, and Kentucky rivers. In Tennessee, it was known from the Tennessee, Cumberland, Powell, Clinch, Holston, Elk, Duck, and Buffalo rivers. It was found in Virginia in the Powell, Clinch, and Holston rivers and in Alabama in the Tennessee River.

Current Distribution

Only three populations of the cracking pearly mussel are known to survive: in the Clinch River, Hancock County, Tennessee, and Scott County, Virginia; in the Powell River, Hancock County, Tennessee, and Lee County, Virginia; and in the Elk River, Lincoln County, Tennessee. It is possible that small populations persist in the Green River, Hart and Edmonson counties, Kentucky, as well as in the Tennessee River below Pickwick Dam.

In 1979, the Tennessee Valley Authority (TVA) sampled 78 sites over almost 100 miles of the Powell River and found the cracking pearly mussel at only three sites. A 1980 survey of 108 sites over 172 miles of the Elk River found the species at only two sites.

The largest population of this mussel is in the Clinch River. A TVA survey of 141 sites over 174 miles in 1978 and 1983 found the species at 16 sites.

No live cracking pearly mussels have been taken from the Green or Tennessee rivers in recent years, but there remains suitable habitat in each river and shells have been found, leading researchers to believe that small populations persist.

Conservation and Recovery

The cracking pearly mussel has declined over its historic range because of the alteration and pollution of its streambed habitat. The extensive series of dams constructed in the area by TVA has altered much of the original aquatic environment inhabited by freshwater mussels. The dam reservoirs convert stream environments into lakes, producing a corresponding change in the aquatic life. In addition, the water quality of the Powell River and, to a lesser extent, the Clinch River has been degraded by pollution associated with coal mining. In the past, the Clinch River has suffered large fish and mussel kills from toxic discharges from a power plant. Oil and gas production, cold water discharges from reservoirs, channel maintenance, and gravel dredging are other activities that have contributed to the decline of freshwater mussels.

Additional Sources

Ahlstedt, S. A. 1986. "Cumberland Mollusk Conservation Program Activity 1: Mussel Distribution Surveys." Tennessee Valley Authority, Norris, Tennessee.

Ahlstedt, S. A., and J. J. Jenkinson. 1987. "A Mussel Die-off in the Powell River, Virginia and Tennessee, in 1983." In *Proceedings of the Workshop on Die-offs of Freshwater Mussels in the United States, June 23-25, 1986,* edited by Richard Neves. Davenport, Iowa.

Bates, J. M., and S. D. Dennis. 1985. "Mussel Resource Survey—State of Tennessee." Tennessee Wildlife Resources Agency Technical Report No. 85-3.

Contacts

Regional Office of Endangered Species
U. S. Fish and Wildlife Service
Richard B. Russell Federal Building
75 Spring Street, S.W.
Atlanta, Georgia 30303

Richard G. Biggins
Asheville Field Office
U.S. Fish and Wildlife Service
330 Ridgefield Court
Asheville, North Carolina 28806

Arkansas Fatmucket

Lampsilis powelli

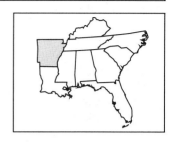

A. E. Spreitzer/OSU Museum of Zoology

Status	Threatened
Listed	April 5, 1990
Family	Unionidae (Freshwater Mussel)
Description	Medium-sized, olive-brown, elliptical shell with a pearly, bluish white interior.
Habitat	Deep pools and backwaters with sand or gravel bottoms.
Threats	Impoundments, channel alteration, water pollution.
Region 4	Arkansas

Description

The Arkansas fatmucket is a medium-sized freshwater mussel, whose shell occasionally reaches 10 centimeters (3.9 in) in length. The exterior is shiny olive-brown and lacks rays; the interior is pearly, bluish white. It has also been known as *Unio powelli,* and *Actinonaias ligamentina.*

Habitat

The Arkansas fatmucket is found in deep pools or backwater areas with sand or gravel bottoms. It requires a sufficient current to prevent silt and detritus buildup on the bottom. It is not generally found in impoundments or riffle areas.

Freshwater mussels feed by filtering food particles from the water. Their reproductive life cycle involves a stage when the mussel larvae attach to the gills of host fish species. For a general discussion of the freshwater mussel life cycle see the species account of the birdwing pearly mussel (*Conradilla caelata*) on page 955 of volume two of this guide.

Historic Range

The historic range of the Arkansas fatmucket cannot be known with certainty because of the lack of collection records. A likely range, however, can be described, based upon the mussel's preferred habitat and the alterations of the river systems where it is now found. The species likely occurred in Arkansas in the Caddo River, from Norman downstream to the Ouachita River, including the lower reach of the South Fork Caddo River. It probably was found in the Ouachita River from Malvern upstream to its current range and the entire length of the South Fork Ouachita River. It most likely occurred in all four forks and the main stem of the Saline River drainage, from the fall line upstream.

Current Distribution

The Arkansas fatmucket survives in parts of the Ouachita, Saline, and Caddo river systems. In the Ouachita system it is found in the Ouachita River upstream of Lake Ouachita in Montgomery and Polk counties, and in the South Fork Ouachita River upstream of Lake Ouachita in Montgomery County. In the Saline River system, the mussel occurs in the Alum, Middle, and North forks and in the Saline River from its formation downstream to about the fall line. The species is known from three locations in the Caddo River.

Conservation and Recovery

The main causes of the decline of the Arkansas fatmucket have been construction of dams, alteration of channels, gravel dredging, and decline in water quality. On the Ouachita River dams have created Lake Ouachita, Lake Hamilton, and Lake Catherine. The DeGray Reservoir has been constructed on the Caddo River. The Army Corps of Engineers has studied the feasibility of constructing dams on the Saline River near Benton. The Soil Conservation Service is in the process of constructing three dams on the South Fork Ouachita River. Even if these dams do not directly destroy Arkansas fatmucket populations, the resulting change in water flows often has harmful effects on mussels.

Channel alterations of the South Fork Ouachita River made during highway repairs in the mid-1980s has increased siltation at the site of one Arkansas fatmucket population. Such channel alteration is common at highway crossings and will continue to threaten local mussel populations.

Gravel dredging and degradation of water quality are other factors that affect the Arkansas fatmucket. Dredging destroys the species' habitat and contributes to increased siltation. The region's water quality has been degraded by the runoff from mining operations and improperly treated sewage. In addition, feed lot runoff, timber harvesting, road construction, and fertilization contribute to stream pollution.

Additional Source

Lawson, E. R. 1985. "Effects of Forest Practices on Water Quality in the Ozark-Ouachita Highlands." In *Proceedings in Forestry and Water Quality: A Mid-South Symposium*, edited by B. G. Blackmon. University of Arkansas, Monticello.

Contacts

Regional Office of Endangered Species
U. S. Fish and Wildlife Service
Richard B. Russell Federal Building
75 Spring Street, S.W.
Atlanta, Georgia 30303

James Stewart
Jackson Field Office
U.S. Fish and Wildlife Service
6578 Dogwood View Parkway, Suite A
Jackson, Mississippi 39213

Ring Pink Mussel
Obovaria retusa

A. E. Spreitzer/OSU Museum of Zoology

Status	Endangered
Listed	September 29, 1989
Family	Unionidae
	(Freshwater Mussel)
Description	Medium to large, yellow-green to brown shell with a salmon to purple interior.
Habitat	Gravel or sand river bottoms.
Threats	Lack of reproduction, water pollution, dredging.
Region 4	Kentucky, Tennessee

Description

The ring pink mussel has a medium to large, yellow-green to brown shell. The inside is salmon to deep purple, with a white border. The species is also known as the golf stick pearly mussel.

Habitat

The ring pink inhabits the silt-free gravelly bottoms of large rivers. Freshwater mussels feed by filtering food particles from the water. Their reproductive life cycle involves a stage when the mussel larvae attach to the gills of host fish species. For a general discussion of the freshwater mussel life cycle see the species account of the birdwing pearly mussel (*Conradilla caelata*) on page 955 of volume two of this guide.

Historic Range

The ring pink mussel was once found in the Ohio River and its large tributaries in Pennsylvania, West Virginia, Ohio, Indiana, Illinois, Kentucky, Tennessee, and Alabama.

Current Distribution

Today, small, apparently nonreproducing populations of the ring pink mussel occur in two stretches of the Tennessee River (Livingston, Marshall, and McCracken counties, Kentucky, and Hardin County, Tennessee). Nonreproducing populations are also found in the Cumberland River, Wilson, Trousdale, and Smith counties, Tennessee, and the Green River, Hart and Edmonson counties, Kentucky.

Conservation and Recovery

The decline of the ring pink mussel is attributed to the conversion of large sections of its riverine habitat to a series of large impoundments. This vastly reduced the gravel and sand habitat and most likely affected the distribution of the mussel's fish host.

Since it is probable that all individuals in the known populations are beyond reproductive age, the species will soon be extinct if no unknown, reproducing populations exist. Surviving ring pink mussel in the Green River are threatened by water pollution from oil and gas production. In the Cumberland and Tennessee rivers the species is threatened by gravel dredging and channel maintenance.

Additional Sources

Bates, J. M., and S. D. Dennis. 1985. "Mussel Resource Survey—State of Tennessee." Tennessee Wildlife Resources Agency Technical Report No. 85-3.

Parmalee, P. W., W. E. Klippel, and A. E. Bogan. 1980. "A Relic Population of *Obovaria retusa* in the Middle Cumberland River, Tennessee." *The Nautilus* 96(1): 30-32.

Sickel, James B. 1985. "Biological Assessment of the Freshwater Mussels in the Kentucky Dam Tailwaters of the Tennessee River." Kentucky Division of Water, Frankfort, Kentucky.

Contacts

Regional Office of Endangered Species
U. S. Fish and Wildlife Service
Richard B. Russell Federal Building
75 Spring Street, S.W.
Atlanta, Georgia 30303

Richard G. Biggins
Asheville Field Office
U.S. Fish and Wildlife Service
330 Ridgefield Court
Asheville, North Carolina 28806

Cumberland Pigtoe
Pleurobema gibberum

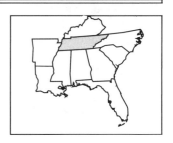

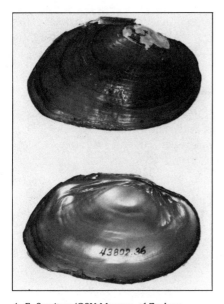

A. E. Spreitzer/OSU Museum of Zoology

Status . . . . Endangered
Listed . . . . May 7, 1991
Family . . . . Unionidae
(Freshwater Mussel)
Description . . . . . . Small, triangular, yellowish brown to mahogany shell with a peach to orange interior.
Habitat . . . . Gravel or sand stream bottoms.
Threats . . . . Water pollution.
Region 4 . . . . Tennessee

Description

The Cumberland pigtoe is a small freshwater mussel, rarely exceeding 6 centimeters (2.3 in) in length. The heavy triangular shell is yellowish brown on young mussels, turning dark mahogany with age. The shell interior is peach to orange.

Habitat

Like many other freshwater mussels, the Cumberland pigtoe prefers stream riffle areas of gravel or sand (occasionally mud or cobble). Freshwater mussels feed by filtering food particles from the water. Their reproductive life cycle involves a stage when the mussel larvae attach themselves to the gills of host fish species. For a general discussion of the freshwater mussel life cycle see the species account of the birdwing pearly mussel (*Conradilla caelata*) on page 955 of volume two of this guide.

Historic Range

The Cumberland pigtoe is known only from the Caney Fork River system in Tennessee. Historical records indicate that the mussel has been collected from five Caney Fork tributaries, all above the Great Falls Reservoir, which was constructed in the 1910s. Historic mussel collection records are very limited and given the amount of suitable habitat that was flooded by the impoundment, it is very likely that the Cumberland pigtoe was more widely distributed.

Current Distribution

At present there are four known populations of the Cumberland pigtoe on Caney Fork tributaries: Barren Fork (Warren County), Calfkiller River (White County), Cane Creek (Van Buren County), and Collins River (Warren and Grundy counties). A 1990 survery of the river system failed to find Cumberland pigtoe mussels in the main stem of Caney Fork or any other tributaries.

Conservation and Recovery

Decline of the Cumberland pigtoe mussel most likely began with the construction of the Great Falls Reservoir in the 1910s, which flooded a large portion of the mussel's preferred habitat. The species' distribution has declined over the years as a result of water pollution associated with coal mining, poor land use practices, and waster discharge.

Although no projects with federal involvement that would affect surviving Cumberland pigtoe populations are currently being planned, federal listing of the species ensures that any actions that might affect the species would face close examination. Such actions would include the construction of reservoirs, or hydroelectric and wastewater facilities, channel maintenance or stream alterations.

Additional Sources

Anderson, R. M. 1990. "Status Survey of the Cumberland Pigtoe Pearly Mussel, *Pleurobema gibberum*." Tennessee Cooperative Fishery Research Unit, Tennessee Techno-
logical University, Cookeville, Tennessee. U.S. Fish and Wildlife Service, Asheville, North Carolina.

Gordon, M. E., and J. B. Layzer. 1989. "Mussels (Bivalvia: Unionidae) of the Cumberland River: Review of Life Histories and Ecological Relationships." U.S. Fish and Wildlife Service Biological Report 89(15).

Contacts

Regional Office of Endangered Species
U. S. Fish and Wildlife Service
Richard B. Russell Federal Building
75 Spring Street, S.W.
Atlanta, Georgia 30303

Richard G. Biggins
Asheville Field Office
U.S. Fish and Wildlife Service
100 Otis St., Room 224
Asheville, North Carolina 28801

Inflated Heelsplitter
Potamilus inflatus

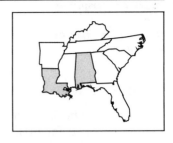

A. E. Spreitzer/OSU Museum of Zoology

Status	Threatened
Listed	September 28, 1990
Family	Unionidae (Freshwater Mussel)
Description	Large, thin, oval, brown to black shell with a pink to purple interior.
Habitat	Soft, stable stream bottoms with slow to moderate currents.
Threats	Impoundments, gravel dredging, channel maintenance.
Region 4	Alabama, Louisiana

Description

The inflated heelsplitter is a medium to large freshwater mussel that reaches a shell length of 14 centimeters (5.5 in). The thin, oval shell is brown to black and, in young individuals, often has green rays. The interior is pink to purple. It was first described as *Symphynota inflata* in 1831. Since its discovery there has been disagreement over the correct genus. It has been variously placed in *Unio, Lampsilis, Metaptera, Margaita, Margaron,* and *Proptera.* It is also widely known as the Alabama heelsplitter.

Habitat

This mussel species prefers soft, stable stream bottoms with slow or moderate currents. It has been found in sand, mud, silt, and sandy gravel, usually on the protected side of bars and often in depths over 6.7 meters (20 ft).

Freshwater mussels feed by filtering food particles from the water. Their reproductive life cycle involves a stage when the mussel larvae attach to the gills of host fish species. For a general discussion of the freshwater mussel life cycle see the species account of the birdwing pearly mussel

(*Conradilla caelata*) on page 955 of volume two of this guide.

Historic Range

The inflated heelsplitter has been found in the Amite and Tangipahoa rivers in Louisiana; in the Pearl River in Mississippi; and in the Tombigbee, Black Warrior, Alabama, and Coosa rivers in Alabama.

Current Distribution

This mussel species is known to survive in the Amite River in Louisiana and in the Black Warrior and Tombigbee rivers in Alabama. In the Black Warrior River it occurs at a single site below Selden Dam, near Eutaw, Alabama. In a 1989 survey two freshly dead mussels were found there. In the Tombigbee River the inflated heelsplitter survives in at least two locations: Gainesville Bendway and in a 12-mile area downstream of Coffeeville Dam.

Conservation and Recovery

The inflated heelsplitter is threatened by gravel dredging, impoundments, and channel maintenance activities. The Tombigbee River has been extensively modified by the construction of the Tennessee-Tombigbee Waterway, which eliminated a great deal of mussel habitat. The population below Coffeeville Dam is threatened by the frequent dredging required to maintain the navigation channel. Spoil is deposited on bars along the channel. From there it washes onto mussel habitat, suffocating mussels.

In the Amite River, the species is threatened by gravel mining and a proposed reservoir. A recent study estimated that since 1976, 30 percent of the range of the inflated heelsplitter on the Amite River has been lost to gravel mining. The Army Corps of Engineers is currently studying flood control proposals for the river. One proposal calls for the construction of a reservoir near Darlington, upstream of inflated heelsplitter habitat. Although this impoundment would not directly affect the species, cold water releases from the dam would probably have a negative effect on mussels. Interrupted flows could strand mussel populations on dry bars and reduce the current's ability to flush sediment. An alternative proposal to widen and channelize the river would likely eliminate the species entirely in the Amite River.

Additional Sources

Hartfield, P. 1988. "Status Survey of the Alabama Heelsplitter Mussel, *Potamilus inflatus* (Lea, 1831)." U.S. Fish and Wildlife Service.

———. 1989. "Mussel Survey of the Amite River, Louisiana." Espy Huston and Associates, Austin, Texas.

U.S. Army Corps of Engineers. 1987. "Final Supplement to the Final Environmental Impact Statement: Black Warrior and Tombigbee Rivers, Alabama (Maintenance)." U.S. Army Corps of Engineers, Mobile, Alabama.

Contacts

Regional Office of Endangered Species
U. S. Fish and Wildlife Service
Richard B. Russell Federal Building
75 Spring Street, S.W.
Atlanta, Georgia 30303

James H. Stewart
Jackson Field Office
U.S. Fish and Wildlife Service
6578 Dogwood View Parkway, Suite A
Jackson, Mississippi 39213

Winged Mapleleaf
Quadrula fragosa

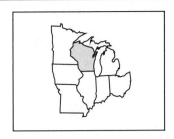

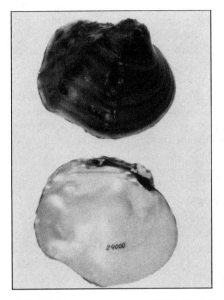

A. E. Spreitzer
OSU Museum of Zoology

Color Plate C-8

Status	Endangered
Listed	June 20, 1991
Family	Unionidae (Freshwater Mussel)
Description	Similar to the common mapleleaf, but with a more inflated shell.
Habitat	Riffle areas of large, clear-water streams.
Threats	Low numbers, reproductive failure.
Region 3	Wisconsin

Description

The winged mapleleaf is a freshwater mussel closely related to the mapleleaf, a common mussel species in eastern North America. It can be distinguished by its more inflated shell, which is more quadrate in outline, and the beaks on the shell, which are turned forward and more elevated.

Habitat

This species occupies gravel bars in the shallow, clear water of large rivers. Freshwater mussels feed by filtering food particles from the water. Their reproductive life cycle involves a stage when the mussel lar-

vae attach to the gills of host fish species. For a general discussion of the freshwater mussel life cycle see the species account of the birdwing pearly mussel (*Conradilla caelata*) on page 955 of volume two of this guide.

Historic Range

The winged mapleleaf has been found in four river systems in eleven states: the Mississippi, Tennessee, Ohio, and Cumberland systems in Ohio, Indiana, Missouri, Tennessee, Kansas, Nebraska, Iowa, Illinois, Wisconsin, Oklahoma, and Kentucky. Collections of the winged mapleleaf were not unusual until about 1920, after which they became rare and many experts considered the species extinct.

Current Distribution

Today a single, small population of the winged mapleleaf survives in the St. Croix River along the border of Minnesota and Wisconsin. This population is restricted to less than five miles of river within a national scenic riverway administered by the National Park Service.

The population density at this one remaining site was one individual per 52 square meters, constituting less than 0.02 percent of the mussel community. This community consists of 32 species of mussels, including rare species such as the federally Endangered Higgins' eye (*Lampsilis higginsi*) and the spectacle case (*Cumberlandia monodonta*) and salamander mussel (*Simpsonaias ambigua*), which are candidates for federal listing.

Conservation and Recovery

The preferred habitat of the winged mapleleaf—riffles or gravel bars in large clearwater streams—has been largely eliminated by impoundment, channelization, and sedimentation.

The sole surviving population is at extreme risk because of an apparent reproductive failure. During surveys in 1988 and 1989, researchers failed to find any individuals less than four years old or to find females carrying eggs. Related species that were collected during the survey included individuals of all age classes. If this population is truly failing to reproduce, its extinction is certain.

Additional Sources

Doolittle, Thomas C. J. 1988. "Distribution and Relative Abundance of Freshwater Mussels in the Saint Croix National Scenic Riverway." Cable Natural History Museum, Sigurd Olson Environmental Institute, Ashland, Wisconsin.

Havlik, M. E. and L. L. Marking. 1980. "A Quantitative Analysis of Naiad Mollusks from the Prairie du Chien, Wisconsin, Wisconsin Dredge Material Site on the Mississippi River." *Bulletin of the American Malacological Union.* 1977:9-12.

Contacts

James M. Engel
U.S. Fish and Wildlife Service
Federal Building, Fort Snelling
Twin Cities, Minnesota 55111

Squirrel Chimney Cave Shrimp

Palaemonetes cummingi

Chip Clark   Kentucky cave shrimp (*Palaemonias ganteri*)

Status	Threatened
Listed	June 21, 1990
Family	Palaemonidae
Description	Transparent shrimp with reduced eyes.
Habitat	Flooded cave.
Food	Plant matter, insects, algae.
Reproduction	Females probably lay about 20 eggs.
Threats	Water pollution.
Region 4	Florida

Description

The Squirrel Chimney cave shrimp is transparent and measures about 3 centimeters (1.2 in) in length. The body and eyes are without pigment and the eyes are smaller than surface dwelling species. It is also known by the common name Florida cave shrimp. A photograph of this species could not be located, the similar Kentucky cave shrimp (*Palaemonias ganteri*) is pictured above.

Behavior

Little is known of the reproductive cycle or diet of this species, although it is assumed to be similar to that of other cave-dwelling shrimp. The Endangered Kentucky cave shrimp (*Palaemonias ganteri*) feeds on plant detritus, insects, algae, and fungi. It breeds year round, with females producing from 16 to 24 eggs.

Habitat

This cave shrimp inhabits a single sinkhole and flooded cave system near Gainesville, Florida. The 30-meter (100-ft) deep system supports one of the richest cave invertebrate faunas in the United States, including McLane's cave crayfish (*Troglocambarus maclanei*), the light-fleeing crayfish (*Procambarus lucifugus*), the pallid cave crayfish (*Procambarus pallidus*), and Hobbs' cave ambhipod (*Crangonyx hobbsi*).

Historic Range

The Squirrel Chimney cave shrimp was described in 1954, after its discovery in Squirrel Chimney, a sinkhole in Alachua County, Florida, on the outskirts of Gainesville.

Current Distribution

This cave shrimp has not been found in any other cave system. No population estimates are available.

Conservation and Recovery

Because of the limited range of the Squirrel Chimney cave shrimp and the fragile nature of its habitat, any change in the sinkhole or the underlying aquifer could be devastating to the species and perhaps lead to its extinction.

The surrounding land consists of oak hammock and pine plantation. The area, situated on the outskirts of Gainesville, is undergoing residential development. The current owners have indicated a willingness to offer The Nature Conservancy the first option on the land surrounding the sinkhole if they decide to sell. However, this will not prevent the development of nearby areas. The increased erosion and pollution from septic tanks, pesticides, and herbicides resulting from such development could threaten the fragile cave fauna.

Construction of a proposed business/industrial park near the cave could pose a danger to this shrimp and other rare cave species. Alachua County has approved the development at a site about six miles from Squirrel Chimney. Some scientists fear that the system of caves and underground streams that make up the aquifer could become contaminated by industrial pollution. The county development plan is awaiting state approval. Meanwhile, a local citizen's group has filed a complaint with the county government, the first step in trying to block the development in the courts.

In 1983 Squirrel Chimney was proposed for recognition as a National Natural Landmark. The National Park Service has not yet taken action on this proposal.

Additional Sources

Chace, F. A., Jr. 1954. "Two New Subterranean Shrimp (Decapoda: Caridea) from Florida and the West Indies, with a Revised Key to the American Species." *Journal of the Washington Academy of Sciences* 44: 318-324.

Mohr, C. E., and T. L. Poulson. 1966. *Life of the Cave.* McGraw-Hill, New York.

Contacts

Regional Office of Endangered Species
U. S. Fish and Wildlife Service
Richard B. Russell Federal Building
75 Spring Street, S.W.
Atlanta, Georgia 30303

David J. Wesley
U.S. Fish and Wildlife Service
Jacksonville Field Office
3100 University Boulevard, South, Suite 120
Jacksonville, Florida 32216

Kanab Ambersnail
Oxyloma haydeni ssp. *kanabensis*

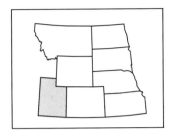

Blaine Lunceford/Bureau of Land Management

Status	Endangered
Listed	August 8, 1991
Family	Succineidae (Land Snail)
Description	Small snail with an amber whirled shell.
Habitat	Perennially wet soils in marshes and meadows.
Threats	Destruction of habitat.
Region 6	Utah

Description

The Kanab ambersnail is a small terrestrial snail about 14 to 19 millimeters (0.5 to 0.8 in) long. The mottled, grayish to yellowish amber shell has three or four whorls in an elongated spire and a broad, expanded aperture. The snail's eyes are borne on the ends of long stalks; the tentacles are small protuberances at the base of the eyestalks.

This species has also been known as *Succinea hawkinsi*. Some specialists believe that the current taxonomic status of the snail should be reevaluated to determine whether it deserves classification as a full species.

Behavior

Almost nothing is known about the specific behavior of the Kanab ambersnail. Other members of the genus feed on microscopic plants and lay about a dozen jelly-like eggs at the base of plants. The eggs hatch after two or three weeks. Young snails reach full size after about two years, and die soon after.

Habitat

The Kanab ambersnail lives in marshes which are constantly watered by springs and seeps at the base of sandstone cliffs. It is found in close association with cattail

(*Typha domingensis*) which it uses as vegetative cover and protection from predation by birds. It is always associated with perennially wet soils and has never been found in drier habitats, or even in places which are attractive to other land snails, such as underneath logs.

Historic Range

This snail species was first collected in 1909 from an area known as "The Greens," on Kanab Wash, six miles above Kanab, Utah. It has only been found at two locations in Kane County in extreme southern Utah.

Current Distribution

The two known populations of the Kanab ambersnail are just over a mile apart on privately owned land. A colony inhabiting a marsh beneath a cliff in Kanab Creek Canyon has almost vanished. Although once common at this site, the snail population has suffered a dramatic crash. An intensive search in 1990 found only three individuals. The wetland habitat at this site was recently altered by draining much of the water to provide for domestic livestock.

The only remaining large population occurs in marshes in Three Lakes Canyon, a tributary drainage of Kanab Creek, about six miles northwest of Kanab. In June 1990, the Kanab ambersnail population was estimated at 100,000. However, soon afterward, the landowner began modifying the marshes in preparation for development. This resulted in the destruction of a portion of the snail population.

Conservation and Recovery

The possible imminent destruction of the only remaining substantial Kanab ambersnail population moved the Fish and Wild-

life Service (FWS) to list the snail as Endangered on an emergency basis on August 8, 1991. This emergency determination expires on April 3, 1992. During this eight-month period FWS will follow its normal process in proposing the species for listing.

Although private landowners had indicated a willingness to protect the snail and negotiate the sale of the property to the federal government or The Nature Conservancy, they were still considering development of the property as a retirement home or recreational vehicle park and campground. The fact that development of the property could happen before a regular listing proposal could be finalized prompted the emergency listing. Discussions are continuing between the landowners and The Nature Conservancy for sale of the property.

Additional Sources

Clarke, A. H. 1991. "Status Survey of Selected Land and Freshwater Gastropods in Utah." U.S. Fish and Wildlife Service, Denver.

Pilsbry, H. A. 1948. *Land Mollusca of North America*. The Academy of Natural Science of Philadelphia Monographs, Philadelphia.

Contacts

Regional Office of Endangered Species
U.S. Fish and Wildlife Service
P.O. Box 25486
Denver Federal Center
Denver, Colorado 80225

Clark D. Johnson
U.S. Fish and Wildlife Service
2078 Administration Building
1745 West 1700 South
Salt Lake City, Utah 84104

Socorro Springsnail
Pyrgulopsis neomexicana

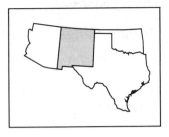

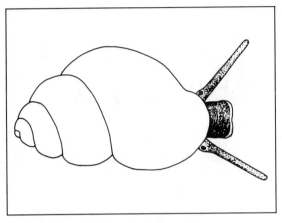

New Mexico Bureau of Mines & Mineral Resources

Status	Endangered
Listed	September 30, 1991
Family	Hydrobilidae (Aquatic Snail)
Description	Minute aquatic snail with an elongated, tan spiral shell.
Habitat	Thermal spring.
Food	Algae and other organic detritus.
Reproduction	Eggs laid in spring and summer.
Threats	Limited range, destruction of habitat.
Region 2	New Mexico

Description

The Socorro springsnail is a minute aquatic snail with an elongated, light tan spiral shell that measures only 2.5 millimeters (0.1 in) in length. Females are larger than males. The body and head are dark gray to black; the tentacles are dark at the base, lightening to pale gray at the tips. Snails of this family breathe through gills rather than lungs and have a lidlike structure on the foot called the operculum. *Pyrgulopsis* species are distinguished by characteristics of the structure of the male sexual organ. This snail has also been known as *Amnicola neomexicana* and *Fontelicella neomexicana*.

Behavior

The Socorro springsnail feeds on algae and elements of the organic film on the water. It lays eggs during the spring and summer.

Habitat

This snail species inhabits slowly flowing water near a thermal spring source. It is found on stones, among aquatic vegetation, and in the upper layer of organic muck on the bottom.

Historic Range

The species was first described in 1916 from specimens taken from thermal springs west of Socorro (Socorro County), New Mexico. It no longer occurs in these springs.

Current Distribution

The Socorro springsnail survives in a single spring in Socorro County. The main spring source has been impounded and only a single small free-flowing source remains. The source pool measures less than a square meter in area; an outflow stream flows about 2.5 meters (8 ft) to an irrigation ditch. The species inhabits the source pool and the outflow stream. The total population has been estimated at 5,000 individuals.

Conservation and Recovery

The greatest threat to the Socorro springsnail is its extremely limited distribution. Inhabiting a single small spring, the species is in danger of extinction through any change in its habitat. Pumping of the source pool, pollution, the introduction of predatory species, or vandalism are threats to the species. The spring is on private land and the owners did not object to the listing of the Socorro springsnail as Endangered.

Additional Sources

Hershler, R. and F. G. Thompson. 1987. "North American Hydrobilidae (Gastropoda: Rissoacea): Redescription and Systematic Relationships of *Tryonia* Stimpson, 1865 and *Pyrgulopsis* Call and Pilsbry, 1886." *Nautilus* 101(1):25-32.

New Mexico Department of Game and Fish. 1985. *Handbook of Species Endangered in New Mexico.* Santa Fe, New Mexico.

Taylor, D. W. 1987. *Fresh Water Mollusks from New Mexico and Vicinity.* Bulletin 116. New Mexico Bureau of Mines and Mineral Resources. Socorro, New Mexico.

Taylor, D. W. 1983. "Report to the State of New Mexico on a Status Investigation of Mollusca in New Mexico." New Mexico Department of Game and Fish, Santa Fe, New Mexico.

Contacts

Regional Office of Endangered Species
U.S. Fish and Wildlife Service
P.O. Box 1306
Albuquerque, New Mexico 87103

Jerry Burton
U.S. Fish and Wildlife Service
3530 Pan American Highway NE, Suite D
Albuquerque, New mexico 87107

Alamosa Springsnail

Tryonia alamosae

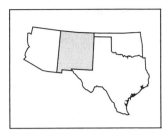

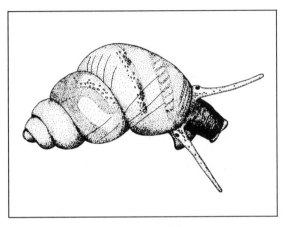

New Mexico Bureau of Mines & Mineral Resources

Status	Endangered
Listed	September 30, 1991
Family	Hydrobildae (Aquatic Snail)
Description	Minute aquatic snail with a translucent, spiral shell.
Habitat	Thermal springs.
Food	Algae and organic detritus.
Reproduction	Eggs hatch within the female's body.
Threats	Limited distribution, disruption of spring flow.
Region 2	New Mexico

Description

The Alamosa springsnail is a minute aquatic snail with a thin, translucent spiral shell up to 3.0 millimeters (0.1 in) in length. Females are about 50 percent larger than males. The body varies from black to gray and the tentacles are speckled with dark spots. This species breathes by means of gills rather than lungs.

Behavior

This snail feeds on algae and organic detritus. The eggs develop within the body of the female, and reproduction does not appear to be seasonal.

Habitat

This springsnail inhabits the slow-flowing currents of thermal springs. It is found on stones and submerged vegetation, but is absent from swift flowing water and muddy bottoms.

Historic Range

The Alamosa springsnail was discovered in 1979 in Ojo Caliente (Socorro County), one of the largest thermal springs in New Mexico.

Current Distribution

It is currently known only from Ojo Caliente and a nearby system of smaller thermal springs. Although no population estimates have been made, the snail is considered abundant on gravel and vegetation in the shallow, slow-moving portions of the spring outflows.

Conservation and Recovery

The greatest threat to the Alamosa springsnail is its extremely limited distribution. Found in only a few thermal spring outflows, the species could face extinction through any change in its aquatic habitat. Impounding of the springs, pollution, the introduction of predatory species, or vandalism are ever-present threats to the species.

These thermal spring is on private land and the owners did not object to the listing of the Alamosa springsnail as Endangered. However, several of the smaller springs have been dug and impounded in the past. At present the spring water flows through a canyon and then is diverted for irrigation use and to supply water to villages downstream. Future development of the springs to increase the water supply could threaten the Alamosa springsnail.

Additional Sources

Hershler, R. and F. G. Thompson. 1987. "North American Hydrobilidae (Gastropoda: Rissoacea): Redescription and Systematic Relationships of *Tryonia* Stimpson, 1865 and *Pyrgulopsis* Call and Pilsbry, 1886." *Nautilus* 101(1):25-32.

New Mexico Department of Game and Fish. 1985. *Handbook of Species Endangered in New Mexico*. Santa Fe, New Mexico.

Taylor, D. W. 1987. *Fresh Water Mollusks from New Mexico and Vicinity*. Bulletin 116. New Mexico Bureau of Mines and Mineral Resources. Socorro, New Mexico.

Taylor, D. W. 1983. "Report to the State of New Mexico on a Status Investigation of Mollusca in New Mexico." New Mexico Department of Game and Fish, Santa Fe, New Mexico.

Contacts

Regional Office of Endangered Species
U.S. Fish and Wildlife Service
P.O. Box 1306
Albuquerque, New Mexico 87103

Jerry Burton
U.S. Fish and Wildlife Service
3530 Pan American Highway NE, Suite D
Albuquerque, New mexico 87107

Tulotoma Snail
Tulotoma magnifica

Malcolm Pierson   *Color Plate C-8*

Status	Endangered
Listed	January 9, 1991
Family	Viviparidae (Live-bearing Snails)
Description	Aquatic snail with a globular shell, with spiral lines of knobs.
Habitat	Moderately flowing rivers with rocky bottoms.
Food	Filter-feeder.
Reproduction	Bears live young.
Threats	Alteration of habitat, water pollution, siltation.
Region 4	Alabama

Description

The tulotoma snail is a gill-breathing aquatic snail with a globular shell that grows to a size slightly larger than a golf ball. The shell is ornamented with spiral lines of knob-like structures. Its size and ornamentation, as well as its oblique aperture with a concave margin, distinguish the species from other freshwater snails occuring in the same habitat.

The species was first described in 1834 as *Paludina magnifica* from specimens taken from the Alabama River. Over the next seven years three additional species of *Paludina* were described from the Alabama-Coosa River system. In 1840 all four species were transferred to the the subgenus *Tulotoma*. The original distinctions between these four species were minor differences in shell size and shape, and most scientists now consider them a single species. The species is also known as the Alabama live-bearing snail.

Behavior

The tulotoma snail is usually found during the day clinging to the bottoms of large rocks. Little of its natural history is known apart from the fact that it is a filter-feeder and broods its young.

Habitat

This snail inhabits cool, well-oxygenated, free-flowing water in both mainstream rivers and major tributaries. It shows a preference for riffles and shoals with boulder or cobble bottoms.

Historic Range

Since its discovery, the tulotoma snail has only been found in the Alabama and Coosa River systems in Alabama. In the Coosa River system it occurred from St. Clair County south to the confluence with the Tallapoosa River. It was known from two locations in the Alabama River system: from the Alabama River near Claiborne in Monroe County and from Chilachee Creek, southwest of Selma, in Dallas County.

Current Distribution

The tulotoma snail currently survives in a single short stretch of the Coosa River and in four of its tributaries. In the Coosa River it occurs between Jordan Dam and Wetumpka in Elmore County.

The tributaries that support populations are: Kelly Creek (St. Clair and Shelby counties), Weogufka and Hatchet creeks (Coosa County), and Ohatchee Creek (Calhoun County). All of these populations, except that at Ohatchee Creek, are believed to be self-sustaining.

Conservation and Recovery

Decline in the number and range of the tulotoma snail has been documented for the last fifty years. By the mid-1930s the species was no longer found in the Ala-

bama River; a fall in the population of all snails in the Coosa River was noted by the mid-1940s. Since the 1950s collections of the tulotoma snail have been rare.

The decline of tulotoma snail was caused by the modification of its river habitat by channel dredging and dam construction. Dredging of the Alabama River began in the late nineteenth century and continues today. A series of locks and dams that converted virtually the entire river into a series of impoundments was completed in the 1960s. Six large hydroelectric dams constructed on the Coosa River between 1914 and 1966 have impounded that river for 230 miles above its confluence with the Tallapoosa River. These impoundments have destroyed tulotoma snail habitat in the rivers and modified habitat in the lower reaches of many tributaries. In all, the snail's range has declined 98 percent in the main river channels and about 50 percent in tributaries.

Additional Sources

Hershler, R. J. 1989. "Status Survey of *Tulotoma magnifica* (Conrad)." U.S. Fish and Wildlife Service, Atlanta, Georgia.

Stein, C. B. 1976. "Gastropods." In *Endangered and Threatened Plants and Animals of Alabama*, edited by H. Boschung. *Bulletin of the Museum of Natural History* 2:24-25.

Contacts

Regional Office of Endangered Species
U. S. Fish and Wildlife Service
Richard B. Russell Federal Building
75 Spring Street, S.W.
Atlanta, Georgia 30303

Paul D. Hartfield
Jackson Field Office
U.S. Fish and Wildlife Service
6578 Dogwood View Parkway
Jackson, Mississippi 39213

Uncompahgre Fritillary Butterfly
Boloria acrocnema

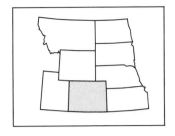

Paul A. Opler

Status	Endangered
Listed	June 24, 1991
Family	Nymphalidae
	(Brush-Footed Butterfly)
Description	Small, rusty brown
	butterfly, with upper wings
	crisscrossed in black.
Habitat	Patches of snow willow on
	cool, wet mountain slopes.
Host Plant	Snow willow.
Threats	Collectors.
Region 6	Colorado

Description

The Uncompahgre fritillary is a small butterfly with a 2.5 centimeter (1.0 in) wingspan. The upperwings are rusty brown, crisscrossed with black bars. The forewing is light ocher below, and the hindwing has a jagged white bar separating the crimson-brown inner half from the purple-gray outer half. Females are generally lighter above than males. The body has a rusty brown thorax and a brownish black abdomen. The species is considered by some to be *Boloria improba* ssp. *acrocnema*, a subspecies of the dingy arctic fritillary. It has also been classified as *Clossiana acrocnema*.

Behavior

Adults feed on a variety of alpine flowers. Females lay eggs on snow willow (*Salix reticulata* ssp. *nivalis*), which is the larval food plant.

Researchers believe that the Uncompahgre fritillary has a biennial life cycle. Eggs laid in the summer become caterpillars the following summer and mature into adult butterflies during the third summer. There are thus separate even- and odd-year populations within the same habitat area.

This butterfly is relatively sedentary and a weak flyer that stays close to the ground, making it an easy target for collectors.

Habitat

The Uncompahgre fritillary inhabits cool, moist mountain slopes above 4,040 meters (13,200 ft). It is always associated with patches of snow willow (*Salix reticulata* ssp. *nivalis*) which provide larval food and cover.

Historic Range

This species has the smallest range of any North American butterfly. It was discovered on Uncompahgre Peak in Hinsdale County, Colorado, in 1978. Another site was discovered in 1982 on land mangaged by the Bureau of Land Management (BLM). In 1988 a few individuals were captured at two additional sites. The total known range includes the San Juan Mountains and southern Sawatch Range in Gunnison, Hinsdale, and possibley Chaffee counties in southwestern Colorado.

Current Distribution

Since this species was only recently discovered, its current range is the same as its historic range, and it is not known whether the species was formerly more widespread. The original Uncomprahgre Peak population is in the Big Blue Wilderness in the Uncompahgre National Forest. The second population is in a wilderness study area administered by BLM. The two additional sites where some individuals were found in 1988 require more study to determine whether they support viable populations. Reports that four additional colonies have been discovered are as yet unconfirmed.

Recent surveys indicate that populations at the major colonies have declined in recent years. The even-year brood at Uncompahgre Peak has declined from about 800 in 1978 to about 200 in 1988. The pop-ulation at the BLM site has declined from over 1,000 in 1984 to about 500 in 1988. The odd-year brood at Uncompahgre Peak, which has been documented in the past, may be extinct, and the status of the odd-year brood at the BLM site is unclear. The Fish and Wildlife Service estimates the total current population to be about 1,000.

Conservation and Recovery

The overwhelming threat to the Uncompahgre fritillary is butterfly collectors. As one of the few North American species discovered in this century, it is in great demand by collectors, and individual specimens are often sold for more than a hundred dollars. Although collecting has been banned by the Forest Service at the Uncompahgre Peak area, some collection apparently continues. There has been no ban on collecting at the BLM site. Now that the Uncompahgre fritillary has been listed as Endangered, collecting the species is illegal and can be prosecuted by federal authorities.

The small size of the known population and the need for a cool, wet habitat also threaten the long-term viability of the Uncompahgre fritillary. Besides the pressures of collecting, the species is vulnerable to such unpredictable natural events as prolonged drought or climactic change.

In 1984 the Forest Service and BLM came to an agreement on conservation of the Uncompahgre fritillary. Besides banning collecting on Forest Service land, trails near the BLM site have been rerouted to reduce recreational traffic in the habitat area.

Additional Sources

Brussard, P. F., and H. Britten. 1989. "Final Report on the Uncomprahgre Fritillary (*Boloria acrocnema*)." Final report prepared for the U.S. Forest Service, Bureau of Land Management, and Fish and Wildlife Service. Montana State University, Bozeman.

Gall, L. F. 1984. "Population Structure and Recommendations for Conservation of the Narrowly Endemic Alpine Butterfly, *Boloria acrocnema* (Lepidoptera: Nymphalidae)." *Biological Conservation* 28:111-138.

Interagency Agreement. 1984. "Interagency Agreement and Species Management Perspective for Mt. Uncompahgre Fritillary Butterfly (*Boloria acrocenema*)." U.S. Forest Service and U.S. Bureau of Land Management. Gunnison, Colorado.

Contacts

Regional Office of Endangered Species
U.S. Fish and Wildlife Service
P.O. Box 25486
Denver Federal Center
Denver, Colorado 80225

John Anderson
U.S. Fish and Wildlife Service
529 25½ Road, Suite B-113
Grand Junction, Colorado 81505

Northeastern Beach Tiger Beetle

Cicindela dorsalis dorsalis

C. Barry Knisley   *Color Plate C-8*

Status	Threatened
Listed	August 7, 1990
Family	Cicindelidae (Tiger Beetle)
Description	Bronze-green head and thorax, white to light tan wing covers.
Habitat	Beaches.
Food	Small invertebrates.
Reproduction	Larvae metamorphose after two years.
Threats	Habitat disruption by humans.
Region 5	Maryland, Massachusetts, Virginia

Description

The northeastern beach tiger beetle is about 14 millimeters (0.5 in) in length. It has a bronze-green head and thorax and white to tan wing covers.

This species was described in 1817. During the 1950s it, along with three previously described species, were considered subspecies of a single species. Recent taxonomic study indicates that *Cicindela dorsalis* is most likely a full species. Until that research is published, however, the Fish and Wildlife Service will continue to consider the northeastern beach tiger beetle a subspecies.

Behavior

Both adult and larval tiger beetles prey on small arthropods. The adults grasp their prey with their mandables in a "tiger-like" manner. The larvae, which live in ground burrows, attach themselves near the entrance with abdominal hooks and extend quickly to capture passing prey.

Northeastern beach tiger beetle larvae burrow directly into the sand in and above the high-tide zone. They overwinter twice as larvae and metamorphose into adults in their third summer. They emerge in early June through August, and scavenge on dead fish and invertebrates.

Habitat

The northeastern beach tiger beetle occurs on fine sand beaches that are exposed to a vigorous tidal action and have low human and vehicular activity.

Historic Range

In the past, the northeastern beach tiger beetle occurred on sandy beaches from Cape Cod, Massachusetts, south to central New Jersey, and along the Chesapeake Bay in Maryland and Virginia. In the early part of the century, the species was so abundant that contemporary accounts refer to "swarms" of the insect occurring in July. Over the years, the population has declined dramatically. By the mid-1980s the species was believed to have vanished from the upper Atlantic Coast.

Current Distribution

In 1989 a small population of this tiger beetle was discovered on a privately owned beach on Martha's Vineyard, Massachusetts. Numbering fewer than 40 individuals, it is the only known population north of the Chesapeake Bay.

In Maryland there are currently two large and two medium-sized populations along the Chesapeake Bay in Calvert County. Three of these are on private land owned by housing subdivisions; one is in a county park.

In 1989 an intensive survey of possible beetle habitat in Virginia found 40 new populations, concentrated in Northumberland, Mathews, and Northampton counties, with additional sites in Accomack and Gloucester counties. A number of these populations are on isolated beaches that are relatively free from threats.

Conservation and Recovery

The decline in the northeastern beach tiger beetle from relative abundance to near extinction in the northern portion of its range was caused by the increased residential and recreational use of ocean beaches. The larvae, which must spend two years in beach burrows, are particularly vulnerable to crushing and the compaction of their sand habitat. The destructive effect of human and vehicular traffic was demonstrated in a recent study of a closely related beetle species. On Assateague Island, off the Maryland and Virgina coasts, the absence of beetles was diretly correlated with human or vehicular traffic. On those parts of the island that receive heavy recreational traffic, no beetles are found, while beetles were present on beaches where there was little or no traffic.

Continuing recreational and developmental pressure on Atlantic and Chesapeake Bay beaches will threaten the northeastern beach tiger beetle for the forseeable future.

In Maryland the northeastern beach tiger beetle is somewhat protected by the state's "critical areas" legislation, enacted to help conserve and restore the Chesapeake Bay ecosystem. According to this legislation, "critical areas" are those within 1,000 feet of the bay or its tributaries. Development of these areas is curtailed and often prohibited when a state-designated threatened species is present. In addition, four of the Maryland sites are designated "Natural Heritage Areas," giving them further protection from disturbance.

Collectors pose an additional threat to this beetle. Tiger beetles are without doubt the most intensely collected of any insect genus. Although collectors are not considered a factor in the species' decline, the

harmful effects of collection are magnified
when population numbers are low.

Additional Sources

Boyd, H. P. 1978. "The Tiger Beetles
(Coleoptera: Cicindelidae) of New Jersey,
with Specieal Reference to their Ecological
Relationships." *Transactions of the American
Entomological Society* 104:191-242.

Knisley, C. B. 1987. "Final Report: Status Survey of Two Candidate Tiger Beetles,
Cicindela puritana G. Horn and *C. dorsalis*
Say." U.S. Fish and Wildlife Service, Newton Corner, Massachusetts.

Knisley, C. B., and J. M. Hill. 1990. "Studies
of Two Endangered Tiger Beetles, *Cicindela
dorsalis dorsalis* and *Cicindela puritana* in
Maryland, 1989." Maryland Natural Heritage Program, Annapolis.

Contacts

Regional Office of Endangered Species
U.S. Fish and Wildlife Service
One Gateway Center, Suite 700
Newton Corner, MA 02158

Judy Jacobs
Annapolis Field Office
U.S. Fish and Wildlife Service
1825 Virginia Street
Annapolis, Maryland 21401

Puritan Tiger Beetle
Cicindela puritana

C. Barry Knisley   *Color Plate C-8*

Status	Threatened
Listed	August 7, 1990
Family	Cicindelidae (Tiger Beetle)
Description	Brownish bronze above and metallic blue below, marginal white bands on wing covers.
Habitat	Beaches and adjacent cliffs.
Food	Small invertebrates.
Reproduction	Larva with three stages.
Threats	Habitat disruption by humans.
Region 5	Connecticut, Maryland, Massachusetts

Description

The Puritan tiger beetle measures about 1.2 centimeters (0.5 in) in length. It is brownish bronze above with a metallic blue underside. The wing covers (elytrons) are marked with narrow marginal and transverse white bands.

In the past it has been considered a subspecies of *Cicindela cuprascens* and of *C. macra*. It was again recognized as a separate species in 1967.

Behavior

Both adult and larval tiger beetles prey on small arthropods. The adults grasp their prey with their mandables in a "tiger-like" manner. The larvae, which live in ground burrows, attach themselves near the entrance with abdominal hooks and extend quickly to capture passing prey.

Adult Puritan tiger beetles appear in mid-June, with numbers peaking in early July and declining by late July. After mating, females move from beaches to nearby cliffs where they deposit their eggs. The newly hatched larvae dig burrows in the cliffs, where they pass through three larval stages (instars). Recent studies indicate that they do not metamorphose into adults until the second year.

Habitat

The Puritan tiger beetle inhabits beach areas with adjacent sand or clay cliffs. Adult beetles feed and mate along the beach and use the sparsely vegetated cliff areas for depositing eggs. Larvae inhabit the cliff sites, moving to the beach as adults.

Historic Range

The Puritan tiger beetle was once known from scattered locations along the Connecticut River in Vermont, New Hampshire, Massachusetts, and Connecticut. It has also been found along the Chesapeake Bay in Calvert County, Maryland, and along a short stretch of the Sassafras River in Kent and Cecil counties on Maryland's Eastern Shore.

Most New England collections date from the early 1900s, and until recently it was believed that the beetle had been extirpated from that region. However, recently two new populations have been discovered.

Current Distribution

The Puritan tiger beetle survives at two locations in New England and two locations around the Chesapeake Bay in Maryland. In 1986 a small population of fewer than 100 adult beetles was discovered in Hampshire County, Massachusetts, on a small island in the Connecticut River and on a nearby sandy beach. In 1989 a larger population was found near Cromwell in Middlesex County, Connecticut. This site is unusual since there are no adjacent cliffs or clay banks, and the larvae burrow in the ground.

Five large populations of over 600 adults and four small populations of fewer than a hundred are scattered along 26 miles of the Chesapeake Bay in Clavert County, Maryland. The Sassafras County populations, which were only discovered in 1989, occur on a 1.5-mile section of the Sassafras River. These consist of fewer than four medium-sized populations of from 100 to 500 adults.

Conservation and Recovery

Decline of the Puritan tiger beetle has been caused by degradation of its beach and cliff habitat, natural and man-made flooding, urbanization, and cliff stabilization projects. A recent study of the beetle's historic collection sites along the Connecticut River determined that 23 percent have been flooded by dams, 38 percent heavily urbanized, and 8 percent altered by stabilization projects. It is believed that severe flooding in New England during the 1920s and 1930s contributed to the loss of Puritan tiger beetles in that region.

The only remaining Massachusetts population is threatened by human recreational use. From May through September the beach is heavily used by power boats, motorcycles, and all-terrain vehicles. In Maryland, the principal threat to beetle populations is cliff stabilization projects. Continued breakdown of the cliffs is necessary to provide the exposed areas needed by the larvae. Stabilized cliffs are often quickly overgrown by vegetation.

The Puritan tiger beetle is somewhat protected by Maryland's "critical areas" legislation, enacted to help reverse the degradation of the Chesapeake Bay ecosystem. "Critical areas," according to this legislation, are those within 1,000 feet of the bay or its tributaries. Development of these areas is curtailed and often prohibited when a state-designated threatened species is present. In addition, four of the Maryland sites are designated "Natural

Heritage Areas," giving them further protection from disturbance. Without this strong state protection, the Fish and Wildlife Service would have classified the Puritan tiger beetle as Endangered rather than Threatened.

Collectors pose an additional threat to this beetle species. Tiger beetles are without doubt the most intensely collected of any insect genus. Although collection is not considered a factor in the beetle's decline, the harmful effects are magnified when the species' population is low.

Additional Sources

Boyd, H. P. 1978. "The Tiger Beetles (Coleoptera: Cicindelidae) of New Jersey, with Special Reference to their Ecological Relationships." *Transactions of the American Entomological Society* 104:191-242.

Knisley, C. B. 1987. "Final Report: Status Survey of Two Candidate Tiger Beetles, *Cicindela puritana* G. Horn and *C. dorsalis* Say." U.S. Fish and Wildlife Service, Newton Corner, Massachusetts.

Knisley, C. B., and J. M. Hill. 1990. "Studies of Two Endangered Tiger Beetles, *Cicindela dorsalis dorsalis* and *Cicindela puritana* in Maryland, 1989." Maryland Natural Heritage Program, Annapolis.

Nothnagel, P. 1987. "*Cicindela puritana*— The Puritan Tiger Beetle: Its Current Status in Massachusetts." Massachusetts Natural Heritage Program, Boston.

_____. 1989. "Current Status of the Puritan Tiger Beetle (*Cicindela puritana*) in Connecticut." Eastern Heritage Task Force, The Nature Conservancy, Boston.

Contacts

Regional Office of Endangered Species
U.S. Fish and Wildlife Service
One Gateway Center, Suite 700
Newton Corner, MA 02158

Judy Jacobs
Annapolis Field Office
U.S. Fish and Wildlife Service
1825 Virginia Street
Annapolis, Maryland 21401

Mitchell's Satyr Butterfly
Neonympha mitchellii mitchellii

Larry West   *Color Plate C-8*

Status	Endangered
Listed	June 25, 1991
Family	Nymphalidae (Brush-Footed Butterfly)
Description	Brown butterfly, with yellow-ringed, black and silver eyespots.
Habitat	Wetland fens.
Host Plants	Sedges.
Threats	Collectors, conversion of wetland habitat.
Region 3	Indiana, Michigan

Description

Mitchell's satyr is a medium-sized butterfly of the Satyrinae subfamily of the Nymphalidae family. It has a wingspan of from 38 to 44 millimeters (1.4 to 1.8 in) and is rich brown overall. The lower surfaces of all four wings show a series of yellow-ringed, black, circular eyespots with silvery centers. There are two orange bands across the posterior wing edges and lighter orange bands across the wing centers. The species has also been known by the names *Cissia mitchellii* and *Euptychia mitchellii*.

Behavior

The host plant for Mitchell's satyr is believed to be a sedge, possibly more than one species. Adults are active during a brief two- to three-week period in the summer. In early to mid-July females lay eggs, which hatch in 7 to 11 days. The larvae overwinter on sedge leaves and emerge the following May to continue their growth and pupation. The species has a single, short flight period each summer, which lasts about a week for the individual butterfly, and for about three weeks for the local population (late June through mid-July). Mitchell's satyr is relatively sedentary and has a slow, low-level flight pattern.

Habitat

This butterfly is restricted to wetland habitats known as prairie fens, which are characterized by calcareous soils fed by carbonate-rich water from seeps and springs. This uncommon habitat, which is often part of larger wetland complexes, is characterized by tamarak (*Larix laricina*), poison sumac (*Toxicodendron vernix*), dogwood (*Cornus* spp.), and a ground cover of sedges (*Carex* spp.), shrubby cinquefoil (*Potentilla fruticosa*), and other prairie species.

Historic Range

Mitchell's satyr was first described in 1889 from specimens collected in Cass County, Michigan. It has been known from about 30 locations in four states. Its historic range included southern Michigan, northeastern Indiana, and northwestern Ohio. In addition several separate populations were known from New Jersey.

Current Distribution

It is believed that Mitchell's satyr survives at only 15 sites in nine counties in southwestern Michigan and northeastern Indiana. Intensive surveys of historical sites and suitable habitat were conducted between 1985 and 1990. No populations were found in Ohio, and a population found in New Jersey was eliminated by collectors soon after the area was surveyed.

Conservation and Recovery

The main threats to surviving populations of Mitchell's satyr are collectors and the conversion of the butterfly's unique wetland fen habitat. One Michigan site has been destroyed by urban development, and several other sites in Michigan and Ohio have been converted to agricultural use.

Collectors, however, are the greatest immediate threat to the species. Mitchell's

satyr is considered a prize specimen by many butterfly collectors and it is clear that collectors have been responsible for the loss of a number of populations, including two in New Jersey. Several Michigan sites are under strong collecting pressure. About one-third of the surviving populations are extremely vulnerable to local extinction through collection, and all known sites are susceptible to this danger.

Because of the continuing threat from collectors and the fact that half of the known populations have vanished in a period of five years, on June 25, 1991, the Fish and Wildlife Service (FWS) listed Mitchell's satyr as Endangered on an emergency basis. This gave the species protection under the Endangered Species Act during its 1991 flight period, and, it is hoped, eased the pressure from collectors. FWS has initiated the regular process of proposing that Mitchell's satyr be listed as Endangered.

Additional Sources

Martin, M. L. 1987. "Mitchell's Satyr (*Neonympha mitchellii*) in Indiana." Michigan Natural Features Inventory, Lansing.

McAlpine, W. S., S. P. Hubbell, and T. E. Pliske. 1960. "The Distribution, Habits, and Life History of *Euptychia mitchellii* (Satyridae)." *Journal of the Lepidopterist Society* 14(4):209-225.

Contacts

William F. Harrison
U.S. Fish and Wildlife Service
Federal Building, Fort Snelling
Twin Cities, Minnesota, 55111

Appendix I
State by State Occurrence
(For Species Listed in Volume 3)

ALABAMA

Price's Potato-Bean   *Apios priceana*
Leafy Prairie Clover   *Dalea foliosa*
Lyrate Bladder-Pod   *Lesquerella lyrata*
Kral's Water-Plantain   *Sagittaria secundifolia*
Tennessee Yellow-Eyed Grass   *Xyris tennesseensis*
Gulf Sturgeon   *Acipenser oxyrhynchus desotoi*
Pygmy Sculpin   *Cottus pygmaeus*
Cahaba Shiner   *Notropis cahabae*
Inflated Heelsplitter   *Potamilus inflatus*
Tulotoma Snail   *Tulotoma magnifica*

ALASKA

Steller Sea-Lion   *Eumetopias jubatus*

ARIZONA

Sentry Milk-Vetch   *Astragalus cremnophylax* var. *cremnophylax*
Virgin River Chub   *Gila robusta seminuda*
Razorback Sucker   *Xyrauchen texanus*

ARKANSAS

Pallid Sturgeon   *Scaphirhynchus albus*
Ouachita Rock-Pocketbook   *Arkansia wheeleri*
Arkansas Fatmucket   *Lampsilis powelli*

CALIFORNIA

Baker's Sticky Seed   *Blennosperma bakeri*
California Jewelflower   *Caulanthus californicus*
Kern Mallow   *Eremalche kernensis*
Hoover's Wooly-Star   *Eriastrum hooveri*
Burke's Goldfields   *Lasthenia burkei*
San Joaquin Wooly-Threads   *Lembertia congdonii*

CALIFORNIA, cont.

Sebastopol Meadowfoam	*Limnanthes binculans*
Bakersfield Cactus	*Opuntia treleasei*
Steller Sea-Lion	*Eumetopias jubatus*
Northern Spotted Owl	*Strix occidentalis caurina*
Chinook Salmon	*Oncorhynchus tshawytscha*
(Sacarmento River Winter Run)	

COLORADO

Dudley Bluffs Bladderpod	*Lesquerella congesta*
Dudley Bluffs Twinpod	*Physaria obcordata*
Razorback Sucker	*Xyrauchen texanus*
Uncompahgre Fritillary	*Boloria acrocnema*

CONNECTICUT

Puritan Tiger Beetle	*Cicindela puritana*

FLORIDA

Garrett's Mint	*Dicerandra christmanii*
Fringed Campion	*Silene polypetala*
Gentian Pinkroot	*Spigelia gentianoides*
Florida Salt Marsh Vole	*Microtus pennsylvanicus dukecambelli*
Silver Rice Rat	*Oryzomys palustris natator*
Lower Keys Rabbit	*Sylvilagus palustris hefneri*
Gulf Sturgeon	*Acipenser oxyrhynchus desotoi*
Squirrel Chimney Cave Shrimp	*Palaemonetes cummingi*

GEORGIA

Michaux's Sumac	*Rhus michauxii*
Kral's Water-Plantain	*Sagittaria secundifolia*
Fringed Campion	*Silene polypetala*
Virginia Spiraea	*Spiraea virginiana*
Tennessee Yellow-Eyed Grass	*Xryris tennesseensis*

HAWAII

No common name	*Abutilon sandwicense*
No common name	*Abutilon eremitopetalum*
No common name	*Alsinidendron obovatum*
No common name	*Alsinidendron trinerve*

HAWAII, cont.

No common name	*Centaurium sebaeoides*
Akoko	*Chamaesyce celastroides* var. *kaenana*
No common name	*Chamaesyce kuwaleana*
Cyanea Superba	*Cyanea superba*
No common name	*Cyanea undulata*
Haha	*Cyanea pinnatifida*
No common name	*Cyanea marcrostegia* var. *gibsonii*
No common name	*Diellia falcata*
No common name	*Dubautia pauciflorula*
Na'ena'e	*Dubautia herbstobatae*
No common name	*Gahnia lanaiensis*
No common name	*Gouania meyenii*
No common name	*Hedyotis parvula*
No common name	*Hedyotis degeneri*
Na Pali Beach Hedyotis	*Hedyotis st.-johnii*
No common name	*Hesperomannia lydgatei*
No common name	*Hesperomannia arbuscula*
Aupaka	*Isodendrion hosakae*
No common name	*Labordia lydgatei*
No common name	*Lipochaeta lobata* var. *leptophylla*
Nehe	*Lipochaeta tenuifolia*
No common name	*Lobelia niihauensis*
No common name	*Neraudia angulata*
Kulu'i	*Nototrichium humile*
No common name	*Phyllostegia mollis*
No common name	*Phyllostegia glabra* var. *lanaiensis*
Kauai Remya	*Remya kauaiensis*
Maui Remya	*Remya mauiensis*
No common name	*Remya montgomeryi*
No common name	*Sanicula mariversa*
ma'oli'oli	*Schiedea apokremnos*
No common name	*Schiedea kaalae*
No common name	*Silene perlmanii*
No common name	*Tetramolopium filiforme*
No common name	*Tetramolopium lepidotum* ssp. *lepidotum*
No common name	*Tetramolopium remyi*
Opuhe	*Urera kaalae*
Pamakani	*Viola chamissoniana* ssp. *chamissoniana*
No common name	*Viola lanaiensis*
No common name	*Viola helenae*

IDAHO

Sockeye Salmon (Snake River)	*Oncorhynchus nerka*

ILLINOIS

Leafy Prairie Clover	*Dalea foliosa*
Eastern Prairie Fringed Orchid	*Platanthera leucophaea*
Pallid Sturgeon	*Scaphirhynchus albus*
Fanshell	*Cyprogenia stegaria*

INDIANA

Fanshell	*Cyprogenia stegaria*
Mitchell's Satyr Butterfly	*Neonympha mitchellii mitchellii*

IOWA

Eastern Prairie Fringed Orchid	*Platanthera leucophaea*
Western Prairie Fringed Orchid	*Platanthera praeclara*
Pallid Sturgeon	*Scaphirhynchus albus*

KANSAS

Western Prairie Fringed Orchid	*Platanthera praeclara*
Neosho Madtom	*Noturus placidus*
Pallid Sturgeon	*Scaphirhynchus albus*

KENTUCKY

Price's Potato-Bean	*Apios priceana*
Cumberland Rosemary	*Conradina verticillata*
Virginia Spiraea	*Spiraea virginiana*
Pallid Sturgeon	*Scaphirhynchus albus*
Fanshell	*Cyprogenia stegaria*
Purple Cat's Paw Pearly Mussel	*Epioblasma obliquata*
Cracking Pearly Mussel	*Hemistena lata*
Ring Pink Mussel	*Obovaria retusa*

LOUISIANA

Gulf Sturgeon	*Acipenser oxyrhynchus desotoi*
Pallid Sturgeon	*Scaphirhynchus albus*
Inflated Heelsplitter	*Potamilus inflatus*

MAINE

Eastern Prairie Fringed Orchid	*Platanthera leucophaea*

MARYLAND

Northeastern Bulrush	*Scirpus ancistrochaetus*
Dwarf Wedge Mussel	*Alasmidonta heterodon*
Northeastern Beach Beetle	*Cicindela dorsalis dorsalis*
Puritan Tiger Beetle	*Cicindela puritana*

MASSACHUSETTS

Northeastern Bulrush	*Scirpus ancistrochaetus*
Puritan Tiger Beetle	*Cicindela puritana*
Northeastern Beach Beetle	*Cicindela dorsalis dorsalis*

MICHIGAN

Michigan Monkey-Flower	*Mimulus glabratus* var. *michiganensis*
Eastern Prairie Fringed Orchid	*Platanthera leucophaea*
MItchell's Satyr Butterfly	*Neonympha mitchellii mitchellii*

MINNESOTA

Western Prairie Fringed Orchid	*Platanthera praeclara*

MISSISSIPPI

Price's Potato-Bean	*Apios priceana*
Yellow-Blotched Map Turtle	*Graptemys flavimaculata*
Gulf Sturgeon	*Acipenser oxyrhynchus desotoi*
Pallid Sturgeon	*Scaphirhynchus albus*

MISSOURI

Western Prairie Fringed Orchid	*Platanthera praeclara*
Neosho Madtom	*Noturus placidus*
Pallid Sturgeon	*Scaphirhynchus albus*

MONTANA

Pallid Sturgeon	*Scaphirhynchus albus*

NEBRASKA

Western Prairie Fringed Orchid	*Platanthera praeclara*
Pallid Sturgeon	*Scaphirhynchus albus*

NEVADA

Virgin River Chub	*Gila robusta seminuda*
Independence Valley Speckled Dace	*Rhinichthys osculus lethoporus*
Clover Valley Speckled Dace	*Rhinichthys osculus oligoporus*
Razorback Sucker	*Xyrauchen texanus*

NEW HAMPSHIRE

Dwarf Wedge Mussel	*Alasmidonta heterodon*

NEW JERSEY

Knieskern's Beaked-Rush	*Rhynchospora knieskernii*

NEW MEXICO

Sacramento Prickly-Poppy	*Argemone pleiacantha* ssp. *pinnatisecta*
Socorro Springsnail	*Pyrgulopsis neomexicana*
Alamosa Springsnail	*Tryonia alamosae*

NORTH CAROLINA

Small-Anthered Bittercress	*Cardamine micranthera*
Spreading Avens	*Geum radiatum*
Roan Mountain Bluet	*Hedyotis purpurea* var. *montana*
Schweinitz's Sunflower	*Helianthus schweinitzii*
Michaux's Sumac	*Rhus michauxii*
Virginia Spiraea	*Spiraea virginiana*
White Irisette	*Sisyrinchium dichotomum*
Dwarf Wedge Mussel	*Alasmidonta heterodon*

NORTH DAKOTA

Western Prairie Fringed Orchid	*Planathera praeclara*
Pallid Sturgeon	*Scaphirhynchus albus*

OHIO

Eastern Prairie Fringed Orchid	*Platanthera leucophaea*
Fanshell	*Cyprogenia stegaria*

OKLAHOMA

Neosho Madtom	*Noturus placidus*
Ouachita Rock-Pocketbook	*Arkansia wheeleri*

OREGON

Steller Sea-Lion	*Eumetopias jubatus*
Northern Spotted Owl	*Strix occidentalis caurina*
Sockeye Salmon (Snake River)	*Oncorhynchus nerka*

PENNSYLVANIA

Northeastern Bulrush	*Scirpus ancistrochaetus*

SOUTH CAROLINA

Schweinitz's Sunflower	*Helianthus schweinitzii*

SOUTH DAKOTA

Pallid Sturgeon	*Scaphirhynchus albus*

TENNESSEE

Price's Potato-Bean	*Apios priceana*
Guthrie's Ground-Plum	*Astragalus bibullatus*
Cumberland Rosemary	*Conradina verticillata*
Leafy Prairie Clover	*Dalea foliosa*
Spreading Avens	*Geum radiatum*
Roan Mountain Bluet	*Hedyotis purpurea* var. *montana*
Virginia Spiraea	*Spiraea virginiana*
Tennessee Yellow-Eyed Grass	*Xyris tennesseensis*
Pallid Sturgeon	*Scaphirhynchus albus*
Fanshell	*Cyprogenia stegaria*
Purple Cat's Paw Pearly Mussel	*Epioblasma obliquata*
Cracking Pearly Mussel	*Hemistena lata*
Ring Pink Mussel	*Obovaria retu*
Cumberland Pigtoe Mussel	*Pleurobema gibberum*

TEXAS

Terlingua Creek Cat's Eye	*Cryptantha crassipes*
Walker's Manioc	*Manihot walkerae*
Texas Trailing Phlox	*Phlox nivalis* ssp. *texensis*
Little Aguja Pondweed	*Potamogeton clystocarpus*
Golden-Cheeked Warbler	*Dendroica chrysoparia*
Gulf Sturgeon	*Acipenser oxyrhynchus desotoi*

UTAH

Barneby Ridge-Cress	*Lepidium barnebyanum*
Virgin River Chub	*Gila robusta seminuda*
Razorback Sucker	*Xyrauchen texanus*
Kanab Ambersnail	*Oxyloma haydeni kanabensis*

VERMONT

Northeastern Bulrush	*Scirpus ancistrochaetus*
Dwarf Wedge Mussel	*Alasmidonta heterodon*

VIRGINIA

Northeastern Bulrush	*Scirpus ancistrochaetus*
Eastern Prairie Fringed Orchid	*Platanthera leucophaea*
Virginia Spiraea	*Spiraea virginiana*
Shenandoah Salamander	*Plethodon shenandoah*
Roanoke Logperch	*Percina rex*
Fanshell	*Cyprogenia stegaria*
Cracking Pearly Mussel	*Hemistena lata*
Northeastern Beach Beetle	*Cicindela dorsalis dorsalis*

WASHINGTON

Steller Sea-Lion	*Eumetopias jubatus*
Northern Spotted Owl	*Strix occidentalis caurina*
Sockeye Salmon (Snake River)	*Oncorhynchus nerka*

WEST VIRGINIA

Northeastern Bulrush	*Scirpus ancistrochaetus*
Virginia Spiraea	*Spiraea virginiana*
Cheat Mountain Salamander	*Plethodon nettingi*
Fanshell	*Cyprogenia stegaria*

WISCONSIN

Eastern Prairie Fringed Orchid	*Platanthera leucophaea*
Winged Mapleleaf Mussel	*Quadrula fragosa*

PUERTO RICO

Pelos del Diablo	*Aristida portoricensis*
Palma de Manaca	*Calyptronoma rivalis*

PUERTO RICO, cont.

No common name   *Cassia mirabilis*
Cranichis Ricartii   *Cranichis ricartii*
Higo Chumbo   *Harrisia portoricensis*
Lepanthes Eltorensis   *Lepanthes eltorensis*
Palo de Rosa   *Ottoschulzia rhodoxylon*
Schoepfia Arenaria   *Schoepfia arenaria*
Cobana Negra   *Stahlia monosperma*

CANADA

Eastern Prairie Fringed Orchid   *Platanthera leucophaea*
Western Prairie Fringed Orchid   *Platanthera praeclara*
Steller Sea-Lion   *Eumetopias jubatus*
Northern Spotted Owl   *Strix occidentalis caurina*

Appendix II
Species Currently Proposed for Listing
(December 1991)

NOTE: Proposed species are generally listed within a year.

Scientific Name	Common Name	Date Proposed	States
PLANTS			
Acaena exigua	Liliwai	05/24/91	HI
Aeschynomene virginica	Sensitive Joint-Vetch	07/26/91	NJ,MD,VA,NC
Alectryon macrococcus	Mahoe	05/24/91	HI
Arenaria paludicola	Marsh Sandwort	09/30/91	CA
Argyroxiphium kauense	Ka'u Silversword	08/06/90	HI
Argyroxiphium sandwicense ssp. *macrocephalum*	Haleakala Silversword	05/24/91	HI
Astragalus albens	Cushenbury Milk-Vetch	11/19/91	CA
Astragalus applegatei	Applegate's Milk-Vetch	11/26/91	OR
Bidens micrantha ssp. *kalealaha*	Ko'oko'olau	05/24/91	HI
Bidens wiebkei	Ko'oko'olau	09/20/91	HI
Brighamia insignis	'Olulu	10/30/91	HI
Brighamia rockii	Pua 'ala	09/20/91	HI
Callicarpa ampla	Capa Rosa	04/19/91	PR
Canavalia molokaiensis	'Awikiwiki	09/20/91	HI
Chamaesyce halemanui	None	09/26/90	HI
Chorizanthe howellii	Howell's Spineflower	03/22/91	CA
Chorizanthe pungens var. *hartwegiana*	Ben Lomond Spineflower	10/24/91	CA
Chorizanthe pungens var. *pungens*	Monterey Spineflower	10/24/91	CA
Chorizanthe robusta var. *hartwegii*	Scotts Valley Spineflower	10/24/91	CA
Chorizanthe robusta var. *robusta*	Robust Spineflower	10/24/91	CA
Chorizanthe valida	Sonoma Spineflower	03/22/91	CA
Clematis morefieldii	Morefield's Leather Flower	10/21/91	AL
Clermontia oblongifolia ssp. *mauiensis*	'Oha Wai	05/24/91	HI
Clermontia oblongifolia ssp. *brevipes*	'Oha Wai	09/20/91	HI
Cyanea asarifolia	Haha	10/30/91	HI
Cyanea lobata	Haha	05/24/91	HI
Cyanea mannii	Haha	09/20/91	HI

Scientific Name	Common Name	Date Proposed	States
Cyanea mceldowneyi	Haha	05/24/91	HI
Cyanea procera	Haha	09/20/91	HI
Cyrtandra limahuliensis	Ha'iwale	10/30/91	HI
Cyrtandra munroi	Ha'iwale	05/24/91	HI
Delissea rhytidosperma	None	10/30/91	HI
Diellia laciniata	None	10/30/91	HI
Dubautia latifolia	None	09/26/90	HI
Echinacea laevigata	Smooth Coneflower	12/09/91	VA,NC,SC,GA
Erigeron parishii	Parish's Daisy	11/19/91	CA
Eriogonum ovalifolium var. vineum	Cushenbury Buckwheat	11/19/91	CA
Eryngium aristulatum var. parishii	San Diego Button-Celery	11/12/91	CA
Erysimum menziesii	Menzies' Wallflower	03/22/91	CA
Erysimum teretifolium	Ben Lomond Wallflower	10/24/91	CA
Euphorbia telephioides	Telephus Spurge	12/18/90	FL
Eutrema penlandii	Penland Alpine Fen Mustard	10/15/90	CO
Exocarpos luteolus	Heau	10/30/91	HI
Geranium arboreum	Hawaiian Red-Flowered Geranium	01/23/91	HI
Geranium multiflorum	Nohoanu	05/24/91	HI
Gilia tenuiflora ssp. arenaria	Monterey Gilia	03/22/91	CA
Hedyotis cookiana	'Awiwi	10/30/91	HI
Hedyotis coriacea	Kio'ele	05/24/91	HI
Hedyotis mannii	Pilo	09/20/91	HI
Hibiscus arnottianus ssp. immaculatus	Koki'o Ke'oke'o	09/20/91	HI
Hibiscus clayi	Clay's Hibiscus	10/30/91	HI
Ilex sintenisii	None	04/19/91	PR
Isoetes louisianensis	Louisiana Quillwort	10/21/91	LA
Layia carnosa	Beach Layia	03/22/91	CA
Lesquerella kingii ssp. bernardina	San Bernardino Mts. Bladderpod	11/19/91	CA
Limnanthes floccosa ssp. californica	Butte County Meadowfoam	02/15/91	CA
Lipochaeta fauriei	Nehe	10/30/91	HI
Lipochaeta kamolensis	Nehe	05/24/91	HI
Lipochaeta micrantha	Nehe	10/30/91	HI
Lipochaeta waimeaensis	Nehe	10/30/91	HI
Lupinus tidestromii	Clover Lupine	03/22/91	CA

Proposed Species

Scientific Name	Common Name	Date Proposed	States
Lycopodium mannii	Wawae'iole	05/24/91	HI
Lysimachia filifolia	None	10/30/91	HI
Lysimachia lydgatei	None	05/24/91	HI
Macbridea alba	White Birds-in-a-Nest	12/18/90	FL
Marsilea villosa	'Ihi'Ihi	02/15/91	HI
Melicope haupuensis	Alani	10/30/91	HI
Melicope knudsenii	Alani	10/30/91	HI
Melicope mucronulata	Alani	05/24/91	HI
Melicope pallida	Alani	10/30/91	HI
Melicope quadrangularis	Alani	10/30/91	HI
Melicope reflexa	Alani	09/20/91	HI
Munroidendron racemosum	None	10/30/91	HI
Nothocestrum peltatum	'Aiea	10/30/91	HI
Orcuttia californica	California Orcutt Grass	11/12/91	CA
Oxytheca parishii var. *goodmaniana*	Cushenbury Oxytheca	11/19/91	CA
Peucedanum sandwicense	Makou	10/30/91	HI
Phyllostegia mannii	None	09/20/91	HI
Phyllostegia waimeae	None	10/30/91	HI
Poa sandvicensis	Hawaiian Bluegrass	09/26/90	HI
Poa siphonoglossa	None	09/26/90	HI
Pogogyne nudiuscula	Otay Mesa Mint	11/12/91	CA
Pritchardia munroi	Loulu	09/20/91	HI
Pteralyxia kauaiensis	Kaulu	10/30/91	HI
Rorippa gambellii	Gambel's Watercress	09/30/91	CA
Schiedea haleakalensis	None	05/24/91	HI
Schiedea lydgatei	None	09/20/91	HI
Schiedea spergulina	None	10/30/91	HI
Schoenocrambe argillacea	Clay Reed-Mustard	04/12/91	UT
Schoenocrambe barnebyi	Barneby Reed-Mustard	04/12/91	UT
Schwalbea americana	American Chaffseed	09/11/91	CT,DE,FL, GA,KY,MA, MD,MS,NC, NJ,NY,SC, TN,VA
Scutellaria floridana	Florida Skullcap	12/18/90	FL
Sedum integrifolium ssp. *leedyi*	Leedy's Roseroot	06/18/91	MN,NY
Sidalcea nelsoniana	Nelson's Checker-Mallow	06/07/91	OR

Scientific Name	Common Name	Date Proposed	States
Silene alexandri	None	09/20/91	HI
Silene lanceolata	None	09/20/91	HI
Solanum sandwicense	Populo'aiakeakua	10/30/91	HI
Spiranthes diluvialis	Ute Ladies'-Tresses	11/13/90	CO,UT
Stenogyne bifida	None	09/20/91	HI
Stenogyne campanulata	None	09/26/90	HI
Stenogyne kanehoana	None	01/23/91	HI
Styrax portoricensis	Palo de Jazmin	04/19/91	PR
Ternstroemia luquillensis	Palo Colorado	04/19/91	PR
Ternstroemia subsessilis	None	04/19/91	PR
Tetramolopium rockii	None	09/20/91	HI
Thelypteris pilosa var. *alabamensis*	Alabama Streak-Sorus Fern	11/29/91	AL
Wilkesia hobdyi	Dwarf Iliau	10/02/89	HI
Xylosma crenatum	None	09/26/90	HI

ANIMALS

Scientific Name	Common Name	Date Proposed	States
Aplodontia rufa nigra	Point Arena Mountain Beaver	02/15/91	CA
Ursus americanus luteolus	Louisiana Black Bear	06/21/90	LA
Brachyramphus marmoratus	Marbled Murrelet	06/20/91	WA,OR,CA
Polioptila californica californica	Coastal California Gnatcatcher	09/17/91	CA
Strix occidentalis lucida	Mexican Spotted Owl	11/04/91	CO,UT,AZ, NM,TX
Cyprinella caerulea	Blue Shiner	04/19/91	AL,GA,TN
Hypomesus transpacificus	Delta Smelt	11/03/91	CA
Oncorhynchus kisutch	Lower Columbia River Coho Salmon	06/27/91	OR,WA
Oncorhynchus tshawytscha	Snake River Spring/Summer Chinook Salmon	06/27/91	OR,WA
Oncorhynchus tshawytscha	Snake River Fall Chinook Salmon	06/27/91	OR,WA
Oregonichthys crameri	Oregon Chub	11/19/91	OR
Percina aurolineata	Goldline Darter	04/19/91	AL,GA
Epioblasma metastriata	Upland Combshell	11/19/91	AL,GA,TN
Epioblasma othcaloogensis	Southern Acornshell	11/19/91	AL,TN,GA
Lampsilis altilis	Fine-Lined Pocketbook	11/19/91	AL,GA

Proposed Species

Scientific Name	Common Name	Date Proposed	States
Lampsilis perovalis	Orange-Nacre Mucket	11/19/91	AL,MS
Medionidus acutissimus	Alabama Moccasinshell	11/19/91	AL,GA,MS
Medionidus parvulus	Coosa Moccasinshell	11/19/91	AL,GA,TN
Pleurobema decisum	Southern Clubshell	11/19/91	AL,GA,MS,TN
Pleurobema furvum	Dark Pigtoe	11/19/91	AL
Pleurobema perovatum	Ovate Clubshell	11/19/91	AL,GA,MS,TN
Pleurobemas georgianum	Southern Pigtoe	11/19/91	AL,GA,TN
Ptychobranchus greeni	Triangular Kidneyshell	11/19/91	AL,GA,TN
Lirceus usdagalun	Lee County Cave Isopod	11/15/91	VA
Streptocephalus woottoni	Riverside Fairy Shrimp	11/12/91	CA
Fontelicella idahoensis	Idaho Springsnail	12/18/90	ID
Hydrobiidae n. sp.	Bliss Rapids Snail	12/18/90	ID
Lanx n. sp.	Banbury Springs Limpet	12/18/90	ID
Physia natricina	Snake River Physa Snail	12/18/90	ID
Valvata utahensis	Utah Valvata Snail	12/18/90	ID
Gryllotalpa major	Prairie Mole Cricket	04/25/90	KS,OK,MO,AR
Speyeria zerene myrtleae	Myrtle's Silverspot Butterfly	03/22/91	CA

Appendix III
Category 1 Candidate Species

* = possibly extinct
** = exists only in cultivation

Scientific Name	Common Name	Historic Range
PLANTS (Notice date: February 21, 1990)		
Abronia alpina	Ramshaw Sand-Verbena	CA
Abronia umbellata ssp. *acutalata**	Rose-Purple Sand-Verbena	WA
Abutilon virginianum	none	PR
Acaena exigua	Lili-Wai	HI
Acanthomintha ilicifolia	San Diego Thornmint	CA
Adenophorus periens	Pendant Kihi Fern	HI
Adiantum vivesii	Helecho	PR
Agalinis caddoensis*	Caddo Purple False-Foxglove	LA
Agrostis aristiglumis	Awned Bentgrass	CA
Alectryon macrococcus	Mahoe	HI
Allium aaseae	Aase's Onion	ID
Allium fimbriatum var. *munzii*	Munz's Onion	CA
Allium gooddingii	none	AZ,NM
Allium hickmanii	Hickman's Onion	CA
Allium sanbornii var. *tuolumnense*	Rawhide Hill Onion	CA
Amaranthus brownii	none	HI
Ambrosia cheiranthifolia	Ragweed	TX
Amorpha ouachitensis	False Indigo	AR,OK
Amsinckia carinata	none	OR
Amsonia tharpii	none	TX
Arabis hoffmannii	Hoffmann's Rock-Cress	CA
Arabis johnstonii	Johnston's Rock-Cress	CA
Arabis perstellata var. *perstellata*	Small Rock Cress	AL,KY
Arctostaphylos imbricata ssp. *imbricata*	San Bruno Mountain Manzanita	CA
Arctostaphylos morroensis	Morro Manzanita	CA
Arctostaphylos pallida	Alameda Manzanita	CA
Arctostaphylos uva-ursi ssp. *myrtifolia*	Lone Manzanita	CA
Arctostaphylos uva-ursi var. *densilfora***	Vine Hill Manzanita	CA
Arctostaphylos uva-ursi var. *franciscana***	San Francisco Manzanita	CA

Category 1 Candidate Species

Scientific Name	Common Name	Historic Range
Arenaria fontinalis	Water Stitchwort	KY,TN
Arenaria paludicola	Marsh Sandwort	CA,OR,WA
Arenaria ursina	Bear Valley Sandwort	CA
Argyroxiphium kauense	Ka'u Silversword	HI
Argyroxiphium sandwicensis ssp. *macrocephalum*	none	HI
Aristida chasae	none	PR
Artemisia campestris var. *wormskioldii*	none	OR,WA
Asclepias viridula	none	FL
Asplenium fragile	none	HI
Aster avitus	none	GA,SC
Aster puniceus ssp. *elliottii* var. *scabricaulis*	none	TX
Astragalus agnicidus	Humboldt Milk-Vetch	CA
Astragalus albens	Cushenbury Milk-Vetch	CA
Astragalus applegatei	none	OR
Astragalus australis var. *olympicus*	none	WA
Astragalus beatleyae	Beatley Milk-Vetch	NV
Astragalus clarianus	Clara Hunt's Milk-Vetch	CA
Astragalus equisolensis	Milk-Vetch	UT
Astragalus lentiginosus var. *coachellae*	Coachella Valley Milk-Vetch	CA
Astragalus lentiginosus var. *micans*	Shiny Milk-Vetch	CA
Astragalus lentiginosus var. *piscinensis*	Fish Slough Milk-Vetch	CA
Astragalus lentiginosus var. *sesquimetralis*	Sodaville Milk-Vetch	CA,NV
Astragalus oophorus var. *clokeyanus*	none	NV
Astragalus pycnostachyus var. *lanosissimus**	Ventura Marsh Milk-Vetch	CA
Astragalus tener var. *titi*	Coastal Dunes Rattleweed	CA
Astragalus xiphoides	Gladiator Milk-Vetch	AZ
Auerodendron pauciflorum	none	PR
Aureolaria patula	none	AL,GA,KY,TN
Baccharis vanessae	Encinitis Coyote Bush	CA
Berberis nevinii	Nevin's Barberry	CA
Bidens micrantha ssp. *kalealaha*	Ko'oko'olau	HI
Bidens wiebkei	Ko'oko'olau	HI
Bonamia menziesii	none	HI
Botrychium pumicola	Crater Lake Grape Fern	CA,OR
Botrychium subbifoliatum*	Makou	HI
Brachionidium ciliolatum	none	PR

Scientific Name	Common Name	Historic Range
*Brachymenium andersonii**	none	NC
Brighamia insignis	Alula	HI
Brighamia rockii	Pua 'ala	HI
Brodiaea filifolia	Thread-Leaved Brodiaea	CA
Brodiaea pallida	Chinese Camp Brodiaea	CA
Calamintha ashei	none	FL,GA
Calamovilfa arcuata	Sand Grass	OK,TN
Callicarpa ampla	Capa Rosa	PR
Calochortus clavatus var. *avius*	Pleasant Valley Mariposa	CA
*Calochortus monanthus**	Shasta River Mariposa	CA
Calochortus nitidus	none	ID,WA
Calochortus westonii	Shirley Meadows Mariposa	CA
Calyptranthes luquillensis	none	PR
Calyptranthes thomasiana	none	PR
Canavalia molokaiensis	Molokai Jack-Bean	HI
Carex albida	White Sedge	CA
Carpenteria californica	Carpenteria	CA
Castanea pumila var. *ozarkensis*	Ozark Chinquapin	AL,AR,MO,OK
Castilleja aquariensis	Aquarius Indian Paintbrush	UT
Castilleja christii	Christ's Paintbrush	ID
Castilleja elongata	none	TX
*Castilleja leschkeana**	Point Reyes Paintbrush	CA
Castilleja levisecta	none	OR,WA,Canada
Castilleja neglecta	Tiburon Paintbrush	CA
Castilleja salsuginosa	Monte Neva Paintbrush	NV
Castilleja uliginosa	Pitkin Marsh Paintbrush	CA
Ceanothus ferrisae	Coyote Valley California-Lilac	CA
Ceanothus roderickii	Pine Hill Ceanothus	CA
Cenchrus agrimonioides var. *laysanensis**	Laysan Argimony Sandbur	HI
Cercocarpus traskiae	Catalina Mountain-Mahogany	CA
Chamaecrista lineata var. *keyensis*	Florida Keys Senna	FL
Chamaesyce celastroides var. *tomentella**	none	HI
Chamaesyce deltoidea ssp. *serpyllum*	Wedge Spurge	FL
Chamaesyce deppeana	none	HI
Chamaesyce halemanui	none	HI
Chamaesyce hooveri	Hoover's Spurge	CA
Chamaesyce remyi var. *hanaleiensis*	none	HI

Category 1 Candidate Species

Scientific Name	Common Name	Historic Range
Chlorogalum purpureum var. *purpureum*	Purple Amole	CA
Chlorogalum purpureum var. *reductum*	Cammatta Canyon Amole	CA
Chorizanthe howellii	Howell's Spineflower	CA
Chorizanthe orcuttiana*	Orcutt's Spineflower	CA
Chorizanthe parryi var. *fernandina**	San Fernando Valley Spineflower	CA
Chorizanthe valida	Sonoma Spineflower	CA
Chrysothamnus molestus	none	AZ
Cimicifuga arizonica	Arizona Bugbane	AZ
Cirsium fontinale var. *fontinale*	Fountain Thistle	CA
Cirsium hydrophilum var. *hydrophilum*	Suisun Thistle	CA
Cirsium loncholepis	La Graciosa Thistle	CA
Cirsium rhothophilum	Surf Thistle	CA
Clarkia franciscana	Presidio Clarkia	CA
Clarkia imbricata	Vine Hill Clarkia	CA
Clarkia lingulata	Merced Clarkia	CA
Clarkia speciosa ssp. *immaculata*	Pismo Clarkia	CA
Clarkia springvillensis	Springville Clarkia	CA
Claytonia lanceolata var. *peirsonii*	Peirson's Spring Beauty	CA
Clematis hirsutissima var. *arizonica*	Arizona Leather Flower	AZ
Clermontia lindseyana	none	HI
Clermontia oblongifolia ssp. *brevipes*	none	HI
Clermontia oblongifolia ssp. *mauiensis*	none	HI
Clermontia peleana	none	HI
Clermontia pyrularia	none	HI
Clitoria fragrans	none	FL
Coccoloba rugosa	none	PR
Collomia rawsoniana	Rawson's Flaming Trumpet	CA
Colubrina oppositifolia	Kauila	HI
Conostegia hotteana	none	PR
Conradina glabra	Apalachicola Rosemary	FL
Cordia wagnerorum	none	PR
Cordylanthus mollis ssp. *mollis*	Soft Bird's-Beak	CA
Cordylanthus nidularius	Mt. Diablo Bird's-Beak	CA
Cordylanthus rigidus ssp. *littoralis*	Seaside Bird's-Beak	CA
Cordylanthus tenuis ssp. *capillaris*	Pennell's Bird's-Beak	CA
Coryphantha albicolumnaria	none	TX

Scientific Name	Common Name	Historic Range
Coryphantha recurvata	Santa Cruz Beehive Cactus	AZ
Coryphantha scheeri var. *robustispina*	none	AZ
Ctenitis squamigera*	none	HI
Cuphea aspera	none	FL
Cupressus stephensonii	Cuyamaca Cypress	CA
Cuscuta attenuata	Dodder	OK
Cyanea asarifolia	none	HI
Cyanea copelandii ssp. *copelandii*	none	HI
Cyanea hamatiflora ssp. *carlsonii*	none	HI
Cyanea lobata	none	HI
Cyanea longissima*	none	HI
Cyanea manii	none	HI
Cyanea mceldowneyi	none	HI
Cyanea procera*	none	HI
Cyanea shipmanii	none	HI
Cyanea stictophylla	none	HI
Cyanea truncata	none	HI
Cylindrocolea andersoni*	none	NC
Cyrtandra crenata	none	HI
Cyrtandra giffardii	none	HI
Cyrtandra limahuliensis	none	HI
Cyrtandra munroi	none	HI
Cyrtandra polyantha	none	HI
Cyrtandra tintinnabula	none	HI
Dalea tentaculoides	Gentry's Indigobush	AZ
Delissea rhytidosperma	none	HI
Delissea undulata*	none	HI
Delphinium bakeri	Baker's Larkspur	CA
Delphinium luteum	Yellow Larkspur	CA
Delphinium variegatum ssp. *thornei*	Thorne's Royal Larkspur	CA
Delphinium viridescens	Wenatchee Larkspur	WA
Descurainia torulosa	none	WY
Dicliptera krugii	none	PR
Diellia erecta	none	HI
Diellia laciniata*	none	HI
Diellia unisora*	none	HI
Diplazium molokaiense	none	HI

Category 1 Candidate Species

Scientific Name	Common Name	Historic Range
*Dissanthelium californicum**	California Dissanthelium	CA
Downingia concolor var. *brevior*	Cuyamaca Lake Downingia	CA
Dubautia latifolia	none	HI
Dudleya brevifolia	Short-Leaved Dudleya	CA
Dudleya cymosa ssp. *nov./ined.*	Pierpoint Springs Liveforever	CA
Dudleya densiflora	San Gabriel Mountains Dudleya	CA
Dudleya parva	Conejo Dudleya	CA
Dudleya setchellii	Santa Clara Valley Dudleya	CA
Dudleya stolonifera	Laguna Beach Liveforever	CA
Dudleya viscida	Sticky-Leaved Liveforever	CA
Echinomastus erectocentrus var. *acunensis*	Acuna Cactus	AZ
Elaphoglossum serpens	none	PR
*Elodea linearis**	Nashville Waterweed	TN
Encyclia kranzlinii	none	PR
*Eragrostis fosbergii**	Fosberg's Love Grass	HI
*Eragrostis hosakai**	none	HI
Erigeron basalticus	Basalt Daisy	WA
Erigeron decumbens var. *decumbens*	none	OR
Erigeron kuschei	Chiricahua Fleabane	AZ
Eriodictyon altissimum	Indian Knob Mountain Balm	CA
Eriodictyon capitatum	Lompoc Yerba Santa	CA
Eriogonum apricum var. *apricum*	Lone Buckwheat	CA
Eriogonum apricum var. *prostratum*	Irish Hill Buckwheat	CA
Eriogonum argophyllum	Buckwheat	NV
Eriogonum brandegei	Brandegee Wild Buckwheat	CO
Eriogonum chrysops	Golden Buckwheat	OR
Eriogonum kelloggii	Red Mountain Buckwheat	CA
Eriogonum longifolium var. *gnaphalifolium*	Scrub Wild Buckwheat	FL
Eriogonum longifolium var. *harperi*	none	AL,KY,TN
Eriogonum ovalifolium var. *vineum*	Cushenbury Buckwheat	CA
Eriophyllum latilobum	San Mateo Wooly-Sunflower	CA
Eryngium aristulatum var. *parishii*	San Diego Button-Celery	CA
Erysimum menziesii	Menzies' Wallflower	CA
Erysimum teretifolium	Ben Lomond Wallflower	CA
Erythrina eggersii	Pinon Espinoso	PR
Eugenia haematocarpa	Uvillo	PR

Scientific Name	Common Name	Historic Range
Eugenia koolauensis	Nioi	HI
Euphorbia telephioides	Telephus Spurge	FL
Eutrema penlandii	Penland Eutrema	CO
Exocarpos luteolus	Heau	HI
Flaveria macdougallii	none	AZ
Flueggea neowawraea	none	HI
Forestiera segregata var. *pinetorum*	none	FL
*Franklinia alatamaha***	Franklin Tree	GA
Fremontodendron decumbens	Pine Hill Flannelbush	CA
Gaura neomexicana ssp. *coloradensis*	Colorado Butterfly Plant	CO,WY
Geranium arboreum	Hawaiian Red-Fowered Geranium	HI
Geranium multiflorum	Native Geranium	HI
Gesneria pauciflora	none	PR
Gilia caespitosa	Rabbit Valley Gilia	UT
Gilia tenuiflora ssp. *arenaria*	Monterey Gilia	CA
*Gouania vitifolia**	none	HI
Hackelia cronquistii	Cronquist's Stickseed	OR
Hackelia venusta	Showy Stickseed	WA
Haplopappus insecticruris	none	ID
Haplopappus radiatus	Goldenweed	ID,OR
Hastingsia bracteosa	none	OR
Hedeoma graveolens	Mock Pennyroyal	FL
Hedyotis cookiana	none	HI
*Hedyotis coriacea**	Kio'ele	HI
Hedyotis mannii	none	HI
Helenium virginicum	none	VA
Helianthus nuttallii ssp. *parishii**	Los Angeles Sunflower	CA
Helianthus paradoxus	Sunflower	NM,TX
Hemizonia arida	Red Rock Tarweed	CA
Hemizonia increscens ssp. *villosa*	Gaviota Tarweed	CA
*Hemizonia mohavensis**	Mojave Tarweed	CA
Hesperocnide sandwicensis	none	HI
Hesperolinon congestum	Marin Dwarf-Flax	CA
Hesperolinon didymocarpum	Lake County Dwarf-Flax	CA
Hesperomannia arborescens	Lana'i Hesperomannia	HI
*Hibiscadelphus crucibracteatus**	none	HI

Category 1 Candidate Species

Scientific Name	Common Name	Historic Range
*Hibiscadelphus giffardianus***	Kilauea Hau Kuahiwi	HI
Hibiscadelphus hualalaiensis	Hualalai Hau Kuahiwi	HI
Hibiscus arnottianus ssp. *immaculatus*	none	HI
Hibiscus brackenridgei	Native Yellow Hibiscus	HI
Hibiscus clayi	Clay's Hibiscus	HI
Holocarpha macradenia	Santa Cruz Tarweed	CA
Howellia aquatilis	Howellia	CA,ID,MT, OR,WA
Ischaemum byrone	none	HI
Ivesia aperta var. *canina*	Dog Valley Ivesia	CA
Juncus leiospermus var. *ahartii*	Ahart's Rush	CA
Lasthenia conjugens	Contra Costa Goldfields	CA
Layia carnosa	Beach Layia	CA
Leavenworthia exigua var. *laciniata*	Glade Cress	KY
Lepidium bidentatum var. *remyi**	Remy's 'Anaunau	HI
Lepidium montanum var. *stellae*	none	UT
Leptocereus grantianum	none	PR
Lesquerella kingii ssp. *bernardina*	San Bernardino Bladder-Pod	CA
Lesquerella perforata	Spring Creek Bladder-Pod	TN
Lesquerella stonensis	Stones River Bladder-Pod	TN
Lessingia germanorum var. *germanorum*	San Francisco Lessingia	CA
Lilium maritimum	Coast Lily	CA
Lilium occidentale	Western Lily	CA,OR
Lilium pitkinense	Pitkin Marsh Lily	CA
Limnanthes floccosa ssp. *californica*	Butte County Meadowfoam	CA
Limnanthes floccosa ssp. *pumila*	Dwarf Meadowfoam	OR
*Lipochaeta degeneri**	Small-Leaved Nehe	HI
Lipochaeta fauriei	Faurie Nehe	HI
Lipochaeta kamolensis	none	HI
Lipochaeta micrantha	none	HI
Lipochaeta waimeaensis	none	HI
Lobelia oahuensis	none	HI
Lomatium cookii	Cook's Lomatium	OR
Lomatium erythrocarpum	Red-Fruited Desert-Parsley	OR
Lomatium greenmanii	Greenman's Desert-Parsley	OR
Luina serpentina	none	OR
Lunania buchii	none	PR

Scientific Name	Common Name	Historic Range
Lupinus aridus ssp. *ashlandensis*	Ashland Lupine	OR
Lupinus nipomensis	Nipomo Mesa Lupine	CA
Lupinus tidestromii var. *layneae*	Point Reyes Clover Lupine	CA
Lupinus tidestromii var. *tidestromii*	Tidestrom's Clover Lupine	CA
Lycopodium mannii	none	HI
Lycopodium nutans	none	HI
Lyonia truncata var. *proctorii*	none	PR
Lysimachia filifolia	none	HI
Lysimachia lydgatei	none	HI
Macbridea alba	White Birds-in-a-Nest	FL
Mariscus fauriei	none	HI
Mariscus pennatiformis	none	HI
*Mariscus rockii**	none	HI
Marsilea villosa	none	HI
Maytenus ponceana	Cuero de Sapo	PR
*Melicope balloui**	none	HI
*Melicope degeneri**	none	HI
Melicope haupuensis	none	HI
Melicope knudsenii	none	HI
*Melicope lydgatei**	none	HI
Melicope mucronulata	Alani	HI
*Melicope ovalis**	none	HI
*Melicope pallida**	Alani	HI
*Melicope quadrangularis**	none	HI
*Melicope reflexa**	none	HI
*Micranthemum micranthemoides**	Nuttall's Micranthemum	DE,DC,MD,NJ, NY,PA,VA
*Mimulus brandegei**	Santa Cruz Island Monkey-flower	CA
Mimulus shevockii	Kelso Creek Monkeyflower	CA
*Mimulus traskiae**	Santa Catalina Monkeyflower	CA
*Mimulus whipplei**	Whipple's Monkeyflower	CA
Mitracarpus maxwelliae	none	PR
*Monardella leucocephala**	Merced Monardella	CA
*Monardella pringlei**	Pringle Monardella	CA
Munroidendron racemosum	none	HI
Myrcia paganii	Ausu	PR

Category 1 Candidate Species

Scientific Name	Common Name	Historic Range
Narthecium americanum	none	DE,NJ,NC,SC
Navarretia plieantha	Many-Flowered Navarretia	CA
Navarretia setiloba	Piute Mountains Navarretia	CA
Neostapfia colusana	Colusa Grass	CA
Neraudia sericea	none	HI
Nolina brittoniana	Britton's Bear-Grass	FL
Nolina interrata	Dehesa Bear-Grass	CA
Nothocestrum breviflorum	none	HI
Nothocestrum peltatum	'Aiea	HI
Ochrosia kilaueaensis	Holei	HI
Oenothera psammophila	Evening-Primrose	ID
Oenothera wolfii	Wolf's Evening-Primrose	CA,OR
Ophioglossum coccinnum	Adder's-Tongue	HI
Opuntia whipplei var. *multigeniculata*	none	NV
Orcuttia californica	California Orcutt Grass	CA
Orcuttia inequalis	San Joaquin Orcutt Grass	CA
Orcuttia pilosa	Pilose Orcutt Grass	CA
Orcuttia tenuis	Slender Orcutt Grass	CA
Orcuttia viscida	Sacramento Orcutt Grass	CA
Paronychia congesta	Bushy Whitlow-Wort	TX
Parvisedum leiocarpum	Lake County Stonecrop	CA
Pediocactus paradinei	Kaibab Pincushion Cactus	AZ
Pediocactus peeblesianus var. *fickeiseniae*	Fickeisen Pincushion Cactus	AZ
Pediocactus winkleri	none	UT
Penstemon albifluvis	White River Beardtongue	CO,UT
Penstemon discolor	Cataiina Beardtongue	AZ
Penstemon grahamii	Graham Beardtongue	CO,UT
Pentachaeta lyonii	Lyon's Pentachaeta	CA
*Peperomia degeneri**	none	HI
Peperomia megalopoda	none	PR
Petrophytum cinerascens	Chelan Rockmat	WA
*Phacelia cinerea**	Ashy Phacelia	CA
Phacelia submutica	Phacelia	CO
Phaseolus supinus	Supine Bean	AZ
Phlox hirsuta	Yreka Phlox	CA
Phlox idahonis	Clearwater Phlox	ID
*Phyllostegia imminuta**	none	HI

Scientific Name	Common Name	Historic Range
Phyllostegia mannii	none	HI
Phyllostegia waimeae	none	HI
Pinguicula ionantha	Butterwort	FL
Plagiobothrys hirtus	Popcornflower	OR
Plagiobothrys strictus	Calistoga Allocarya	CA
Plantago hawaiensis	none	HI
Plantago princeps	Ale	HI
Pleodendron macranthum	Chupagallo	PR
Pleuropogon oregonus	Oregon Semaphore Grass	OR
Poa altropurpurea	San Bernardino Bluegrass	CA
Poa mannii*	Mann's Bluegrass	HI
Poa napensis	Napa Bluegrass	CA
Poa sandvicensis	Hawaiian Bluegrass	HI
Poa siphonoglossa	none	HI
Pogogyne nudiuscula	Otay Mesa Mint	CA
Polemonium pectinatum	none	WA
Polyctenium williamsiae	Combleaf	NV
Polygala lewtonii	Lewton's Polygala	FL
Polygonella macrophylla	Large-Leaved jointweed	AL,FL
Polygonella myriophylla	Jointweed	FL
Polystichum calderonense	none	PR
Portulaca sclerocarpa	Ihi-Makole	HI
Potentilla basaltica	Soldier Meadows Cinquefoil	NV
Potentilla hickmanii	Hickman's Cinquefoil	CA
Potentilla multijuga*	Ballona Cinquefoil	CA
Pritchardia affinis	none	HI
Pritchardia aylmer-robinsonii	Hawane	HI
Pritchardia munroii	none	HI
Pritchardia remota	none	HI
Pseudobahia peirsonii	Tulare Pseudobahia	CA
Psidium sintenisii	Hoja Menuda	PR
Psoralea macrophylla*	Scurf-Pea	NC
Psoralea stipulata*	Scurf-Pea	IN,KY
Pteralyxia kauaiensis	Kauai Pteralyxia	HI
Pteris lidgatei	none	HI
Ranunculus reconditus	none	OR,WA
Rollandia crispa	none	HI

Category 1 Candidate Species

Scientific Name	Common Name	Historic Range
Rorippa gambelii	Gambel's Watercress	CA
Rorippa subumbellata	Tahoe Yellow-Cress	CA,NV
Roystonea elata	Florida Royal Palm	FL
Rubus nigerrimus	none	WA
Rumex orthoneurus	Blumer Dock	AZ
Salix arizonica	White Mountains Willow	AZ
Schiedea haleakalensis	Ma'oli'oli	HI
Schiedea lydgatei	Ma'oli'oli	HI
Schiedea spergulina var. *leiopoda**	none	HI
Schiedea spergulina var. *spergulina*	Ma'oli'oli	HI
Schiedea verticillata	none	HI
Schizachyrium niveum	none	FL
Schoenocrambe barnebyi	none	UT
Schwalbea americana	Chaffseed	CT,DE,FL,GA, KY,MA,MD, MS,NC,NJ, NY,SC,TN,VA
Scrophularia micrantha	Figwort	NM
Scutellaria floridana	none	FL
Sedum laxum ssp. *eastwoodiae*	Red Mountain Stonecrop	CA
Senecio ertterae	Ertter's Ragwort	OR
Senecio huachucanus	Huachuca Groundsel	AZ
Sesbania tomentosa	'Ohai	HI
Sibara filifolia	Island Rock Cress	CA
*Sidalcea keckii**	Keck's Sidalcea	CA
Sidalcea nelsoniana	Nelson's Checkermallow	OR
Sidalcea oregana ssp. *valida*	Kenwood Marsh Checkermallow	CA
Sidalcea oregana var. *calva*	none	WA
Sidalcea stipularis	Scadden Flat Checkerbloom	CA
Silene alexandri	none	HI
Silene campanulata ssp. *campanulata*	Red Mountain Campion	CA
Silene hawaiiensis	none	HI
Silene lanceolata	none	HI
Solanum carolinense var. *hirsutum**	Horse-Nettle	GA
Solanum incompletum	Thorny Popolo	HI
Solanum sandwicense	none	HI

Scientific Name	Common Name	Historic Range
*Solidago plumosa**	Goldenrod	NC
Spermolepis hawaiiensis	none	HI
Sphaeromeria compacta	Tansy	NV
Spiranthes diluvialis	Ute Ladies'-Tresses	CO,UT
Stenogyne bifida	none	HI
Stenogyne campanulata	none	HI
*Stenogyne haliakalae**	Haleakala Stenogyne	HI
Stenogyne kanehoana	none	HI
Streptanthus albidus ssp. *albidus*	Metcalf Canyon Jewelflower	CA
Streptanthus albidus ssp. *peramoenus*	Uncommon Jewelflower	CA
Streptanthus brachiatus ssp. *brachiatus*	Contact Mine Streptanthus	CA
Streptanthus brachiatus ssp. *hoffmanii*	Freed's Jewelflower	CA
Streptanthus morrisonii ssp. *elatus*	Three Peaks Jewelflower	CA
Streptanthus morrisonii ssp. *hirtiflorus*	Dorr's Cabin Jewelflower	CA
Streptanthus niger	Tiburon Jewelflower	CA
Synthyris ranunculina	Kittentails	NV
Taraxacum californicum	California Dandelion	CA
Taxus floridana	Florida Yew	FL
Tectaria estremerana	none	PR
Ternstroemia luquillensis	Palo Colorado	PR
Ternstroemia subsessilis	none	PR
*Tetramolopium capillare**	none	HI
Tetramolopium rockii	none	HI
Tetraplasandra gymnocarpa	none	HI
Thelypodium howellii var. *spectabilis*	none	OR
Thelypteris inabonensis	none	PR
Thelypteris verecunda	none	PR
Thelypteris yaucoensis	none	PR
*Thismia americana**	none	IL
Thlaspi montanum var. *californicum*	Kneeland Prairie Penny-Cress	CA
Tillandsia baileyi	none	TX
Trichostema austromontanum ssp. *compactum*	Hidden Lake Bluecurls	CA
Trifolium polyodon	Pacific Grove Clover	CA
Trifolium thompsonii	Thompson's Clover	WA
Trifolium trichocalyx	Del Monte Clover	CA
Tuctoria greenei	Greene's Orcutt Grass	CA

Category 1 Candidate Species

Scientific Name	Common Name	Historic Range
Verbena californica	Red Hills Vervain	CA
Verbena tampensis	Vervain	FL
Verbesina chapmannii	Chapman's Crownbeard	FL
Verbesina heterophylla	none	FL
Vernonia proctori	none	PR
Vicia ocalensis	Ocala Vetch	FL
Vigna o-wahuensis	O'ahu Vigna	HI
Wilkesia hobdyi	Dwarf Iliau	HI
Xylosma crenatum	none	HI
Zanthoxylum hawaiiense	A'e	HI

ANIMALS (Notice date: January 6, 1989)

Mammals

Aplodontia rufa nigra	Point Arena Mountain Beaver	CA
Sorex vagrans halicoetes	Salt Marsh Vagrant Shrew	CA
Sorex ornatus sinuosus	Suisun Ornate shrew	CA
Spermophilus brunneus ssp.	Northern Idaho Ground Squirrel	ID
Sylvilagus bachmani riparius	Riparian Brush Rabbit	CA

Birds

Laterallus jamaicensis coturniculus	California Black Rail	AZ,CA
Thryomanes bewickii altus	Appalachian Bewick's Wren	AL,GA,KY, MD,NC,OH, PA,SC,TN,

Reptiles

Phrynosoma mcalli	Flat-Tailed Horned Lizard	CA,AZ

Amphibians

Batrachoseps campi	Inyo Mountains Slender Salamander	CA
Gyrinophilis palleucus gulolineatus	Berry Cave Salamander	TN
Plethodon neomexicanus	Jemez Mountain Salamander	NM
Rana tarahumarae	Tarahumara Frog	AZ,VA,WV,CD

Scientific Name	Common Name	Historic Range
Fishes		
Coregonus reighardi	Shortnose Cisco	IL,IN,MI,NY, WI,CA
Cyprinodon nevadensis shoshone	Shoshone Pupfish	CA
Cyprinodon pecosensis	Pecos Pupfish	NM,TX
Elassoma sp.	Spring Pygmy Sunfish	AL
Gila bicolor ssp.	Summer Basin Tui Chub	OR
Gila bicolor vaccaceps	Cowhead Lake Tui Chub	CA
Hypomesus transpacificus	Delta Smelt	CA
Iotichthys phlegethontis	Least Chub	UT
Lentipes concolor	O'opu Alamo'o	HI
Crustaceans		
Spelaeorchestia koloana	Kauai Cave Amphipod	HI
Snails		
Assiminea pecos	Pecos Assiminea Snail	NM,TX
Binneya notabilis	Santa Barbara Shelled Slug	CA
Fontelicella chupaderae	Chupadera Springsnail	NM
Fontelicella gilae	Gila Springsnail	NM
Fontelicella roswellensis	Rosewell Springsnail	NM
Fontelicella thermalis	New Mexico Hotspring Snail	NM
Helminthoglypta walkeriana	Banded Dune Snail	CA
Io fluvialis	Spiny Riversnail	TN,VA
Micrarionta facta	Santa Barbara Islandsnail	CA
Physa sp.	Snake River Physa Snail	ID
Prygulopsis cristalis	Crystal Spring Springsnail	NV
Prygulopsis erythopoma	Ash Meadows Pebblesnail	NV
Prygulopsis fairbanksensis	Fairbanks Springsnail	NV
Prygulopsis isolatus	Elongate-Gland Springsnail	NV
Prygulopsis nanus	Distal-gland Springsnail	NV
Prygulopsis pisteri	Median-gland Nevada Springsnail	NV
Stenotrema pilsbryi	Rich Mountain Slitmouth	AR,OK
Tryonia adamantina	Diamond Y Spring Snail	TX
Tryonia angulata	Sportinggoods Tryonia Snail	NV
Tryonia elata	Point of Rocks Tryonia Snail	NV

Category 1 Candidate Species

Scientific Name	Common Name	Historic Range
Tryonia ericae	Minute Tryonia Snail	NV
Tryonia stocktonensis	Gonzales Spring Snail	TX
Undescribed	Virile Amargosa Snail	NV
Undescribed	Bliss Rapids Snail	ID
Vespericola karokorum	Karok Indian Snail	CA

Insects and Arachnids

Scientific Name	Common Name	Historic Range
Adelocosa anops	Kauai Cave Wolf Spider	HI
Coelus gracilis	San Joaquin Dune Beetle	CA
Goeracea oregona	Sagehen Creek Goeracean Caddisfly	CA
Lepidostoma sp.	Cold Spring Caddisfly	CA
Megalagrion pacificum	Pacific Megalagrion Damselfly	HI
Proceratium californicum	Valley Oak Ant	CA
Trigonoscuta doyeni	Doyen's Trigonoscuta Dune Weevil	CA

Appendix IV
Recovery Status of Listed Species

Fish and Wildlife Service's evaluation of the status of Threatened and Endangered species in its December 1990 report to Congress.

Common Name	Scientific Name	Status
PLANTS		
Large-Fruited Sand-Verbena	*Abronia macrocarpa*	Declining
Ko'oloa'ula	*Abutilon menziesii*	Improving
San Mateo Thornmint	*Acanthomintha obovata* ssp. *duttonii*	Declining
Achyranthes	*Achyranthes rotundata*	Stable
Northern Wild Monkshood	*Aconitum noveboracense*	Improving
Sandplain Gerardia	*Agalinis acuta*	Stable
Arizona Agave	*Agave arizonica*	Unknown
Crenulate Lead-Plant	*Amorpha crenulata*	Stable
Little Amphianthus	*Amphianthus pusillus*	Stable
Large-Flowered Fiddleneck	*Amsinckia grandiflora*	Improving
Kearney's Blue-Star	*Amsonia kearneyana*	Unknown
Tobusch Fishhook Cactus	*Ancistrocactus tobuschii*	Unknown
Price's Potato-Bean	*Apios priceana*	Declining
McDonald's Rock-Cress	*Arabis macdonaldiana*	Stable
Shale Barren Rock-Cress	*Arabis serotina*	Stable
Dwarf Bear-Poppy	*Arctomecon humilis*	Declining
Presidio Manzanita	*Arctostaphylos pungens* var. *ravenii*	Improving
Cumberland Sandwort	*Arenia cumberlandensis*	Unknown
Sacramento Prickly Poppy	*Argemone pleiacantha pinnatisecta*	Unknown
Ahinahina	*Argyroxiphium sandwicense* ssp. *sandwicense*	Stable
Pelos del Diablo	*Aristida portoricensis*	Declining
Mead's Milkweed	*Asclepias meadii*	Stable
Welsh's Milkweed	*Asclepias welshii*	Declining
Four-Petal Pawpaw	*Asimina tetramera*	Declining
Mancos Milk-Vetch	*Astragalus humillimus*	Declining
Heliotrope Milk-Vetch	*Astragalus montii*	Unknown
Osterhout Milk-Vetch	*Astragalus osterhoutii*	Declining
Ash Meadows Milk-Vetch	*Astragalus phoenix*	Stable
Jesup's Milk-Vetch	*Astragalus robbinsii* var. *jesupi*	Stable

Recovery Status of Listed Species

Common Name	Scientific Name	Status
Palo de Ramon	*Banara vanderbiltii*	Declining
Hairy Rattleweed	*Baptisia arachnifera*	Declining
Virginia Round-Leaf Birch	*Betula uber*	Improving
Cuneate Bidens	*Bidens cuneata*	Extinct
Decurrent False Aster	*Boltania decurrens*	Improving
Florida Bonamia	*Bonamia grandiflora*	Declining
Vahl's Boxwood	*Buxus vahlii*	Declining
Texas Poppy-Mallow	*Callirhoe scabriuscula*	Declining
Palma de Manaca	*Calyptronoma rivialis*	Declining
San Benito Evening-Primrose	*Camissonia benitensis*	Unknown
Brooksville Bellflower	*Campanula robinsiae*	Unknown
Small Anthered Bittercress	*Cardomine micranthera*	Declining
Navajo Sedge	*Carex specuicola*	Unknown
None	*Cassia mirabilis*	Declining
San Clemente Island Indian Paintbrush	*Castelleja grisea*	Improving
California Jewelflower	*Caulanthus californicus*	Declining
Spring-Loving Centaury	*Centaurium namophilum*	Stable
Slender-Horned Spineflower	*Centrostegia leptoceras*	Declining
Fragrant Prickly-Apple Cactus	*Cereus eriophorus* var. *fragrans*	Declining
Key Tree Cactus	*Cereus robinii*	Stable
Pygmy Fringe Tree	*Chionanthus pygmaeus*	Declining
Florida Golden Aster	*Chrysopsis floridana*	Declining
Pitcher's Thistle	*Cirsium pitcheri*	Stable
Sacramento Mountains Thistle	*Cirsium vinaceum*	Stable
Alabama Leather Flower	*Clematis socialis*	Stable
Salt Marsh Bird's-Beak	*Cordylanthus maritimus* ssp. *maritimus*	Unknown
Palmate-Bracted Bird's-Beak	*Cordylanthus palmatus*	Declining
Palo de Nigua	*Cornutia obovata*	Unknown
Nellie Cory Cactus	*Coryphantha minima*	Declining
Bunched Cory Cactus	*Coryphantha ramillosa*	Declining
Cochise Pincushion Cactus	*Coryphantha robbinsorum*	Unknown
Lee Pincushion Cactus	*Coryphantha sneedii* var. *leei*	Stable
Sneed Pincushion Cactus	*Coryphantha sneedii* var. *sneedii*	Declining
Arizona Cliffrose	*Cowania subintegra*	Unknown
Hiquero de Sierra	*Crescentia portoricensis*	Declining
Santa Cruz Cypress	*Cupressus abramsiana*	Stable

Common Name	Scientific Name	Status
Elfin Tree Fern	*Cyathea dryopteroides*	Declining
Jones Cycladenia	*Cycladenia humilis* var. *jonesii*	Stable
Daphnopsis	*Daphnopsis hellerana*	Declining
Beautiful Pawpaw	*Deeringothamnus pulchellus*	Declining
Rugel's Pawpaw	*Deeringothamnus rugelii*	Declining
San Clemente Island Larkspur	*Delphinium kinkiense*	Improving
Garrett's Mint	*Dicerandra christmanii*	Declining
Longspurred Mint	*Dicerandra cornutissima*	Declining
Scrub Mint	*Dicerandra frutescens*	Declining
Lakela's Mint	*Dicerandra immaculata*	Declining
Santa Barbara Island Liveforever	*Dudleya traskiae*	Stable
Tennessee Purple Coneflower	*Echinacea tennesseensis*	Stable
Nichol's Turk's Head Cactus	*Echinocactus horizonthalonius* var. *nicholii*	Unknown
Chisos Mountain Hedgehog Cactus	*Echinocereus chisoensis* var. *chisoensis*	Declining
Kuenzler Hedgehog Cactus	*Echinocereus fendleri* var. *kuenzleri*	Stable
Lloyd's Hedgehog Cactus	*Echinocereus lloydii*	Unknown
Black Lace Cactus	*Echinocereus reichenbachii* var. *albertii*	Declining
Arizona Hedgehog Cactus	*Echinocereus triglochidiatus* var. *arizonicus*	Unknown
Spineless Hedgehog Cactus	*Echinocereus triglochidiotus* var. *inermis*	Improving
Davis' Green Pitaya Cactus	*Echinocereus viridiflorus* var. *davisii*	Declining
Ash Meadows Sunray	*Enceliopsis nudicaulis* var. *corrugata*	Stable
Kern mallow	*Eremalche kernensis*	Declining
Santa Ana River Woolly-Star	*Eriastrum densifolium* ssp. *sanctorum*	Declining
Hoover's Wooly-Star	*Eriastrum hooveri*	Declining
Maguire Daisy	*Erigeron maguirei* var. *maguirei*	Unknown
Zuni Fleabane	*Erigeron rhizomatus*	Stable
Gypsum Wild Buckwheat	*Eriogonum gypsophilum*	Stable
Steamboat Buckwheat	*Eriogonum ovalifolium* var. *williamsiae*	Stable
Clay-Loving Wild Buckwheat	*Eriogonum pelinophilum*	Stable
Loch Lomond Coyote Thistle	*Eryngium constancei*	Improving
Snakeroot	*Eryngium cuneifolium*	Declining
Contra Costa Wallflower	*Erysimum capitatum* var. *angustatum*	Stable
Minnesota Trout-Lily	*Erythronium propullans*	Improving
Deltoid Spurge	*Euphorbia deltoidea*	Declining
Garber's Spurge	*Euphorbia garberi*	Stable

Recovery Status of Listed Species

Common Name	Scientific Name	Status
Ewa Plains Akoko	*Euphorbia skottsbergii* var. *kalaeloana*	Stable
Johnston's Frankenia	*Frankenia johnstonii*	Improving
Small's Milkpea	*Galactia smallii*	Declining
Na'u	*Gardenia brighamii*	Stable
Geocarpon	*Geocarpon minimum*	Stable
Spreading avens	*Geum radiatum*	Declining
Toad-Flax Cress	*Glaucocarpum suffrutescens*	Declining
Beautiful Goetzea	*Goetzea elegans*	Declining
Hillebrand's Gouania	*Gouania hillebrandii*	Stable
Ash Meadows Gumplant	*Grindelia fraxinopratensis*	Stable
Honohono	*Haplostachys haplostachya* var. *angustifolia*	Improving
Harper's Beauty	*Harperocallis flava*	Improving
Higo Chumbo	*Harrisia portoricensis*	Declining
McKittrick Pennyroyal	*Hedeoma apiculatum*	Stable
Todsen's Pennyroyal	*Hedeoma todsenii*	Improving
Roan Mountain Bluet	*Hedyotis purpurea* var. *montana*	Unknown
Swamp Pink	*Helonias bullata*	Stable
Dwarf-Flowered Heartleaf	*Hexastylis naniflora*	Unknown
Kauai Hau Kuahiwi	*Hibiscadelphus distans*	Declining
Slender Rush-Pea	*Hoffmannseggia tenella*	Declining
Mountain Golden Heather	*Hudsonia montana*	Declining
Lakeside Daisy	*Hymenoxys acaulis* var. *glabra*	Stable
Texas Bitterweed	*Hymenoxys texana*	Declining
Highlands Scrub Hypericum	*Hypericum cumulicola*	Declining
Cook's Holly	*Ilex cookii*	Declining
Peter's Mountain Mallow	*Iliamna corei*	Improving
Dwarf Lake Iris	*Iris lacustris*	Stable
Black-Spored Quillwort	*Isoetes melanospora*	Declining
Mat-Forming Quillwort	*Isoetes tegetiformans*	Stable
Small Whorled Pogonia	*Isotria medeoloides*	Improving
Ash Meadows Ivesia	*Ivesia eremica*	Stable
Cooley's Water-Willow	*Justicia cooleyi*	Unknown
Cooke's Kokio	*Kokia cookei*	Stable
Kokio	*Kokia drynarioides*	Stable
San Joaquin Wooly-Threads	*Lembertia congdonii*	Declining
Barneby's Ridge-Cress	*Lepidium barnebyanum*	Declining
Prairie Bush-Clover	*Lespedeza leptostachya*	Improving

Common Name	Scientific Name	Status
Dudley Bluffs Baldderpod	*Lesquerella congesta*	Stable
Missouri Bladder-Pod	*Lesquerella filiformis*	Improving
Lyrate Bladderpod	*Lesquerella lyrata*	Declining
White Bladderpod	*Lesquerella pallida*	Declining
Heller's Blazing Star	*Liatris helleri*	Unknown
Scrub Blazing Star	*Liatris ohlingerae*	Declining
Pondberry	*Lindera melissifolia*	Unknown
Lipochaeta	*Lipochaeta venosa*	Stable
Bradshaw's Lomatium	*Lomatium bradshawii*	Unknown
San Clemente Island Broom	*Lotus dendroideus* var. *traskiae*	Improving
Scrub Lupine	*Lupinus aridorum*	Declining
Rough-Leaved Loosestrife	*Lysimachia asperulaefolia*	Unknown
Truckee Barberry	*Mahonia sonnei*	Stable
San Clemente Island Bush-Mallow	*Malacothamnus clementinus*	Improving
Mohr's Barbara's-Buttons	*Marshallia mohrii*	Stable
Ash Meadows Blazing Star	*Mentzelia leucophylla*	Stable
Uhiuhi	*Mezoneuron kavaiense*	Declining
Michigan Monkey-Flower	*Mimulus glabratus* var. *michiganensis*	Stable
MacFarlane's Four O'Clock	*Mirabilis macfarlanei*	Improving
Lloyd's Mariposa Cactus	*Neolloydia mariposensis*	Declining
Amargosa Niterwort	*Nitrophila mohavensis*	Stable
Eureka Valley Evening-Primrose	*Oenothera avita* ssp. *eurekensis*	Stable
Antioch Dunes Evening-Primrose	*Oenothera deltoides* ssp. *howellii*	Stable
Bakersfield Cactus	*Opuntia treleasei*	Declining
Palo de Rosa	*Ottoschulzia rhodoxylon*	Declining
Canby's Dropwort	*Oxypolis canbyi*	Declining
Fassett's Locoweed	*Oxytropis campestris* var. *chartacea*	Stable
Carter's Panicgrass	*Panicum carteri*	Stable
Papery Whitlow-Wort	*Paronychia chartacea*	Declining
Furbish Lousewort	*Pedicularis furbishiae*	Stable
Brady Pincushion Cactus	*Pediocactus bradyi*	Unknown
San Rafael Cactus	*Pediocactus despainii*	Declining
Knowlton Cactus	*Pediocactus knowltonii*	Stable
Peebles Navajo Cactus	*Pediocactus peeblesianus* var. *peeblesianus*	Unknown

Recovery Status of Listed Species

Common Name	Scientific Name	Status
Siler Pincushion Cactus	*Pediocactus sileri*	Unknown
Blowout Penstemon	*Penstemon haydenii*	Stable
Penland Beardtongue	*Penstemon penlandii*	Stable
Wheeler's Peperomia	*Peperomia wheeleri*	Declining
Clay Phacelia	*Phacelia argillacea*	Declining
North Park Phacelia	*Phacelia formosula*	Unknown
American Hart's-Tongue Fern	*Phyllitis scolopendrium* var. *americana*	Unknown
Dudley Bluffs Twinpod	*Physaria obcordata*	Stable
Ruth's Golden Aster	*Pityopsis ruthii*	Declining
Eastern Prairie Fringed Orchid	*Platanthera leucophaea*	Stable
Western Prairie Fringed Orchid	*Platanthera praeclara*	Stable
San Diego Mesa Mint	*Pogogyne abramsii*	Declining
Tiny Polygala	*Polygala smallii*	Stable
Wireweed	*Polygonella basiramia*	Declining
Aleutian Shield Fern	*Polystichum aleuticum*	Stable
Robbins' Cinquefoil	*Potentilla robbinsiana*	Stable
Maguire Primrose	*Primula maguirei*	Declining
Scrub Plum	*Prunus geniculata*	Declining
Harperella	*Ptilimnium nodosum*	Stable
Hinckley Oak	*Quercus hinckleyi*	Declining
Autumn Buttercup	*Ranunculus acriformis* var. *aestivalis*	Declining
Chapman's Rhododendron	*Rhododendron chapmanii*	Declining
Michaux's Sumac	*Rhus michauxi*	Unknown
Miccosukee Gooseberry	*Ribes echinellum*	Stable
Bunched Arrowhead	*Sagittaria fasciculata*	Declining
Kral's Water-Plantain	*Sagittaria secundifolia*	Declining
Lanai Sandalwood	*Santalum freycinetianum* var. *lanaiense*	Stable
Green Pitcher Plant	*Sarracenia oreophila*	Improving
Alabama Canebrake Pitcher Plant	*Sarracenia rubra* ssp. *alabamensis*	Declining
Mountain Sweet Pitcher Plant	*Sarracenia rubra* ssp. *jonesii*	Declining
Dwarf Naupaka	*Scaevola coriacea*	Stable
Diamond Head Schiedea	*Schiedea adamantis*	Stable
Uinta Basin Hookless Cactus	*Sclerocactus glaucus*	Stable
Mesa Verde Cactus	*Sclerocactus mesae-verdae*	Stable
Wright Fishhook Cactus	*Sclerocactus wrightiae*	Stable
Large-Flowered Skullcap	*Scutellaria montana*	Unknown

Common Name	Scientific Name	Status
San Francisco Peaks Groundsel	*Senecio franciscanus*	Unknown
Pedate Checker-Mallow	*Sidalcea pedata*	Declining
Erubia	*Solanum drymophilum*	Declining
White-Haired Goldenrod	*Solidago albopilosa*	Stable
Houghton's Goldenrod	*Solidago houghtonii*	Stable
Short's Goldenrod	*Solidago shortii*	Stable
Blue Ridge Goldenrod	*Solidago spithamaea*	Unknown
Navasota Ladies'-Tresses	*Spiranthes parksii*	Declining
Virginia Spiraea	*Spirea virginiana*	Declining
Cobana Negra	*Stahlia monosperma*	Stable
Stenogyne	*Stenogyne angustifolia* var. *angustifolia*	Stable
Malheur Wire Lettuce	*Stephanomeria malheurensis*	Unknown
Texas Snowbells	*Styrax texana*	Declining
Eureka Valley Dunegrass	*Swallenia alexandrae*	Stable
Cooley's Meadowrue	*Thalictrum cooleyi*	Unknown
Slender-Petaled Mustard	*Thelypodium stenopetalum*	Declining
Ashy Dogweed	*Thymophylla tephroleuca*	Declining
Florida Torreya	*Torreya taxifolia*	Declining
Last Chance Townsendia	*Townsendia aprica*	Unknown
Bariaco	*Trichilia triacantha*	Declining
Running Buffalo Clover	*Trifolium stoloniferum*	Improving
Persistent Trillium	*Trillium persistens*	Stable
Relict Trillium	*Trillium reliquum*	Declining
Solano Grass	*Tuctoria mucronata*	Stable
Tumamoc Globeberry	*Tumamoca macdougalii*	Unknown
Hawaiian Vetch	*Vicia menziesii*	Stable
Wide-Leaf Warea	*Warea amplexifolia*	Declining
Carter's Mustard	*Warea carteri*	Declining
St. Thomas Prickly-Ash	*Zanthoxylum thomassianum*	Declining
Texas Wildrice	*Zizania texana*	Declining
Florida Ziziphus	*Ziziphus celata*	Declining

MAMMALS

Sonoran Pronghorn	*Antilocapra americana sonoriensis*	Declining
Gray Wolf	*Canis lupus*	Improving
Red Wolf	*Canis rufus*	Improving

Recovery Status of Listed Species

Common Name	Scientific Name	Status
Utah Prairie Dog	*Cynomys parvidens*	Improving
Morro Bay Kangaroo Rat	*Dipodomys heermanni morroensis*	Declining
Giant Kangaroo Rat	*Dipodomys ingens*	Declining
Fresno Kangaroo Rat	*Dipodomys nitratoides exilis*	Declining
Tipton Kangaroo Rat	*Dipodomys nitratoides nitratoides*	Declining
Stephens' Kangaroo Rat	*Dipodomys stephensi*	Declining
Southern Sea Otter	*Enhydra lutris nereis*	Stable
Florida Panther	*Felis concolor coryi*	Stable
Eastern Cougar	*Felis concolor couguar*	Extinct
Ocelot	*Felis pardalis*	Stable
Jaguarundi	*Felis yagouaroundi*	Unknown
Carolina Northern Flying Squirrel	*Glaucomys sabrinus coloratus*	Stable
Virginia Northern Flying Squirrel	*Glaucomys sabrinus fuscus*	Stable
Hawaiian Hoary Bat	*Lasiurus cinereus semotus*	Unknown
Mexican Long-Nosed Bat	*Leptonycteris nivalis*	Unknown
Sanborn's Long-Nosed Bat	*Leptonycteris sanborni*	Unknown
Amargosa Vole	*Microtus californicus scirpensis*	Declining
Hualapai Vole	*Microtus mexicanus hualpaiensis*	Declining
Black-Footed Ferret	*Mustela nigripes*	Improving
Gray Bat	*Myotis grisescens*	Improving
Indiana Bat	*Myotis sodalis*	Declining
Key Largo Woodrat	*Neotoma floridana smalli*	Stable
Columbian White-Tailed Deer	*Odocoileus virginianus leucurus*	Improving
Florida Key Deer	*Odocoileus virginianus clavium*	Declining
Key Largo Cotton Mouse	*Peromyscus gossypinus allapaticola*	Stable
Perdido Key Beach Mouse	*Peromyscus polionotus trissyllepsis*	Improving
Anastasia Island Beach Mouse	*Peromyscus polionotus phasma*	Improving
Alabama Beach Mouse	*Peromyscus polionotus allophrys*	Improving
Southeastern Beach Mouse	*Peromyscus polionotus niveiventris*	Declining
Choctawhatchee Beach Mouse	*Peromyscus polionotus ammobates*	Unknown
Virginia Big-Eared Bat	*Plecotus townsendii virginianus*	Improving
Ozark Big-Eared Bat	*Plecotus townsendii ingens*	Unknown
Woodland Caribou	*Rangifer tarandus caribou*	Improving
Salt Marsh Harvest Mouse	*Reithrodontomys raviventris*	Declining
Delmarva Fox Squirrel	*Sciurus niger cinereus*	Stable

Common Name	Scientific Name	Status
Dismal Swamp Southeastern Shrew	*Sorex longirostris fisheri*	Improving
Lower Keys Rabbit	*Sylvilagus palustrus hefneri*	Declining
Mount Graham Red Squirrel	*Tamiasciurus hudsonicus grahamensis*	Declining
West Indian Manatee	*Trichechus manatus*	Declining
Grizzly Bear	*Ursus arctos horribilis*	Stable
San Joaquin Kit Fox	*Vulpes macrotis mutica*	Declining

BIRDS

Common Name	Scientific Name	Status
Nihoa Millerbird	*Acrocephalus familiaris kingi*	Stable
Yellow-Shouldered Blackbird	*Agelaius xanthomus*	Stable
Puerto Rican Parrot	*Amazona vittata*	Declining
Cape Sable Seaside Sparrow	*Ammodramus maritimus mirabilis*	Stable
Florida Grasshopper Sparrow	*Ammodramus savannarum floridanus*	Declining
San Clemente Island Sage Sparrow	*Amphispiza belli clementeae*	Declining
Laysan Duck	*Anas laysanensis*	Stable
Hawaiian Duck	*Anas wyvilliana*	Stable
Florida Scrub Jay	*Aphelocoma coerulescens coerulescens*	Declining
Aleutian Canada Goose	*Branta canadensis leucopareia*	Increasing
Hawaiian Hawk	*Buteo solitarius*	Stable
Ivory-Billed Woodpecker	*Campephilus principalis*	Extinct
Puerto Rican Nightjar	*Caprimulgus noctitherus*	Stable
Piping Plover	*Charadrius melodus*	Declining
Masked Bobwhite	*Colinus virginianus ridgwayi*	Increasing
Puerto Rican Plain Pigeon	*Columba inornata wetmorei*	Stable
Hawaiian Crow	*Corvus hawaiiensis*	Declining
Golden-Cheeked Warbler	*Dendroica chrysoparia*	Declining
Kirtland's Warbler	*Dendroica kirtlandii*	Increasing
Northern Aplomado Falcon	*Falco femoralis septentrionalis*	Unknown
American Peregrine Falcon	*Falco peregrinus anatum*	Increasing
Arctic Peregrine Falcon	*Falco peregrinus tundrius*	Increasing
Hawaiian Coot	*Fulica americana alai*	Stable
Hawaiian Common Moorhen	*Gallinula chloropus sandvicensis*	Stable
Whooping Crane	*Grus americana*	Increasing
Mississippi Sandhill Crane	*Grus canadensis pulla*	Increasing

Recovery Status of Listed Species

Common Name	Scientific Name	Status
California Condor	*Gymnogyps californianus*	Increasing
Bald Eagle	*Haliaeetus leucocephalus*	Increasing
Kauai Nukupuu	*Hemignathus lucidus hanapepe*	Declining
Akiapolaau	*Hemignathus munroi*	Stable
Kauai Akialoa	*Hemignathus procerus*	Unknown
Hawaiian Stilt	*Himantopus mexicanus knudseni*	Stable
San Clemente Island Loggerhead Shrike	*Lanius ludovicianus mearnsi*	Declining
Palila	*Loxioides bailleui*	Stable
Akepa	*Loxops coccineus* ssp.	Declining
Poo-uli	*Melamprosops phaeosoma*	Declining
Kauai Oo	*Moho braccatus*	Declining
Molokai Thrush	*Myadestes lanaiensis rutha*	Declining
Large Kauai Thrush	*Myadestes myadestinus*	Declining
Small Kauai Thrush	*Myadestes palmeri*	Stable
Wood Stork	*Mycteria americana*	Stable
Hawaiian Goose	*Nesochen sandvicensis*	Declining
Eskimo Curlew	*Numenius borealis*	Unknown
Hawaii Creeper	*Oreomystis mana*	Stable
Crested Honeycreeper	*Palmeria dolei*	Stable
Molokai Creeper	*Paroreomyza flammea*	Declining
Brown Pelican	*Pelecanus occidentalis*	Increasing
Red-Cockaded Woodpecker	*Picoides borealis*	Declining
Inyo Brown Towhee	*Pipilo fuscus eremophilus*	Stable
Audubon's Crested Caracara	*Polyborus plancus audubonii*	Stable
Maui Parrotbill	*Pseudonestor xanthophys*	Stable
Ou	*Psittirostra psittacea*	Declining
Dark-Rumped Petrel	*Pterodroma phaeopygia sandwichensis*	Stable
Newell's Townsend's Shearwater	*Puffinus auricularis newelli*	Stable
Light-Footed Clapper Rail	*Rallus longirostris levipes*	Declining
California Clapper Rail	*Rallus longirostris obsoletus*	Declining
Yuma Clapper Rail	*Rallus longirostris yumanensis*	Stable
Florida Snail Kite	*Rostrhamus sociabilis plumbeus*	Stable
Least Tern	*Sterna antillarum antillarum*	Increasing
California Least Tern	*Sterna antillarum browni*	Declining
Roseate Tern	*Sterna dougallii dougallii*	Stable

Common Name	Scientific Name	Status
Northern Spotted Owl	*Strix occidentalis caurina*	Declining
Laysan Finch	*Telespyza cantans*	Stable
Nihoa Finch	*Telespyza ultima*	Stable
Attwater's Prairie Chicken	*Tympanuchus cupido attwateri*	Declining
Bachman's Warbler	*Vermivora bachmanii*	Unknown
Black-Capped Vireo	*Vireo atricapillus*	Declining
Least Bell's Vireo	*Vireo belli pusillus*	Increasing

REPTILES

Culebra Island Giant Anole	*Anolis roosevelti*	Unknown
Loggerhead Sea Turtle	*Caretta caretta*	Declining
Green Sea Turtle	*Chelonia mydas*	Unknown
American Crocodile	*Crocodylus acutus*	Unknown
New Mexican Ridgenose Rattlesnake	*Crotalus willardi obscurus*	Unknown
Mona Ground Iguana	*Cyclura stegnegeri*	Stable
Leatherback Sea Turtle	*Dermochelys coriacea*	Unknown
Eastern Indigo Snake	*Drymarchon corais couperi*	Declining
Puerto Rican Boa	*Epicrates inornatus*	Stable
Mona Boa	*Epicrates monensis monensis*	Unknown
Hawksbill Sea Turtle	*Eretmocheyls imbricata*	Unknown
Blue-Tailed Mole Skink	*Eumeces egregius lividus*	Declining
Blunt-Nosed Leopard Lizard	*Gambelia silus*	Declining
Desert Tortoise	*Gopherus agassizii*	Declining
Gopher Tortoise	*Gopherus polyphemus*	Declining
Ringed Sawback Turtle	*Graptemys oculifera*	Stable
Kemp's Ridley Sea Turtle	*Lepidochelys kempii*	Declining
Olive Ridley Sea Turtle	*Lepidochelys olivacea*	Declining
Sand Skink	*Neoseps reynoldsi*	Declining
Atlantic Salt Marsh Snake	*Nerodia fasciata taeniata*	Declining
Concho Water Snake	*Nerodia harteri paucimaculata*	Stable
Alabama Red-Bellied Turtle	*Pseudemys alabamensis*	Unknown
Plymouth Red-Bellied Turtle	*Pseudemys rubriventris bangsii*	Stable
Monito Gecko	*Sphaerodactylus micropithecus*	Unknown
Flattened Musk Turtle	*Sternotherus depressus*	Unknown
San Francisco Garter Snake	*Thamnophis sirtalis tetrataenia*	Declining

Recovery Status of Listed Species

Common Name	Scientific Name	Status
Coachella Valley Fringe-Toed Lizard	*Uma inornata*	Declining
Island Night Lizard	*Xantusia riversiana*	Stable

AMPHIBIANS

Common Name	Scientific Name	Status
Santa Cruz Long-Toed Salamander	*Ambystoma macrodactylum croceum*	Stable
Desert Slender Salamander	*Batrachoseps aridus*	Unknown
Wyoming Toad	*Bufo hemiophrys baxteri*	Declining
Houston Toad	*Bufo houstonensis*	Unknown
Golden Coqui	*Eleutherodactylus jasperi*	Stable
San Marcos Salamander	*Eurycea nana*	Unknown
Puerto Rican Crested Toad	*Peltophryne lemur*	Unknown
Red Hills Salamander	*Phaeognathus hubrichti*	Declining
Cheat Mountain Salamander	*Plethodon nettingi*	Stable
Shenandoah Salamander	*Plethodon shenandoah*	Stable
Texas Blind Salamander	*Typhlomolge rathbuni*	Unknown

FISHES

Common Name	Scientific Name	Status
Ozark Cavefish	*Amblyopsis rosae*	Increasing
Modoc Sucker	*Catostomus microps*	Declining
Warner Sucker	*Catostomus warnerensis*	Unknown
Shortnose Sucker	*Chamistes brevirostris*	Declining
Cui-ui	*Chamistes cujus*	Unknown
June Sucker	*Chasmistes liorus*	Declining
Pygmy Sculpin	*Cottus pygmaeus*	Unknown
White River Springfish	*Crenichthys baileyi baileyi*	Stable
Hiko White River Springfish	*Crenichthys baileyi grandis*	Stable
Railroad Valley Springfish	*Crenichthys nevadae*	Stable
Leon Springs Pupfish	*Cyprinodon bovinus*	Stable
Devil's Hole Pupfish	*Cyprinodon diabolis*	Stable
Comanche Springs Pupfish	*Cyprinodon elegans*	Declining
Desert Pupfish	*Cyprinodon macularius*	Stable
Ash Meadows Amargosa Pupfish	*Cyprinodon nevadensis mionectes*	Stable
Warm Springs Pupfish	*Cyprinodon nevadensis pectoralis*	Stable
Owens Pupfish	*Cyprinodon radiosus*	Stable

Common Name	Scientific Name	Status
Lost River Sucker	*Deltistes luxatus*	Declining
Pahrump Killifish	*Empetrichthys latos latos*	Increasing
Desert Dace	*Eremichthys acros*	Stable
Slackwater Darter	*Etheostoma boschungi*	Unknown
Fountain Darter	*Etheostoma fonticola*	Unknown
Niangua Darter	*Etheostoma nianguae*	Unknown
Watercress Darter	*Etheostoma nuchale*	Declining
Okaloosa Darter	*Etheostoma okaloosae*	Declining
Bayou Darter	*Etheostoma rubrum*	Stable
Maryland Darter	*Etheostoma sellare*	Declining
Boulder Darter	*Etheostoma* sp.	Stable
Big Bend Gambusia	*Gambusia gaigai*	Stable
San Marcos Gambusia	*Gambusia georgei*	Extinct
Clear Creek Gambusia	*Gambusia heterochir*	Stable
Pecos Gambusia	*Gambusia nobilis*	Stable
Unarmored Threespine Stickleback	*Gasterosteus aculeatus williamsoni*	Stable
Mohave Tui Chub	*Gila bicolor mohavensis*	Declining
Owens Tui Chub	*Gila bicolor snyderi*	Stable
Hutton Spring Tui Chub	*Gila bicolor* ssp.	Unknown
Borax Lake Chub	*Gila boraxobius*	Stable
Humpback Chub	*Gila cypha*	Stable
Sonora Chub	*Gila ditaenia*	Stable
Bonytail Chub	*Gila elegans*	Declining
Chihuahua Chub	*Gila nigrescens*	Stable
Yaqui Chub	*Gila purpurea*	Stable
Pahranagat Roundtail Chub	*Gila robusta jordani*	Unknown
Virgin River Chub	*Gila robusta seminuda*	Declining
Slender Chub	*Hybopsis cahni*	Unknown
Spotfin Chub	*Hybopsis monacha*	Unknown
Yaqui Catfish	*Ictalurus pricei*	Declining
White River Spinedace	*Lepidomeda albivallis*	Unknown
Big Spring Spinedace	*Lepidomeda mollispinis pratensis*	Unknown
Little Colorado Spinedace	*Lepidomeda vittata*	Unknown
Spikedace	*Meda fulgida*	Stable
Waccamaw Silverside	*Menidia extensa*	Unknown
Moapa Dace	*Moapa coriacea*	Stable

Recovery Status of Listed Species

Common Name	Scientific Name	Status
Beautiful Shiner	*Notropis formosus*	Declining
Cape Fear Shiner	*Notropis mekistocholas*	Unknown
Pecos Bluntnose Shiner	*Notropis simus pecosensis*	Unknown
Smoky Madtom	*Noturus baileyi*	Stable
Yellowfin Madtom	*Noturus flavipinnis*	Unknown
Neosho Madtom	*Noturus placidus*	Declining
Scioto Madtom	*Noturus trautmani*	Unknown
Amber Darter	*Percina antesella*	Stable
Conasauga Logperch	*Percina jenkinsi*	Stable
Leopard Darter	*Percina pantherina*	Stable
Roanoke Logperch	*Percina rex*	Stable
Snail Darter	*Percina tanasi*	Unknown
Blackside Dace	*Phoxinus cumberlandensis*	Unknown
Woundfin	*Plagopterus argentissimus*	Declining
Gila Topminnow	*Poeciliopsis occidentalis occidentalis*	Declining
Yaqui Topminnow	*Poeciliopsis occidentalis sonoriensis*	Declining
Colorado Squawfish	*Ptychocheilus lucius*	Stable
Independence Valley Speckled Dace	*Rhinichthys osculus lethoporus*	Stable
Ash Meadows Speckled Dace	*Rhinichthys osculus nevadensis*	Stable
Clover Valley Speckled Dace	*Rhinichthys osculus oligoporus*	Stable
Foskett Speckled Dace	*Rhinichthys osculus* ssp.	Unknown
Kendall Warm Springs Dace	*Rhinichthys osculus thermalis*	Stable
Apache Trout	*Salmo apache*	Declining
Little Kern Golden Trout	*Salmo aquabonita whitei*	Stable
Lahontan Cutthroat Trout	*Salmo clarki henshawi*	Declining
Paiute Cutthroat Trout	*Salmo clarki seleniris*	Declining
Greenback Cutthroat Trout	*Salmo clarki stomias*	Increasing
Gila Trout	*Salmo gilae*	Declining
Pallid Sturgeon	*Scaphirhynchus albus*	Declining
Alabama Cavefish	*Speoplatyrhinus poulsoni*	Stable
Loach Minnow	*Tiaroga cobitis*	Stable

MUSSELS

Dwarf Wedge Mussel	*Alasmidonta heterodon*	Declining
Birdwing Pearly Mussel	*Conradilla caelata*	Declining
Fanshell	*Cyprogenia stegaria*	Declining

Common Name	Scientific Name	Status
Dromedary Pearly Mussel	*Dromus dromas*	Declining
Tar River Spinymussel	*Elliptio steinstansana*	Declining
Curtis' Pearly Mussel	*Epioblasma florentina curtisi*	Declining
Yellow-Blossom Pearly Mussel	*Epioblasma florentina florentina*	Extinct
Purple Cat's Paw Pearly Mussel	*Epioblasma o. obliquata*	Declining
Penitent Mussel	*Epioblasma penita*	Declining
White Cat's Paw Pearly Mussel	*Epioblasma sulcata delicata*	Unknown
Green-Blossom Pearly Mussel	*Epioblasma torulosa gubernaculum*	Declining
Tubercled-Blossom Pearly Mussel	*Epioblasma torulosa torulosa*	Extinct
Turgid-Blossom Pearly Mussel	*Epioblasma turgidula*	Extinct
Tan Riffle Shell	*Epioblasma walkeri*	Declining
Fine-Rayed Pigtoe Pearly Mussel	*Fusconaia cuneolus*	Declining
Shiny Pigtoe Pearly Mussel	*Fusconaia edgariana*	Declining
Cracking Pearly Mussel	*Hemistena lata*	Declining
Higgins' Eye Pearly Mussel	*Lampsilis higginsi*	Unknown
Pink Mucket Pearly Mussel	*Lampsilis orbiculata*	Declining
Arkansas Fatmucket	*Lampsilis powelli*	Unknown
Speckled Pocketbook Mussel	*Lampsilis streckeri*	Unknown
Alabama Lamp Pearly Mussel	*Lampsilis virescens*	Declining
Louisiana Pearlshell	*Margaritifera hembeli*	Unknown
Ring Pink Mussel	*Obovaria retusa*	Declining
Little-Wing Pearly Mussel	*Pegias fabula*	Declining
White Wartyback Pearly Mussel	*Plethobasus cicatricosus*	Declining
Orange-Footed Pearly Mussel	*Plethobasus cooperianus*	Declining
James River Spinymussel	*Pleurobema collina*	Declining
Curtus' Mussel	*Pleurobema curtum*	Declining
Marshall's Mussel	*Pleurobema marshalli*	Declining
Rough Pigtoe Pearly Mussel	*Pleurobema plenum*	Declining
Judge Tait's Mussel	*Pleurobema taitianum*	Declining
Fat Pocketbook Pearly Mussel	*Potamilus capax*	Increasing
Inflated Heelsplitter	*Potamilus inflatus*	Declining
Cumberland Monkeyface Pearly Mussel	*Quadrula intermedia*	Declining

Common Name	Scientific Name	Status
Appalachian Monkeyface Pearly Mussel	*Quadrula sparsa*	Declining
Stirrup Shell	*Quadrula stapes*	Declining
Pale Lilliput Pearly Mussel	*Toxolasma cylindrellus*	Declining
Cumberland Bean Pearly Mussel	*Villosa trabalis*	Declining

CRUSTACEANS

Madison Cave Isopod	*Antrolana lira*	Stable
Cave Crayfish	*Cambarus zophonastes*	Stable
Nashville Crayfish	*Orconectes shoupi*	Unknown
Shasta Crayfish	*Pacifastacus fortis*	Unknown
Squirrel Chimney Cave Shrimp	*Palaemonetes cummingi*	Declining
Alabama Cave Shrimp	*Palaemonias alabamae*	Declining
Kentucky Cave Shrimp	*Palaemonias ganteri*	Unknown
Hay's Spring Amphipod	*Stygobromus hayi*	Stable
California Freshwater Shrimp	*Syncaris pacifica*	Unknown
Socorro Isopod	*Thermosphaeroma thermophilum*	Increasing

SNAILS

Oahu Tree Snails	*Achatinella sp.*	Declining
Painted Snake Coiled Forest Snail	*Anguispira picta*	Unknown
Iowa Pleistocene Snail	*Discus macclintocki*	Unknown
Noonday Snail	*Mesodon clarki nantahala*	Unknown
Magazine Mountain Shagreen	*Mesodon magazinensis*	Stable
Stock Island Snail	*Orthalicus reses reses*	Declining
Virginia Fringed Mountain Snail	*Polygyriscus virginianus*	Stable
Chittenango Ovate Amber Snail	*Succinea chittenangoensis*	Declining
Flat-Spired Three-Toothed Snail	*Triodopsis platysayoides*	Stable

INSECTS AND ARACHNIDS

Ash Meadows Naucorid	*Ambrysus amargosus*	Unknown
Lange's Metalmark Butterfly	*Apodemia mormo langei*	Stable

Common Name	Scientific Name	Status
San Bruno Elfin Butterfly	*Callophrys mossii bayensis*	Stable
Northeastern Beach Tiger Beetle	*Cicindela dorsalis dorsalis*	Declining
Puritan Tiger Beetle	*Cicindela puritana*	Declining
Valley Elderberry Longhorn Beetle	*Desmocerus californicus dimorphus*	Unknown
Delta Green Ground Beetle	*Elaphrus viridis*	Unknown
El Segundo Blue Butterfly	*Euphilotes battoides allyni*	Unknown
Smith's Blue Butterfly	*Euphilotes enoptes smithi*	Declining
Bay Checkerspot Butterfly	*Euphydryas editha bayensis*	Declining
Kern Primrose Sphinx Moth	*Euproserpinus euterpe*	Unknown
Palos Verdes Blue Butterfly	*Glaucopsyche lygdamus palosverdesensis*	Declining
Schaus Swallowtail Butterfly	*Heraclides aristodemus ponceanus*	Declining
Pawnee Montane Skipper	*Hesperia leonardus montana*	Stable
Mission Blue Butterfly	*Icaricia icarioides missionensis*	Stable
Tooth Cave Spider	*Leptoneta myopica*	Unknown
Lotis Blue Butterfly	*Lycaeides argyrognomon lotis*	Unknown
Tooth Cave Pseudoscorpion	*Microcreagris texana*	Unknown
American Burying Beetle	*Nicrophorus americanus*	Declining
Tooth Cave Ground Beetle	*Rhadine persephone*	Unknown
Oregon Silverspot Butterfly	*Speyeria zerene hippolyta*	Declining
Kretschmarr Cave Mold Beetle	*Texamaurops reddelli*	Unknown
Bee Creek Cave Harvestman	*Texella reddelli*	Unknown

Endangered Species Photo Locator

This directory is divided into three parts—a list of species, a list of sources, and the indexes. The species list contains numbered entries for each plant and animal on the U.S. Endangered Species List together with one or more photo sources. Within each section, i.e. Plants, Mammals, Birds, etc., species are listed alphabetically by their scientific names. Each entry also contains the common name of the species and a page number. The page number refers to the location of the species account and photograph in the *Guide*. Where more than one source is listed, an asterisk indicates the one used.

The source list is an alphabetical listing of photographers and sources, with addresses, telephone numbers, an indication of special areas of endangered species coverage (if any), and a list of the species available from that source.

Two indexes are provided. The first lists species by scientific names; the other by common names. Someone knowing the scientific name of a species can either turn directly to the species list or find out the entry number with the index of scientific names. For those knowing only the common name, a glance at the common name index will quickly locate the species entry number.

The U.S. Fish and Wildlife Service, which has responsibility for endangered species, is a potential source for photos of all federally listed species. We have listed them as a source only for those species for which they furnished the photograph used in the *Guide*. Other general sources for photographs are the fish and game departments and Heritage Programs in the states where the species is found. A listing of Fish and Wildlife Service Offices (including field offices) and state Heritage Programs can be found in an appendix to volume two of the *Guide*. State occurences, as well as other leads for photos, can be found in the species accounts.

For those seeking a photograph of a particular species, the sources given in this directory are a reliable place to begin. For many of these species there undoubtedly are many other photo sources than those listed here. This directory is not intended to be, nor could it be, exhaustive. We invite those who have photos of federally listed species and who would like to be listed in future editions of the directory to write to us (Beacham Publishing, 2100 S St. NW, Washington, DC 20008) with a list of the species you have available.

Threatened and Endangered Species

* denotes photo used in the WWF Guide

Plants

1. *Abronia macrocarpa*
   Large-Fruited Sand-Verbena [pg. 1]
   Montgomery, Paul

2. *Abutilon eremitopetalum*
   NONE [pg. 1181]
   Gustafson, Robert

3. *Abutilon menziesii*
   Ko'oloa'ula [pg. 3]
   Gustafson, Robert J.

4. *Abutilon sandwicense*
   NONE [pg. 1183]
   Obata, John

5. *Acanthomintha obovata* ssp. *duttonii*
   San Mateo Thornmint [pg. 5]
   Bartel, Jim A.*
   Forbes, Holly

6. *Achyranthes rotundata*
   Achyranthes [pg. 7]
   Herbst, Derral

7. *Aconitum noveboracense*
   Northern Wild Monkshood [pg. 9]
   Meyer, Thomas A.
   Moseley, Richard E.*

8. *Agalinis acuta*
   Sandplain Gerardia [pg. 11]
   Droege, Mary F.
   Harris, Jessie M.*
   Wiegand, R. Harrison

9. *Agave arizonica*
   Arizona Agave [pg. 13]
   McMahan, Linda R.*
   Smith, Norm

10. *Alsinidendron obovatum*
    NONE [pg. 1186]
    Obata, John

11. *Alsinidendron trinerve*
    NONE [pg. 1188]
    Gustafson, Robert

12. *Amorpha crenulata*
    Crenulate Lead-Plant [pg. 15]
    Hammer, Roger L.*
    Herndon, Alan

13. *Amphianthus pusillus*
    Little Amphianthus [pg. 17]
    Allison, James R.*
    Nelson, John B.
    Patrick, Thomas S.

14. *Amsinckia grandiflora*
    Large-Flowered Fiddleneck [pg. 19]
    Bartel, Jim A.*
    Forbes, Holly

15. *Amsonia kearneyana*
    Kearney's Blue-Star [pg. 21]
    McLaughlin, Steven P.
    Quinn, Meg*
    Rutman, Susan

16. *Ancistrocactus tobuschii*
    Tobusch Fishhook Cactus [pg. 23]
    Montgomery, Paul

17. *Apios priceana*
    Price's Potato-Bean [pg. 1190]
    Somers, Paul

18. *Arabis macdonaldiana*
    McDonald's Rock-Cress [pg. 25]
    Robinson, Andy

19. *Arabis serotina*
    Shale Barren Rock-Cress [pg. 27]
    Harris, Jessie M.
    Wieboldt, Thomas F.*

20. *Arctomecon humilis*
    Dwarf Bear-Poppy [pg. 29]
    Atwood, Duane

46. *Calyptronoma rivalis*
Palma de Manaca [pg. 1204]
Houghton, William

47. *Camissonia benitensis*
San Benito Evening-Primrose [pg. 71]
Bartel, Jim A.

48. *Campanula robinsiae*
Brooksville Bellflower [pg. 73]
Morin, Nancy

49. *Cardamine micranthera*
Small-Anthered Bittercress [pg. 1206]
Murdock, Nora

50. *Carex specuicola*
Navajo Sedge [pg. 75]
Rutman, Susan

51. *Cassia mirabilis*
NONE [pg. 1208]
Silander, Susan

52. *Castelleja grisea*
**San Clemente Island
Indian Paintbrush** [pg. 77]
Larson, Jan K.

53. *Caulanthus californicus*
California Jewelflower [pg. 1210]
Austin-McDermon, Marianne*
Peterson, B. "Moose"

54. *Centaurium namophilum*
Spring-Loving Centaury [pg. 79]
Cochrane, Susan

55. *Centaurium sebaeoides*
NONE [pg. 1212]
Wilson-Ramsey, Yevonn

56. *Centrostegia leptoceras*
Slender-Horned Spineflower [pg. 81]
Middleton, Susan A.

57. *Cereus eriophorus* var. *fragrans*
Fragrant Prickly-Apple Cactus [pg. 83]
Robinson, Andy

58. *Cereus robinii*
Key Tree Cactus [pg. 85]
Robinson, Andy

59. *Chamaesyce celastoides* var. *kaenana*
Akoko [pg. 1214]
Gustafson, Robert

60. *Chamaesyce kuwaleana*
NONE [pg. 1216]
Perlman, Steve

61. *Chionanthus pygmaeus*
Pygmy Fringe Tree [pg. 87]
Christman, Steve
DeLaney, Kris R.
Shaw, Jonathan*

62. *Chrysopsis floridana*
Florida Golden Aster [pg. 89]
Robinson, Andy

63. *Cirsium pitcheri*
Pitcher's Thistle [pg. 91]
Harris, Jessie M.
Meyer, Thomas A.*

64. *Cirsium vinaceum*
**Sacramento Mountains
Thistle** [pg. 93]
McDonald, Charlie

65. *Clematis socialis*
Alabama Leather Flower [pg. 95]
Pierson, J. Malcolm

66. *Conradina verticillata*
Cumberland Rosemary [pg. 1218]
Somers, Paul

67. *Cordylanthus maritimus*
ssp. *maritimus*
Salt Marsh Bird's-Beak [pg. 97]
Middleton, Susan A.*
Peterson, B. "Moose"

68. *Cordylanthus palmatus*
**Palmate-Bracted
Bird's-Beak** [pg. 100]
Gustafson, Robert J.

69. *Cornutia obovata*
Palo de Nigua [pg. 102]
USFWS Puerto Rico

70. *Coryphantha minima*
    Nellie Cory Cactus [pg. 104]
    Kurz, Don*
    Montgomery, Paul

71. *Coryphantha ramillosa*
    Bunched Cory Cactus [pg. 106]
    Montgomery, Paul

72. *Coryphantha robbinsorum*
    **Cochise Pincushion
    Cactus** [pg. 108]
    Phillips III, Arthur M.

73. *Coryphantha sneedii* var. *leei*
    Lee Pincushion Cactus [pg. 110]
    World Wildlife Fund

74. *Coryphantha sneedii* var. *sneedi*
    Sneed Pincushion Cactus [pg. 112]
    Montgomery, Paul

75. *Cowania subintegra*
    Arizona Cliffrose [pg. 114]
    Phillips, Barbara G.

76. *Cranichis ricartii*
    NONE [pg. 1220]
    Ackerman, James D.

77. *Crescentia portoricensis*
    Higuero de Sierra [pg. 116]
    USFWS Puerto Rico

78. *Cryptantha crassipes*
    Terlingua Creek Cat's Eye [pg. 1222]
    Montgomery, Paul

79. *Cupressus abramsiana*
    Santa Cruz Cypress [pg. 118]
    Austin-McDermon, Marianne
    California Native Plant Society
    Ordano, Jo-Ann*

80. *Cyanea marcrostegia* var. *gibsonii*
    NONE [pg. 1224]
    Lau, Joel

81. *Cyanea pinnatifida*
    Haha [pg. 1226]
    Wilson-Ramsey, Yevonn

82. *Cyanea superba*
    Cyanea Superba [pg. 1228]
    Wilson-Ramsey, Yevonn

83. *Cyanea undulata*
    NONE [pg. 1230]
    Lorence, David

84. *Cyathea dryopteroides*
    Elfin Tree Fern [pg. 120]
    USFWS Puerto Rico

85. *Cycladenia humilis* var. *jonesii*
    Jones Cycladenia [pg. 122]
    Atwood, Duane
    Poulson, Marv*

86. *Dalea foliosa*
    Leafy Prairie Clover [pg. 1232]
    Harris, Jessie M.

87. *Daphnopsis hellerana*
    Daphnopsis [pg. 124]
    USFWS Puerto Rico

88. *Deeringothamnus pulchellus*
    Beautiful Pawpaw [pg. 126]
    Norman, Eliane M.

89. *Deeringothamnus rugelii*
    Rugel's Pawpaw [pg. 126]
    Norman, Eliane M.

90. *Delphinium kinkiense*
    **San Clemente Island
    Larkspur** [pg. 128]
    Larson, Jan K.

91. *Dicerandra christmanii*
    Garrett's Mint [pg. 1235]
    Shaw, Jonathan

92. *Dicerandra cornutissima*
    Longspurred Mint [pg. 130]
    Christman, Steve
    Shaw, Jonathan*

93. *Dicerandra frutescens*
    Scrub Mint [pg. 132]
    Christman, Steve
    DeLaney, Kris R.*

94. *Dicerandra immaculata*
 Lakela's Mint [pg. 134]
 Robinson, Andy*
 Shaw, Jonathan

95. *Diella falcata*
 NONE [pg. 1237]
 Gustafson, Robert

96. *Dubautia herbstobatae*
 Na'ena'e [pg. 1240]
 Herbst, Derral

97. *Dubautia pauciflorula*
 NONE [pg. 1243]
 Carr, G.

98. *Dudleya traskiae*
 Santa Barbara Island
 Liveforever [pg. 136]
 McMahan, Linda R.

99. *Echinacea tennesseensis*
 Tennessee Purple
 Coneflower [pg. 138]
 Harris, Jessie M.
 Somers, Paul*

100. *Echinocactus horizonthalonius*
 var. *nicholii*
 Nichol's Turk's Head
 Cactus [pg. 140]
 World Wildlife Fund

101. *Echinocereus chisoensis* var. *chisoensis*
 Chisos Mountain
 Hedgehog Cactus [pg. 142]
 Kurz, Don*
 Montgomery, Paul

102. *Echinocereus engelmannii* var. *purpureus*
 Purple-Spined
 Hedgehog Cactus [pg. 144]
 Poulson, Marv

103. *Echinocereus fendleri* var. *kuenzleri*
 Kuenzler Hedgehog Cactus [pg. 156]
 McDonald, Charlie

104. *Echinocereus lloydii*
 Lloyd's Hedgehog Cactus [pg. 148]
 Montgomery, Paul

105. *Echinocereus reichenbachii* var. *albertii*
 Black Lace Cactus [pg. 150]
 Montgomery, Paul

106. *Echinocereus triglochidialus* var. *arizonicus*
 Arizona Hedgehog Cactus [pg. 152]
 McMahon, Linda
 Poulson, Marv*

107. *Echinocereus triglochidiotus* var. *inermis*
 Spineless Hedgehog Cactus [pg. 154]
 Poulson, Marv
 Tuhy, Joel*

108. *Echinocereus viridiflorus* var. *davisii*
 Davis' Green Pitaya Cactus [pg. 156]
 Kurz, Don
 Montgomery, Paul*

109. *Enceliopsis nudicaulis* var. *corrugata*
 Ash Meadows Sunray [pg. 158]
 Cochrane, Susan

110. *Eremalche kernensis*
 Kern Mallow [pg. 1245]
 Austin-McDermin, Marianne*
 Peterson, B. "Moose"

111. *Eriastrum densifolium* ssp. *sanctorum*
 Santa Ana River
 Woolly-Star [pg. 160]
 Middleton, Susan A.

112. *Eriastrum hooveri*
 Hoover's Wooly-Star [pg. 1247]
 Austin-McDermon, Marianne

113. *Erigeron maguirei* var. *maguirei*
 Maguire Daisy [pg. 162]
 England, John L.

114. *Erigeron rhizomatus*
 Zuni Fleabane [pg. 164]
 McDonald, Charlie

115. *Eriogonum gypsophilum*
 Gypsum Wild Buckwheat [pg. 166]
 USFWS Region 1

116. *Eriogonum ovalifolium* var. *williamsiae*
 Steamboat Buckwheat [pg. 168]
 Clemmer, Glenn

140. *Hedeoma todsenii*
     Todsen's Pennyroyal [pg. 208]
     USFWS Region 2

141. *Hedyotis degeneri*
     NONE [pg. 1257]

142. *Hedyotis parvula*
     NONE [pg. 1259]
     Obata, John

143. *Hedyotis purpurea* var. *montana*
     Roan Mountain Bluet [pg. 1261]
     Somers, Paul

144. *Hedyotis st.-johnii*
     Na Pali Beach Hedyotis [pg. 1263]
     Wilson-Ramsey, Yevonn

145. *Helianthus schweinitzii*
     Schweinitz's Sunflower [pg. 1265]
     Murdock, Nora

146. *Helonias bullata*
     Swamp Pink [pg. 210]
     Harris, Jessie M.
     Nelson, John B.
     Wiegand, R. Harrison*

147. *Hesperomannia arbuscula*
     NONE [pg. 1267]
     Obata, John

148. *Hesperomannia lydgatei*
     NONE [pg. 1269]
     Wilson-Ramsey, Yevonn

149. *Hexastylis naniflora*
     Dwarf-Flowered Heartleaf [pg. 212]
     Currie, Robert R.

150. *Hibiscadelphus distans*
     Kauai Hau Kuahiwi [pg. 214]
     Herbst, Derral

151. *Hoffmannseggia tenella*
     Slender Rush-Pea [pg. 216]
     Montgomery, Paul

152. *Hudsonia montana*
     Mountain Golden Heather [pg. 218]
     Currie, Robert R.
     Murdock, Nora*

153. *Hymenoxys acaulis* var. *glabra*
     Lakeside Daisy [pg. 220]
     Moseley, Richard E.

154. *Hymenoxys texana*
     Texas Bitterweed [pg. 222]
     Montgomery, Paul

155. *Hypericum cumulicola*
     **Highlands Scrub
     Hypericum** [pg. 224]
     Christman, Steve
     Shaw, Jonathan*

156. *Ilex cookii*
     Cook's Holly [pg. 226]
     USFWS Puerto Rico

157. *Iliamna corei*
     Peter's Mountain Mallow [pg. 228]
     USFWS Region 5

158. *Iris lacustris*
     Dwarf Lake Iris [pg. 230]
     Wilsmann, Leni

159. *Isodendrion hosakae*
     Aupaka [pg. 1271]
     Gustafson, Robert

160. *Isoetes melanospora*
     Black-Spored Quillwort [pg. 232]
     Allison, James R.

161. *Isoetes tegetiformans*
     Mat-Forming Quillwort [pg. 234]
     Allison, James R.
     Patrick, Thomas S.

162. *Isotria medeoloides*
     Small Whorled Pogonia [pg. 236]
     Brackley, Frankie
     Givens, Kerry*
     Nelson, John B.

163. *Ivesia eremica*
     Ash Meadows Ivesia [pg. 238]
     USFWS Region 1

164. *Justicia cooleyi*
     Cooley's Water-Willow [pg. 240]
     Wunderlin, Richard [pg.]

189. *Mahonia sonnei*
Truckee Barberry [pg. 269]
California Native Plant Society
Ordano, Jo-Ann*

190. *Malacothamnus clementinus*
San Clemente Island
Bush-Mallow [pg. 271]
Gustafson, Robert J.*
Larson, Jan K.

191. *Manihot walkerae*
Walker's Manioc [pg. 1298]
Montgomery, Paul M.

192. *Marshallia mohrii*
Mohr's Barbara's-Buttons [pg. 273]
Norquist, Cary

193. *Mentzelia leucophylla*
Ash Meadows Blazing Star [pg. 275]
Reveal, James

194. *Mezoneuron kavaiense*
Uhiuhi [pg. 277]
Herbst, Derral

195. *Mimulus glabratus* var. *michiganensis*
Michigan Monkey-Flower [pg. 1300]
Michigan Natural Features Inventory

196. *Mirabilis macfarlanei*
MacFarlane's Four O'Clock [pg. 279]
Johnson, F. D.

197. *Neolloydia mariposensis*
Lloyd's Mariposa Cactus [pg. 281]
Montgomery, Paul

198. *Neraudia angulata*
NONE [pg. 1302]
Cowan, R.

199. *Nitrophila mohavensis*
Amargosa Niterwort [pg. 283]
Gustafson, Robert J.*
Peterson, B. "Moose"

200. *Nototrichium humile*
Kulu'i [pg. 1305]
Gustafson, Robert

201. *Oenothera avita* ssp. *eurekensis*
Eureka Valley
Evening-Primrose [pg. 285]
USFWS Region 1

202. *Oenothera deltoides* ssp. *howellii*
Antioch Dunes
Evening-Primrose [pg. 287]
Bartel, Jim A.
Forbes, Holly
Ordano, Jo-Ann*

203. *Opuntia treleasei*
Bakersfield Cactus [pg. 1308]
Austin-McDermon, Marianne
Middleton, Susan*
Peterson, B. "Moose"

204. *Ottoschulzia rhodoxylon*
Palo de Rosa [pg. 1310]
Houghton, William

205. *Oxypolis canbyi*
Canby's Dropwort [pg. 289]
Droege, Mary F.

206. *Oxytropis campestris* var. *chartacea*
Fassett's Locoweed [pg. 291]
Meyer, Thomas A.

207. *Panicum carteri*
Carter's Panicgrass [pg. 293]
Herbst, Derral

208. *Paronychia chartacea*
Papery Whitlow-Wort [pg. 295]
Shaw, Jonathan

209. *Pedicularis furbishiae*
Furbish Lousewort [pg. 297]
Harris, Jessie M.

210. *Pediocactus bradyi*
Brady Pincushion Cactus [pg. 299]
Poulson, Marv

211. *Pediocactus despainii*
San Rafael Cactus [pg. 301]
Atwood, Duane
Poulson, Marv*

259. *Sclerocactus glaucus*
   Uinta Basin
      Hookless Cactus [pg. 361]
      Poulson, Marv

260. *Sclerocactus mesae-verdae*
   Mesa Verde Cactus [pg. 363]
      Poulson, Marv

261. *Sclerocactus wrightiae*
   Wright Fishhook Cactus [pg. 365]
      Poulson, Marv

262. *Scutellaria montana*
   Large-Flowered Skullcap [pg. 367]
      Somers, Paul

263. *Senecio franciscanus*
   San Francisco Peaks
      Groundsel [pg. 369]
      Phillips III, Arthur M.

264. *Sidalcea pedata*
   Pedate Checker-Mallow [pg. 371]
      Gustafson, Robert J.*
      Middleton, Susan A.

265. *Silene perlmanii*
   NONE [pg. 1354]
      Obata, John

266. *Silene polypetala*
   Fringed Campion [pg. 1356]
      Harris, Jessie M.

267. *Sisyrinchium dichotomum*
   White Irisette [pg. 1359]
      Murdock, Nora

268. *Solanum drymophilum*
   Erubia [pg. 373]
      USFWS Puerto Rico

269. *Solidago albopilosa*
   White-Haired Goldenrod [pg. 375]
      Barbour, Roger W.*
      Harris, Jessie M.

270. *Solidago houghtonii*
   Houghton's Goldenrod [pg. 377]
      Wilsmann, Leni

271. *Solidago shortii*
   Short's Goldenrod [pg. 379]
      Harris, Jessie M.
      MacGregor, John*

272. *Solidago spithamaea*
   Blue Ridge Goldenrod [pg. 381]
      Robinson, Andy

273. *Spigelia gentianoides*
   Gentian Pinkroot [pg. 1361]
      Missouri Botanical Garden

274. *Spiraea virginiana*
   Virginia Spiraea [pg. 1364]
      Somers, Paul

275. *Spiranthes parksii*
   Navasota Ladies'-Tresses [pg. 383]
      Montgomery, Paul

276. *Stahlia monosperma*
   Cobana Negra [pg. 1366]
      Houghton, William

277. *Stenogyne angustifolia* var. *angustifolia*
   Stenogyne [pg. 385]
      Herbst, Derral

278. *Stephanomeria malheurensis*
   Malheur Wire Lettuce [pg. 387]
      USFWS Region 1

279. *Styrax texana*
   Texas Snowbells [pg. 389]
      Montgomery, Paul

280. *Swallenia alexandrae*
   Eureka Valley Dunegrass [pg. 391]
      USFWS Region 1

281. *Tetramolopium filiforme*
   NONE [pg. 1368]
      Wilson-Ramsey, Yevonn

282. *Tetramolopium lepidotum* ssp. *lepidotum*
   NONE [pg. 1370]
      Obata, John

283. *Tetramolopium remyi*
   NONE [pg. 1372]
      Hobdy, Robert

284. *Thalictrum cooleyi*
Cooley's Meadowrue [pg. 393]
Annand, Frederick W.

285. *Thelypodium stenopetalum*
Slender-Petaled Mustard [pg. 395]
USFWS Region 1
California Native Plant Society*

286. *Thymophylla tephroleuca*
Ashy Dogweed [pg. 397]
Montgomery, Paul

287. *Torreya taxifolia*
Florida Torreya [pg. 399]
Morse, Larry
Robinson, Andy*

288. *Townsendia aprica*
Last Chance Townsendia [pg. 401]
Atwood, Duane
Poulson, Marv*

289. *Trichilia triacantha*
Bariaco [pg. 403]
USFWS Puerto Rico

290. *Trifolium stoloniferum*
Running Buffalo Clover [pg. 405]
Kurz, Don
Moseley, Richard E.*

291. *Trillium persistens*
Persistent Trillium [pg. 407]
Nelson, John B.
Robinson, Andy*

292. *Trillium reliquum*
Relict Trillium [pg. 409]
Patrick, Thomas S.

293. *Tuctoria mucronata*
Solano Grass [pg. 411]
York, Rich

294. *Tumamoca macdougalii*
Tumamoc Globeberry [pg. 413]
Morgan, C. Allan
Smith, Norm*

295. *Urera kaalae*
Opuhe [pg. 1374]
Wilson-Ramsey, Yevonn

296. *Vicia menziesii*
Hawaiian Vetch [pg. 415]
Herbst, Derral
Shallenberger, Robert*

297. *Viola chamissoniana* ssp. *chamissoniana*
Pamakani [pg. 1376]

298. *Viola helenae*
NONE [pg. 1378]
Herbst, Derral

299. *Viola lanaiensis*
NONE [pg. 1380]
Herbst, Derral

300. *Warea amplexifolia*
Wide-Leaf Warea [pg. 47]
Christman, Steve
Shaw, Jonathan*

301. *Warea carteri*
Carter's Mustard [pg. 419]
Christman, Steve
Shaw, Jonathan*

302. *Xyris tennesseenis*
Tennessee Yellow-Eyed Grass [pg. 1382]
Norquist, Cary

303. *Zanthoxylum thomassianum*
St. Thomas Prickly-Ash [pg. 421]
USFWS Puerto Rico

304. *Zizania texana*
Texas Wildrice [pg. 423]
Montgomery, Paul

305. *Ziziphus celata*
Florida Ziziphus [pg. 425]
DeLaney, Kris R.

Mammals

306. *Antilocapra americana sonoriensis*
Sonoran Pronghorn [pg. 427]
Widener, Neil

307. *Arctocephalus townsendi*
Guadalupe Fur Seal [pg. 429]
Blake, Tupper Ansel*
Morgan, C. Allan

308. *Balaena glacialis*
     Right Whale [pg. 431]
        Gallo, Frank
        Morgan, C. Allan
        NOAA*

309. *Balaena mysticetus*
     Bowhead Whale [pg. 434]
        NOAA

310. *Balaenoptera borealis*
     Sei Whale [pg. 436]
        NOAA

311. *Balaenoptera musculus*
     Blue Whale [pg. 438]
        Morgan, C. Allan
        NOAA*

312. *Balaenoptera physalus*
     Finback Whale [pg. 440]
        Morgan, C. Allan
        NOAA*

313. *Bison bison athabascae*
     Wood Bison [pg. 442]
        Carbyn, L. N.

314. *Canis lupus*
     Gray Wolf [pg. 444]
        Rue III, Leonard Lee

315. *Canis rufus*
     Red Wolf [pg. 448]
        USFWS Region 4

316. *Cynomys parvidens*
     Utah Prairie Dog [pg. 451]
        England, John L.

317. *Dipodomys heermanni morroensis*
     Morro Bay Kangaroo Rat [pg. 453]
        Peterson, B. "Moose"

318. *Dipodomys ingens*
     Giant Kangaroo Rat [pg. 455]
        Middleton, Susan A.*
        Peterson, B. "Moose"

319. *Dipodomys nitratoides nitratoides*
     Tipton Kangaroo Rat [pg. 460]
        Williams, Daniel F.*
        Peterson, B. "Moose"

320. *Dipodomys nitratoides exilis*
     Fresno Kangaroo Rat [pg. 458]
        Chesemore, David L.*
        Peterson, B. "Moose"

321. *Dipodomys stephensi*
     Stephens' Kangaroo Rat [pg. 462]
        Peterson, B. "Moose"

322. *Enhydra lutris nereis*
     Southern Sea Otter [pg. 464]
        Peterson, B. "Moose"*
        Morgan, C. Allan

323. *Eschrichtius robustus*
     Gray Whale [pg. 467]
        Mitchell, Robert and Linda*
        Morgan, C. Allan

324. *Eumetopias jubatus*
     Steller Sea-Lion [pg. 1384]
        Rue III, Leonard Lee

325. *Felis concolor couguar*
     Eastern Cougar [pg. 472]
        Barbour, Roger W.

326. *Felis concolor coryi*
     Florida Panther [pg. 469]
        Florida Natural Areas Inventory*
        Maltz, Alan S.
        USFWS Region 4

327. *Felis pardalis*
     Ocelot [pg. 474]
        Barbour, Roger W.
        Mitchell, Robert and Linda*
        Morgan, C. Allan

328. *Felis wiedi*
     Margay [pg. 476]
        Barbour, Roger W.
        Morgan, C. Allan*

329. *Felis yagouaroundi*
     Jaguarundi [pg. 478]
        Hoffman, John H.*
        Morgan, C. Allan

330. *Glaucomys sabrinus coloratus*
     **Carolina Northern
        Flying Squirrel** [pg. 480]
        Rue III, Leonard Lee

331. *Glaucomys sabrinus fuscus*
**Virginia Northern
Flying Squirrel** [pg. 480]
Rue III, Leonard Lee

332. *Lasiurus cinereus semotus*
Hawaiian Hoary Bat [pg. 483]
Telfer, Thomas C.

333. *Leptonycteris nivalis*
Mexican Long-Nosed Bat [pg. 485]
Tuttle, Merlin D.

334. *Leptonycteris sanborni*
Sanborn's Long-Nosed Bat [pg. 487]
Barbour, Roger W.
Morgan, C. Allan
Tuttle, Merlin D.*

335. *Marmota vancouverensis*
Vancouver Island Marmot [pg. 489]
Canadian Wildlife Service
(Western and Northern Region)

336. *Megaptera novaeangliae*
Humpback Whale [pg. 491]
Morgan, C. Allan

337. *Microtus californicus scirpensis*
Amargosa Vole [pg. 494]
USFWS Region 1

338. *Microtus mexicanus hualpaiensis*
Hualapai Vole [pg. 496]
USFWS Region 2

339. *Microtus pennsylvanicus dukecampbelli*
Florida Salt Marsh Vole [pg. 1387]
Woods, Charles A.

340. *Monachus schauinslandi*
Hawaiian Monk Seal [pg. 498]
Shallenberger, Robert
Telfer, Thomas C.*

341. *Mustela nigripes*
Black-Footed Ferret [pg. 500]
USFWS Region 6
Wyoming Game & Fish Dept.*

342. *Myotis grisescens*
Gray Bat [pg. 503]
Tuttle, Merlin D.

343. *Myotis sodalis*
Indiana Bat [pg. 506]
MacGregor, John
Tuttle, Merlin D.*

344. *Neotoma floridana smalli*
Key Largo Woodrat [pg. 509]
Goodyear, Numi C.

345. *Odocoileus virginianus clavium*
Florida Key Deer [pg. 511]
Maltz, Alan S.
Rue III, Leonard Lee*

346. *Odocoileus virginianus leucurus*
**Columbian White-Tailed
Deer** [pg. 514]
USFWS Region 1

347. *Oryzomys palustris natator*
Silver Rice Rat [pg. 1389]
Goodyear, Numi

348. *Peromyscus gossypinus allapaticola*
Key Largo Cotton Mouse [pg. 516]
Goodyear, Numi C.

349. *Peromyscus polionotus allophrys*
Alabama Beach Mouse [pg. 518]
Holler, Nicholas R.

350. *Peromyscus polionotus trissyllepsis*
Perdido Key Beach Mouse [pg. 518]
Holler, Nicholas R.

351. *Peromyscus polionotus ammobates*
Choctawhatchee Beach Mouse [pg. 518]
Holler, Nicholas R.

352. *Peromyscus polionotus niveiventris*
Southeastern Beach Mouse [pg. 521]
Humphrey, Steve

353. *Peromyscus polionotus phasma*
Anastasia Island Beach Mouse [pg. 521]
Humphrey, Steve

354. *Phocoena sinus*
Vaquita [pg. 523]
Brownell, Robert

355. *Physeter catodon*
    Sperm Whale [pg. 525]
    Morgan, C. Allan
    NOAA*

356. *Plecotus townsendii virginianus*
    Virginia Big-Eared Bat [pg. 530]
    MacGregor, John*
    Parnell, James F.

357. *Plecotus townsendii ingens*
    Ozark Big-Eared Bat [pg. 527]
    Clark, Brenda S. and Bryon K.*
    Tuttle, Merlin D.

358. *Rangifer tarandus caribou*
    Woodland Caribou [pg. 533]
    Rue III, Leonard Lee*
    Wilburn, Jack

359. *Reithrodontomys raviventris*
    Salt Marsh Harvest Mouse [pg. 536]
    Blake, Tupper Ansel*
    Peterson, B. "Moose"

360. *Sciurus niger cinereus*
    Delmarva Peninsula
    Fox Squirrel [pg. 538]
    USFWS Region 5

361. *Sorex longirostris fisheri*
    Dismal Swamp
    Southeastern Shrew [pg. 540]
    French, Thomas W.

362. *Sylvilagus palustris hefneri*
    Lower Keys Rabbit [pg. 1392]
    Maltz, Alan S.

363. *Tamiasciurus hudsonicus grahamensis*
    Mount Graham Red Squirrel [pg. 542]
    Smith, Norm

364. *Trichechus manatus*
    West Indian Manatee [pg. 545]
    Maltz, Alan S.
    Morgan, C. Allan
    USFWS Region 4*

365. *Ursus arctos horribilis*
    Grizzly Bear [pg. 548]
    Morgan, C. Allan
    Wilburn, Jack*

366. *Vulpes macrotis mutica*
    San Joaquin Kit Fox [pg. 553]
    Middleton, Susan A.
    Peterson, B. "Moose"*

367. *Vulpes velox hebes*
    Northern Swift Fox [pg. 556]
    Carbyn, L. N.

Birds

368. *Acrocephalus familiaris kingi*
    Nihoa Millerbird [pg. 561]
    Shallenberger, Robert

369. *Agelaius xanthomus*
    Yellow-Shouldered Blackbird [pg. 563]
    Sorrie, Bruce A.

370. *Amazona vittata*
    Puerto Rican Parrot [pg. 565]
    USFWS Puerto Rico

371. *Ammodramus maritimus mirabilis*
    Cape Sable Seaside Sparrow [pg. 568]
    USFWS Region 4

372. *Ammodramus savannarum floridanus*
    Florida Grasshopper Sparrow [pg. 570]
    Delany, Michael F.

373. *Amphispiza belli clementeae*
    San Clemente Island
    Sage Sparrow [pg. 572]
    Larson, Jan K.

374. *Anas laysanensis*
    Laysan Duck [pg. 574]
    USFWS Region 1*
    VIREO

375. *Anas wyvilliana*
    Hawaiian Duck [pg. 576]
    Shallenberger, Robert*
    VIREO

376. *Aphelocoma coerulescens coerulescens*
    Florida Scrub Jay [pg. 579]
    Kuhn, Lee*
    VIREO

377. *Branta canadensis leucopareia*
   Aleutian Canada Goose [pg. 581]
      Smith, Norm*
      VIREO

378. *Buteo solitarius*
   Hawaiian Hawk [pg. 584]
      Shallenberger, Robert

379. *Campephilus principalis*
   Ivory-Billed Woodpecker [pg. 586]
      Elliott, Lang*
      VIREO

380. *Caprimulgus noctitherus*
   Puerto Rican Nightjar [pg. 588]
      Kepler, Cameron B.

381. *Charadrius melodus*
   Piping Plover [pg. 590]
      Parnell, James F.*
      VIREO

382. *Colinus virginianus ridgwayi*
   Masked Bobwhite [pg. 594]
      Hoffman, John H.
      Morgan, C. Allan*
      Smith, Norm
      VIREO

383. *Columba inornata wetmorei*
   Puerto Rican Plain Pigeon [pg. 597]
      USFWS Puerto Rico

384. *Corvus hawaiiensis*
   Hawaiian Crow [pg. 599]
      USFWS Region 1

385. *Dendroica chrysoparis*
   Golden-Cheeked Warbler [pg. 1394]
      VIREO

386. *Dendroica kirtlandii*
   Kirtland's Warbler [pg. 601]
      VIREO
      Wilsmann, Leni*

387. *Falco femoralis septentrionalis*
   Northern Aplomado Falcon [pg. 604]
      USFWS Region 2

388. *Falco peregrinus tundrius*
   Arctic Peregrine Falcon [pg. 607]
      USFWS Region 7

389. *Falco peregrinus anatum*
   American Peregrine Falcon [pg. 607]
      Kuhn, Lee
      Middleton, Susan A.*
      Morgan, C. Allan
      Peterson, B. "Moose"
      VIREO

390. *Fulica americana alai*
   Hawaiian Coot [pg. 610]
      Shallenberger, Robert

391. *Gallinula chloropus sandvicensis*
   Hawaiian Common Moorhen [pg. 613]
      Shallenberger, Robert

392. *Grus americana*
   Whooping Crane [pg. 615]
      Morgan, C. Allan

393. *Grus canadensis pulla*
   Mississippi Sandhill Crane [pg. 618]
      USFWS Region 4

394. *Gymnogyps californianus*
   California Condor [pg. 621]
      Peterson, B. "Moose"
      USFWS Region 1*
      VIREO

395. *Haliaeetus leucocephalus*
   Bald Eagle [pg. 624]
      Gallo, Frank*
      Maltz, Alan S.
      Morgan, C. Allan
      Peterson, B. "Moose"
      VIREO

396. *Hemignathus lucidus hanapepe*
   Kauai Nukupuu [pg. 628]
      Pratt, Douglas

397. *Hemignathus munroi*
   Akiapolaau [pg. 630]
      Pratt, Douglas

398. *Hemignathus procerus*
   Kauai Akialoa [pg. 632]
      Pratt, Douglas

399. *Himantopus mexicanus knudseni*
Hawaiian Stilt [pg. 634]
Shallenberger, Robert*
VIREO

400. *Lanius ludovicianus mearnsi*
**San Clemente Island
Loggerhead Shrike** [pg. 636]
Larson, Jan K.

401. *Loxioides bailleui*
Palila [pg. 638]
Pratt, Douglas

402. *Loxops coccineus* ssp.
Akepa [pg. 640]
Pratt, Douglas

403. *Melamprosops phaeosoma*
Poo-uli [pg. 643]
Pratt, Douglas

404. *Moho braccatus*
Kauai Oo [pg. 645]
Shallenberger, Robert

405. *Myadestes lanaiensis rutha*
Molokai Thrush [pg. 647]
Pratt, Douglas

406. *Myadestes myadestinus*
Large Kauai Thrush [pg. 649]
Pratt, Douglas

407. *Myadestes palmeri*
Small Kauai Thrush [pg. 651]
Pratt, Douglas

408. *Mycteria americana*
Wood Stork [pg. 653]
Kuhn, Lee*
Morgan, C. Allan
Peterson, B. "Moose"
VIREO

409. *Nesochen sandvicensis*
Hawaiian Goose [pg. 656]
Shallenberger, Robert*
VIREO
Wilburn, Jack

410. *Numenius borealis*
Eskimo Curlew [pg. 658]
Kiff, Lloyd

411. *Oreomystis mana*
Hawaii Creeper [pg. 660]
Pratt, Douglas

412. *Palmeria dolei*
Crested Honeycreeper [pg. 662]
Pratt, Douglas

413. *Paroreomyza flammea*
Molokai Creeper [pg. 664]
Pratt, Douglas

414. *Pelecanus occidentalis*
Brown Pelican [pg. 666]
Middleton, Susan A.
Maltz, Alan S.
Morgan, C. Allan
Parnell, James F.
Peterson, B. "Moose"
USFWS Region 1*
VIREO

415. *Picoides borealis*
Red-Cockaded Woodpecker [pg. 670]
Jackson, Jerome A.*
VIREO

416. *Pipilo fuscus eremophilus*
Inyo Brown Towhee [pg. 673]
LaBerteaux, Denise L.*
Peterson, B. "Moose"

417. *Polyborus plancus audubonii*
Audubon's Crested Caracara [pg. 675]
Kuhn, Lee*
Morgan, C. Allan

418. *Pseudonestor xanthophys*
Maui Parrotbill [pg. 677]
Pratt, Douglas*
VIREO

419. *Psittirostra psittacea*
Ou [pg. 679]
Pratt, Douglas

420. *Pterodroma phaeopygia sandwichensis*
Dark-Rumped Petrel [pg. 681]
Shallenberger, Robert*
Telfer, Thomas C.

421. *Puffinus auricularis newelli*
**Newell's Townsend's
Shearwater** [pg. 683]
Shallenberger, Robert
Telfer, Thomas C.*

422. *Rallus longirostris levipes*
Light-Footed Clapper Rail [pg. 685]
Peterson, B. "Moose"*
VIREO

423. *Rallus longirostris obsoletus*
California Clapper Rail [pg. 687]
Middleton, Susan A.
Peterson, B. "Moose"
Wilburn, Jack*

424. *Rallus longirostris yumanensis*
Yuma Clapper Rail [pg. 690]
McKinstry, Ron*
Peterson, B. "Moose"

425. *Rhynchopsitta pachyrhyncha*
Thick-Billed Parrot [pg. 692]
Snyder, Noel F. R.*
VIREO

426. *Rostrhamus sociabilis plumbeus*
Florida Snail Kite [pg. 694]
Dimmitt, Sterling
USFWS Region 4*
VIREO
Wilburn, Jack

427. *Sterna antillarum browni*
California Least Tern [pg. 700]
Peterson, B. "Moose"

428. *Sterna antillarum antillarum*
Least Tern [pg. 697]
USFWS Region 6*
VIREO

429. *Sterna dougallii dougallii*
Roseate Tern [pg. 703]
Gallo, Frank*
VIREO

430. *Strix occidentalis caurina*
Northern Spotted Owl [pg. 1397]
Peterson, B. "Moose"
VIREO

431. *Telespyza cantans*
Laysan Finch [pg. 706]
Shallenberger, Robert*
Telfer, Thomas C.
VIREO

432. *Telespyza ultima*
Nihoa Finch [pg. 708]
Shallenberger, Robert*
Telfer, Thomas C.

433. *Tympanuchus cupido attwateri*
Attwater's Prairie Chicken [pg. 710]
Morgan, C. Allan*
VIREO

434. *Vermivora bachmanii*
Bachman's Warbler [pg. 712]
VIREO

435. *Vireo atricapillus*
Black-Capped Vireo [pg. 714]
VIREO

436. *Vireo belli pusillus*
Least Bell's Vireo [pg. 716]
Peterson, B. "Moose"

Reptiles

437. *Anolis roosevelti*
Culebra Island Giant Anole [pg. 719]
Dodd, C. Kenneth

438. *Caretta caretta*
Loggerhead Sea Turtle [pg. 721]
NOAA
USFWS Region 4*

439. *Chelonia mydas*
Green Sea Turtle [pg. 724]
Maltz, Alan S.
Morgan, C. Allan*
Pritchard, Peter C. H.
Telfer, Thomas C.

440. *Crocodylus acutus*
  American Crocodile [pg. 727]
  Maltz, Alan S.
  USFWS Region 4*

441. *Crotalus willardi obscurus*
  **New Mexican
  Ridgenose Rattlesnake** [pg. 729]
  Dennis, David M.
  Painter, Charles

442. *Cyclura stegnegeri*
  Mona Ground Iguana [pg. 731]
  Dodd, C. Kenneth

443. *Dermochelys coriacea*
  Leatherback Sea Turtle [pg. 733]
  Mitchell, Robert and Linda
  Morgan, C. Allan
  NOAA
  Pritchard, Peter C. H.*

444. *Drymarchon corais couperi*
  Eastern Indigo Snake [pg. 736]
  Ashton, Ray E.

445. *Epicrates inornatus*
  Puerto Rican Boa [pg. 739]
  USFWS Puerto Rico

446. *Epicrates monensis monensis*
  Mona Boa [pg. 741]
  USFWS Puerto Rico

447. *Eretmocheyls imbricata*
  Hawksbill Sea Turtle [pg. 743]
  NOAA
  USFWS Region 4*

448. *Eumeces egregius lividus*
  Blue-Tailed Mole Skink [pg. 745]
  Dodd, C. Kenneth

449. *Gambelia silus*
  Blunt-Nosed Leopard Lizard [pg. 747]
  Middleton, Susan A.*
  Sweet, Samuel S.

450. *Gopherus agassizii*
  Desert Tortoise [pg. 750]
  Dennis, David M.
  Hoffman, John H.
  Morgan, C. Allan
  Middleton, Susan A.*
  Peterson, B. "Moose"

451. *Gopherus polyphemus*
  Gopher Tortoise [pg. 753]
  Dodd, C. Kenneth

452. *Graptemys flavimaculata*
  Yellow-Blotched Map Turtle [pg. 1401]
  Loehefener, Ren
  Vanderventer, Terry L.*

453. *Graptemys oculifera*
  Ringed Sawback Turtle [pg. 755]
  Barbour, Roger W.*
  Dennis, David M.
  Martin, Richard

454. *Lepidochelys kempii*
  Kemp's Ridley Sea Turtle [pg. 757]
  Dennis, David M.
  Morgan, C. Allan

455. *Lepidochelys olivacea*
  Olive Ridley Sea Turtle [pg. 760]
  Pritchard, Peter C. H.*
  Morgan, C. Allan

456. *Neoseps reynoldsi*
  Sand Skink [pg. 762]
  Dodd, C. Kenneth

457. *Nerodia fasciata taeniata*
  Atlantic Salt Marsh Snake [pg. 764]
  Christman, Steve
  Dennis, David M.
  USFWS Region 4*

458. *Nerodia harteri paucimaculata*
  Concho Water Snake [pg. 766]
  Mitchell, Robert and Linda

459. *Pseudemys alabamensis*
  Alabama Red-Bellied Turtle [pg. 768]
  Dobie, James

460. *Pseudemys rubriventris bangsii*
Plymouth Red-Bellied Turtle [pg. 770]
Dennis, David M.
USFWS Region 5*

461. *Sphaerodactylus micropithecus*
Monito Gecko [pg. 772]
Dodd, C. Kenneth

462. *Sternotherus depressus*
Flattened Musk Turtle [pg. 774]
Dodd, C. Kenneth

463. *Thamnophis sirtalis tetrataenia*
San Francisco Garter Snake [pg. 776]
Middleton, Susan A.

464. *Uma inornata*
**Coachella Valley
Fringe-Toed Lizard** [pg. 778]
Dodd, C. Kenneth
Peterson, B. "Moose"*

465. *Xantusia riversiana*
Island Night Lizard [pg. 781]
Larson, Jan K.*
Peterson, B. "Moose"

Amphibians

466. *Ambystoma macrodactylum croceum*
**Santa Cruz Long-Toed
Salamander** [pg. 783]
Ashton, Ray E.*
Dennis, David M.
Sweet, Samuel S.

467. *Batrachoseps aridus*
Desert Slender Salamander [pg. 785]
Foreman, Larry D.
Wake, David B.*

468. *Bufo hemiophrys baxteri*
Wyoming Toad [pg. 787]
Parker, LuRay

469. *Bufo houstonensis*
Houston Toad [pg. 789]
Dodd, C. Kenneth
Morgan, C. Allan*
Hedges, S. Blair

470. *Eleutherodactylus jasperi*
Golden Coqui [pg. 791]
USFWS Puerto Rico

471. *Eurycea nana*
San Marcos Salamander [pg. 793]
Mitchell, Robert and Linda*
Sweet, Samuel S.

472. *Peltophryne lemur*
Puerto Rican Crested Toad [pg. 795]
Dennis, David M.

473. *Phaeognathus hubrichti*
Red Hills Salamander [pg. 797]
Dodd, C. Kenneth

474. *Plethodon nettingi*
Cheat Mountain Salamander [pg. 1403]
Ashton, Ray E.

475. *Plethodon shenandoah*
Shenandoah Salamander [pg. 1405]
Liebman, David

476. *Typhlomolge rathbuni*
Texas Blind Salamander [pg. 799]
Clark, Chip
Mitchell, Robert and Linda*

Fishes

477. *Acipenser brevirostrum*
Shortnose Sturgeon [pg. 801]
Patrick, Thomas S.*
Rohde, Fred

478. *Acipenser oxyrhynchus desotoi*
Gulf sturgeon [pg. 1407]
Moran, John

479. *Amblyopsis rosae*
Ozark Cavefish [pg. 803]
Norton, Russell

480. *Catostomus microps*
Modoc Sucker [pg. 805]
USFWS Region 1

481. *Catostomus warnerensis*
Warner Sucker [pg. 807]
Oregon Nature Conservancy

482. *Chasmistes brevirostris*
Shortnose Sucker [pg. 809]
USFWS Region 1

483. *Chasmistes cujus*
Cui-ui [pg. 813]
USFWS Region 1

484. *Chasmistes liorus*
June Sucker [pg. 811]
USFWS Region 6

485. *Cottus pygmaeus*
Pygmy Sculpin [pg. 1409]
Wallace, Richard

486. *Crenichthys baileyi baileyi*
White River Springfish [pg. 815]
Rinne, John N.

487. *Crenichthys baileyi grandis*
Hiko White River Springfish [pg. 815]
USFWS Region 1

488. *Crenichthys nevadae*
Railroad Valley Springfish [pg. 817]
Baugh, Thomas M

489. *Cyprinodon bovinus*
Leon Springs Pupfish [pg. 819]
Johnson, James E.

490. *Cyprinodon diabolis*
Devil's Hole Pupfish [pg. 821]
Baugh, Thomas M.

491. *Cyprinodon elegans*
Comanche Springs Pupfish [pg. 823]
Johnson, James E.

492. *Cyprinodon macularius*
Desert Pupfish [pg. 825]
Peterson, B. "Moose"*
Morgan, C. Allan

493. *Cyprinodon nevadensis pectoralis*
Warm Springs Pupfish [pg. 829]
Sjoberg, Jon C.

494. *Cyprinodon nevadensis mionectes*
**Ash Meadows Amargosa
Pupfish** [pg. 827]
USFWS Region 1

495. *Cyprinodon radiosus*
Owens Pupfish [pg. 831]
Peterson, B. "Moose"

496. *Deltistes luxatus*
Lost River Sucker [pg. 833]
USFWS Region 1

497. *Empetrichthys latos latos*
Pahrump Killifish [pg. 835]
USFWS Region 1

498. *Eremichthys acros*
Desert Dace [pg. 837]
Etnier, David
Vinyard, Gary*

499. *Etheostoma boschungi*
Slackwater Darter [pg. 839]
Biggins, Richard

500. *Etheostoma fonticola*
Fountain Darter [pg. 841]
Barbour, Roger W.

501. *Etheostoma nianguae*
Niangua Darter [pg. 843]
Roston, Dr. William

502. *Etheostoma nuchale*
Watercress Darter [pg. 845]
Barbour, Roger W.
Roston, William

503. *Etheostoma okaloosae*
Okaloosa Darter [pg. 847]
Barbour, Roger W.*
Roston, William

504. *Etheostoma rubrum*
Bayou Darter [pg. 849]
USFWS Region 4

505. *Etheostoma sellare*
Maryland Darter [pg. 851]
Barbour, Roger W.

506. *Etheostoma sp.*
Boulder Darter [pg. 853]
Biggins, Richard

507. *Gambusia gaigai*
Big Bend Gambusia [pg. 855]
Johnson, James E.

508. *Gambusia georgei*
San Marcos Gambusia [pg. 857]
Edwards, Robert J.

509. *Gambusia heterochir*
Clear Creek Gambusia [pg. 859]
Mills, Glenn

510. *Gambusia nobilis*
Pecos Gambusia [pg. 861]
Johnson, James E.

511. *Gasterosteus aculeatus williamsoni*
**Unarmored Threespine
Stickleback** [pg. 863]
Peterson, B. "Moose"

512. *Gila bicolor snyderi*
Owens Tui Chub [pg. 867]
USFWS Region 1

513. *Gila bicolor ssp.*
Hutton Spring Tui Chub [pg. 869]
Oregon Nature Conservancy

514. *Gila bicolor mohavensis*
Mohave Tui Chub [pg. 865]
USFWS Region 1

515. *Gila boraxobius*
Borax Lake Chub [pg. 871]
Oregon Nature Conservancy

516. *Gila cypha*
Humpback Chub [pg. 873]
USFWS Region 6

517. *Gila ditaenia*
Sonora Chub [pg. 875]
Johnson, James E.*
Morgan, C. Allan

518. *Gila elegans*
Bonytail Chub [pg. 877]
Rinne, John N.

519. *Gila nigrescens*
Chihuahua Chub [pg. 879]
Johnson, James E.

520. *Gila purpurea*
Yaqui Chub [pg. 881]
Johnson, James E.

521. *Gila robusta jordani*
Pahranagat Roundtail Chub [pg. 883]
Rinne, John N.

522. *Gila robusta seminuda*
Virgin River Chub [pg. 1411]
Rinne, John N.

523. *Hybopsis cahni*
Slender Chub [pg. 885]
USFWS Region 4

524. *Hybopsis monacha*
Spotfin Chub [pg. 887]
Roston, Dr. William

525. *Ictalurus pricei*
Yaqui Catfish [pg. 889]
Rinne, John N.

526. *Lepidomeda albivallis*
White River Spinedace [pg. 891]
Rinne, John N.

527. *Lepidomeda mollispinis pratensis*
Big Spring Spinedace [pg. 893]
Sjoberg, Jon C.

528. *Lepidomeda vittata*
Little Colorado Spinedace [pg. 895]
James E. Johnson

529. *Meda fulgida*
Spikedace [pg. 897]
Rinne, John N.

530. *Menidia extensa*
Waccamaw Silverside [pg. 899]
Parnell, James F.

531. *Moapa coriacea*
Moapa Dace [pg. 901]
Rinne, John N.

532. *Notropis cahabae*
Cahaba Shiner [pg. 1414]
Stiles, Robert A.

533. *Notropis formosus*
Beautiful Shiner [pg. 903]
Rinne, John N.

534. *Notropis mekistocholas*
Cape Fear Shiner [pg. 905]
Biggins, Richard

535. *Notropis simus pecosensis*
Pecos Bluntnose Shiner [pg. 907]
Hatch, Michael D.

536. *Noturus baileyi*
Smoky Madtom [pg. 909]
Biggins, Richard

537. *Noturus flavipinnis*
Yellowfin Madtom [pg. 911]
Etnier, David

538. *Noturus placidus*
Neosho Madtom [pg. 1416]
Collins, Suzanne L. and Joseph T.

539. *Noturus trautmani*
Scioto Madtom [pg. 913]
Bonenberger, Lynn

540. *Oncorhynchus nerka*
Sockeye Salmon [pg. 1419]
Bryant, Janet

541. *Oncorhynchus tshawytscha*
Chinook Salmon [pg. 1423]
Vogel, Dave

542. *Percina antesella*
Amber Darter [pg. 915]
Barbour, Roger W.*
Biggins, Richard
Etnier, David

543. *Percina jenkinsi*
Conasauga Logperch [pg. 917]
Thompson, Bruce

544. *Percina pantherina*
Leopard Darter [pg. 919]
Barbour, Roger W.*
James, Paul
Roston, William

545. *Percina rex*
Roanoke Logperch [pg. 1426]
Burkhead, Noel and Robert Jenkins

546. *Percina tanasi*
Snail Darter [pg. 921]
Barbour, Roger W.

547. *Phoxinus cumberlandensis*
Blackside Dace [pg. 924]
Biggins, Richard

548. *Plagopterus argentissimus*
Woundfin [pg. 926]
Rinne, John N.

549. *Poeciliopsis occidentalis sonoriensis*
Yaqui Topminnow [pg. 928]
Johnson, James E.

550. *Poeciliopsis occidentalis occidentalis*
Gila Topminnow [pg. 928]
Johnson, James E.*
Morgan, C. Allan

551. *Ptychocheilus lucius*
Colorado Squawfish [pg. 930]
Tyus, Harold M.*
Morgan, C. Allan

552. *Rhinichthys osculus lethoporus*
**Independence Valley
Speckled Dace** [pg. 1429]
Vinyard, Gary

553. *Rhinichthys osculus nevadensis*
Ash Meadows Speckled Dace [pg. 932]
Sada, Donald W.*
Sjoberg, Jon C.

554. *Rhinichthys osculus oligoporus*
Clover Valley Speckled Dace [pg. 1431]
Vinyard, Gary

555. *Rhinichthys osculus* ssp.
Foskett Speckled Dace [pg. 934]
USFWS Region 1

556. *Rhinichthys osculus thermalis*
Kendall Warm Springs Dace [pg. 936]
Gould, William R.

Mussels

582. *Fusconaia cuneolus*
**Fine-Rayed Pigtoe
Pearly Mussel** [pg. 978]
Spreitzer, A. E.

583. *Fusconaia edgariana*
Shiny Pigtoe Pearly Mussel [pg. 981]
Spreitzer, A. E.

584. *Hemistena lata*
Cracking Pearly Mussel [pg. 1447]
Spreitzer, A. E.

585. *Lampsilis higginsi*
Higgins' Eye Pearly Mussel [pg. 983]
Spreitzer, A. E.

586. *Lampsilis orbiculata*
Pink Mucket Pearly Mussel [pg. 985]
Spreitzer, A. E.

587. *Lampsilis powelli*
Arkansas Fatmucket [pg. 1449]
Spreitzer, A. E.

588. *Lampsilis streckeri*
Speckled Pocketbook Mussel [pg. 987]
Spreitzer, A. E.

589. *Lampsilis virescens*
Alabama Lamp Pearly Mussel [pg. 989]
Spreitzer, A. E.

590. *Margaritifera hembeli*
Louisiana Pearlshell [pg. 991]
Lester, Gary
Spreitzer, A. E.*

591. *Obovaria retusa*
Ring Pink Mussel [pg. 1451]
Spreitzer, A. E.

592. *Pegias fabula*
Little-Wing Pearly Mussel [pg. 993]
Biggins, Richard
Spreitzer, A. E.*

593. *Plethobasus cicatricosus*
**White Wartyback
Pearly Mussel** [pg. 995]
Spreitzer, A. E.

594. *Plethobasus cooperianus*
Orange-Footed Pearly Mussel [pg. 997]
Spreitzer, A. E.

595. *Pleurobema collina*
James River Spinymussel [pg. 999]
Spreitzer, A. E.

596. *Pleurobema curtum*
Curtus' Mussel [pg. 1001]
Spreitzer, A. E.

597. *Pleurobema gibberum*
Cumberland Pigtoe Mussel [pg. 1453]
Spreitzer, A. E.

598. *Pleurobema marshalli*
Marshall's Mussel [pg. 1003]
Spreitzer, A. E.

599. *Pleurobema plenum*
Rough Pigtoe Pearly Mussel [pg. 1005]
Spreitzer, A. E.

600. *Pleurobema taitianum*
Judge Tait's Mussel [pg. 1007]
Spreitzer, A. E.

601. *Potamilus capax*
Fat Pocketbook Pearly Mussel [pg. 1009]
Spreitzer, A. E.

602. *Potamilus inflatus*
Inflated Heelsplitter [pg. 1455]
Spreitzer, A. E.

603. *Quadrula fragosa*
Winged Mapleleaf Mussel [pg. 1457]
Spreitzer, A. E.

604. *Quadrula intermedia*
**Cumberland Monkeyface
Pearly Mussel** [pg. 1011]
Spreitzer, A. E.

605. *Quadrula sparsa*
**Appalachian Monkeyface
Pearly Mussel** [pg. 1014]
Spreitzer, A. E.

606. *Quadrula stapes*
Stirrup Shell [pg. 1016]
Spreitzer, A. E.

607. *Toxolasma cylindrellus*
   Pale Lilliput Pearly Mussel [pg. 1018]
   Spreitzer, A. E.

608. *Villosa trabalis*
   **Cumberland Bean
   Pearly Mussel** [pg. 1020]
   Spreitzer, A. E.

Crustaceans

609. *Antrolana lira*
   Madison Cave Isopod [pg. 1023]
   Holsinger, John
   Norton, Russell*
   White, Christopher P.

610. *Cambarus zophonastes*
   Cave Crayfish [pg. 1025]
   USFWS Region 4

611. *Orconectes shoupi*
   Nashville Crayfish [pg. 1027]
   Biggins, Richard

612. *Pacifastacus fortis*
   Shasta Crayfish [pg. 1029]
   USFWS Region 1

613. *Palaemonetes cummingi*
   Squirrel Chimney Cave Shrimp [pg. 1459]
   None available

614. *Palaemonias alabamae*
   Alabama Cave Shrimp [pg. 1031]
   Cooper, John

615. *Palaemonias ganteri*
   Kentucky Cave Shrimp [pg. 1033]
   Clark, Chip
   MacGregor, John

616. *Stygobromus hayi*
   Hay's Spring Amphipod [pg. 1035]
   Dodd, C. Kenneth

617. *Syncaris pacifica*
   California Freshwater Shrimp [pg. 1037]
   Middleton, Susan A.

618. *Thermosphaeroma thermophilum*
   Socorro Isopod [pg. 1039]
   McDonald, Charlie

Snails

619. *Achatinella sp.*
   Oahu Tree Snails [pg. 1041]
   Mull, William P.

620. *Anguispira picta*
   **Painted Snake Coiled
   Forest Snail** [pg. 1044]
   USFWS Region 4

621. *Discus macclintocki*
   Iowa Pleistocene Snail [pg. 1046]
   Fleckenstein, John
   Frest, Terry*

622. *Mesodon clarki nantahala*
   Noonday Snail [pg. 1048]
   USFWS Region 4

623. *Mesodon magazinensis*
   Magazine Mountain Shagreen [pg. 1050]
   Caldwell, Ron

624. *Orthalicus reses reses*
   Stock Island Snail [pg. 1052]
   Dimmitt, Sterling*
   Thompson, Fred G.

625. *Oxyloma haydeni* ssp. *kanabensis*
   Kanab Ambersnail [pg. 1461]
   Lunceford, Blaine

626. *Polygyriscus virginianus*
   **Virginia Fringed
   Mountain Snail** [pg. 1054]
   Batie, Robert E.

627. *Pyrgulopsis neomexicana*
   Socorro Springsnail [pg. 1463]
   New Mexico Bureau of Mines
   and Mineral Resources

628. *Succinea chittenangoensis*
   **Chittenango Ovate
   Amber Snail** [pg. 1056]
   Nye, Peter

629. *Triodopsis platysayoides*
   **Flat-Spired
   Three-Toothed Snail** [pg. 1058]
   Stihler, Craig W.

Insects & Arachnids

653. *Rhadine persephone*
    Tooth Cave Ground Beetle [pg. 1095]
       Mitchell, Robert and Linda

654. *Speyeria zerene hippolyta*
    Oregon Silverspot Butterfly [pg. 1097]
       Arnold, Richard A.

655. *Texamaurops reddelli*
    Kretschmarr Cave Mold
       Beetle [pg. 1099]
       Mitchell, Robert and Linda

656. *Texella reddelli*
    Bee Creek Cave Harvestman [pg. 1101]
       Mitchell, Robert and Linda

Photographers and Photo Sources

Ackerman, James D.
Dept. of Biology
University of Puerto Rico
P.O. 23360
UPR Station
San Juan, PR 00931
(809) 764-0000 x2023
Photos:
Cranichis ricartii
    NONE
Lepanthes eltorensis
    NONE

Aerni, Sonja
Nebraska Game and Parks Commission
2200 North 33rd
Lincoln, Nebraska 68503
(404) 471-5466
Photos:
Penstemon haydenii
    Blowout Penstemon

Allison, James R.
1574 Mill Run Court
Lawrenceville, GA 30244
(404) 963-4428
Photos:
Amphianthus pusillus
    Little Amphianthus
Isoetes melanospora
    Black-Spored Quillwort
Isoetes tegetiformans
    Mat-Forming Quillwort

Annand, Frederick W.
North Carolina Nature Conservancy
Carr Mill, Suite 223
Carrboro, NC 27510
(919) 967-7007
Photos:
Thalictrum cooleyi
    Cooley's Meadowrue

Arnold, Richard A.
Entomological Consulting Services
104 Mountain View Court
Pleasant Hill, CA 94523
(415) 825-3784
Speciality: West Coast insects
Photos:
Apodemia mormo langei
    Lange's Metalmark Butterfly
Callophrys mossii bayensis
    San Bruno Elfin Butterfly
Desmocerus californicus dimorphus
    Valley Elderberry Longhorn Beetle
Elaphrus viridis
    Delta Green Ground Beetle
Euphilotes battoides allyni
    El Segundo Blue Butterfly
Euphilotes enoptes smithi
    Smith's Blue Butterfly
Euphydryas editha bayensis
    Bay Checkerspot Butterfly
Glaucopsyche lygdamus palosverdesensis
    Palos Verdes Blue Butterfly
Icaricia icarioides missionensis
    Mission Blue Butterfly
Lycaeides argyrognomon lotis
    Lotis Blue Butterfly
Speyeria zerene hippolyta
    Oregon Silverspot Butterfly

Ashton, Ray E.
6821 SW Archer Rd.
Gainesville, FL 32607
(904) 332-5345
Specialty: Reptiles and Amphibians
Photos:
Drymarchon corais couperi
    Eastern Indigo Snake
Ambystoma macrodactylum croceum
    Santa Cruz Long-Toed Salamander
Plethodon nettingi
    Cheat Mountain Salamander

Atwood, Duane
324 25th
Ogden, UT 84403
(801) 625-5599
Specialty: Utah plants
Photos:
  Arctomecon humilis
    Dwarf Bear-Poppy
  Astragalus montii
    Heliotrope Milk-Vetch
  Astragalus perianus
    Rydberg Milk-Vetch
  Cycladenia humilis jonesii
    Jones Cycladenia
  Glaucocarpum suffrutescens
    Toad-Flax Cress
  Pediocactus despainii
    San Rafael Cactus
  Phacelia argillacea
    Clay Phacelia
  Primula maguirei
    Maguire Primrose
  Townsendia aprica
    Last Chance Townsendia

Austin-McDermon, Marianne
P.O. Box 1244
Sonoma, CA 95476
(707) 935-1418
Specialty: West Coast plants
Photos:
  Arctostaphylos pungens ravenii
    Presidio Manzanita
  Blennosperma bakeri
    Baker's Sticky Seed
  Caulanthus californicus
    California Jewelflower
  Cupressus abramsiana
    Santa Cruz Cypress
  Eremalche kernensis
    Kern Mallow
  Eriastrum hooveri
    Hoover's Wooly-Star
  Eryngium constancei
    Loch Lomond Coyote Thistle
  Erysimum capitatum angustatum
    Contra Costa Wallflower
  Lasthenia burkei
    Burke's Goldfields
  Lembertia congdonii
    San Joaquin Wooly-Threads
  Limnanthes vinculans
    Sebastopol Meadowfoam

  Oenothera deltoides howellii
    Antioch Dunes Evening-Primrose
  Opuntia treleasei
    Bakersfield Cactus

Barbour, Roger W.
4880 Tates Creek Pike
Lexington, KY 40515
(606) 272-3925
Photos:
  Solidago albopilosa
    White-Haired Goldenrod
  Felis concolor couguar
    Eastern Cougar
  Felis pardalis
    Ocelot
  Felis wiedi
    Margay
  Leptonycteris sanborni
    Sanborn's Long-Nosed Bat
  Graptemys oculifera
    Ringed Sawback Turtle
  Etheostoma fonticola
    Fountain Darter
  Etheostoma nuchale
    Watercress Darter
  Etheostoma okaloosae
    Okaloosa Darter
  Etheostoma sellare
    Maryland Darter
  Percina antesella
    Amber Darter
  Percina pantherina
    Leopard Darter
  Percina tanasi
    Snail Darter

Bartel, Jim A.
U.S. Fish and Wildlife Service
Office
2800 Cottage Way, Room E-1823
Sacramento, CA 95825
(916) 978-4866
Photos:
  Acanthomintha obovata duttonii
    San Mateo Thornmint
  Amsinckia grandiflora
    Large-Flowered Fiddleneck
  Camissonia benitensis
    San Benito Evening-Primrose

Eryngium constancei
  Loch Lomond Coyote Thistle
Oenothera deltoides howellii
  Antioch Dunes Evening-Primrose

Batie, Robert E.
Department of Biology
Radford University
Radford, VA 24142
(703) 831-5445
Photos:
  Polygyriscus virginianus
    Virginia Fringed Mountain Snail

Baugh, Thomas M.
2115 Nathan West
Jacksonville, FL 32216
(904) 791-2580
Photos:
  Crenichthys nevadae
    Railroad Valley Springfish
  Cyprinodon diabolis
    Devil's Hole Pupfish

Biggins, Richard
U.S. Fish and Wildlife Service
100 Otis, Room 224
Asheville, NC 28801
(704) 259-0321
Photos:
  Etheostoma boschungi
    Slackwater Darter
  Etheostoma
    Boulder Darter
  Notropis mekistocholas
    Cape Fear Shiner
  Noturus baileyi
    Smoky Madtom
  Percina antesella
    Amber Darter
  Phoxinus cumberlandensis
    Blackside Dace
  Elliptio steinstansana
    Tar River Spinymussel
  Pegias fabula
    Little-Wing Pearly Mussel
  Orconectes shoupi
    Nashville Crayfish

Blake, Tupper Ansel
P.O. Box 152
Inverness, CA 94937
(415) 663-8205
Specialty: West Coast mammals and birds
Photos:
  Arctocephalus townsendi
    Guadalupe Fur Seal
  Reithrodontomys raviventris
    Salt Marsh Harvest Mouse

Bonenberger, Lynne
Ohio State University Press
180 Pressey Hall
1070 Carmack Road
Columbus, OH 43210
(614) 292-6930
Line drawing:
  Noturus trautmani
    Scioto Madtom

Bowen, Willaim R.
Biology Dept.
Jacksonville State University
Jacksonville, AL 36265
(205) 782-5642
Photos:
  Sagittaria secundifolia
    Kral's Water-Plantain

Brackley, Frankie
New Hampshire Natural Heritage Inventory
Dept. of Resources and Economic
Development
P.O. Box 856
Concord, NH 03302
(603) 271-3623
Photos:
  Astragalus robbinsii jesupi
    Jesup's Milk-Vetch
  Isotria medeoloides
    Small Whorled Pogonia

Brown, Kevin K.
8329 Santa Fe Lane
Overland Park, KS 66212
(913) 383-2236
Photos:
  Ursus arctos horribilis
    Grizzly Bear

Brownell, Robert
U.S. Fish and Wildlife Service
P.O. Box 70
San Simeon, CA 93452
(805) 927-3893
Photos:
  Phocoena sinus
    Vaquita

Bryant, Janet
Idaho Dept. of Fish and Game
600 S. Walnut
P.O. Box 25
Boise, ID 83707
(208) 334-3476
Photos:
  Oncorhynchus nerka
    Sockeye Salmon (Snake River)

Burkhead, Noel
See USFWS Region 5
  Percina rex
    Roanoke Logperch

Caldwell, Ron
Lincoln Memorial University
P.O. Box 1861
Harrogate, TN 37752
(615) 869-6300
Photos:
  Mesodon magazinensis
    Magazine Mountain Shagreen

California Native Plant Society
909 12th, Suite 116
Sacramento CA 95814
(916) 447-CNPS
Photos:
  Cupressus abramsiana
    Santa Cruz Cypress
  Mahonia sonnei
    Truckee Barberry
  Thelypodium stenopetalum
    Slender-Petaled Mustard
  Tuctoria mucronata
    Solano Grass

Canadian Wildlife Service
Room 230, 4999-98
Edmonton, Alberta T6B 2X3
Canada
(403) 435-7357
Photos:
  Marmota vancouverensis
    Vancouver Island Marmot

Carbyn, L. N.
Canadian Wildlife Service
Room 230, 4999-98
Edmonton, Alberta T6B 2X3
Canada
(403) 435-7357
Photos:
  Bison bison athabascae
    Wood Bison
  Vulpes velox hebes
    Northern Swift Fox

Carr, G.
See USFWS Region 1
  Dubautia pauciflorula
    NONE

Chesemore, David L.
Dept. of Biology
California State University, Fresno
Fresno, CA 93740
(209) 294-2001
Photos:
  Dipodomys nitratoides exilis
    Fresno Kangaroo Rat

Christman, Steve
Box 391
Hawthorne, FL 32640
Specialty: Florida plants
Photos:
  Chionanthus pygmaeus
    Pygmy Fringe Tree
  Dicerandra cornutissima
    Longspurred Mint
  Dicerandra frutescens
    Scrub Mint
  Eryngium cuneifolium
    Snakeroot
  Hypericum cumulicola
    Highlands Scrub Hypericum
  Lupinus aridorum
    Scrub Lupine

Prunus geniculata
    Scrub Plum
Warea amplexifolia
    Wide-Leaf Warea
Warea carteri
    Carter's Mustard
Nerodia fasciata taeniata
    Atlantic Salt Marsh Snake

Clark, Chip
National Museum of Natural History
Smithsonian Insititution
Office of Exhibits
Room 77A
10th & Constitution NW
Washington, DC 20560
(202) 357-2760
Specialty: Cave species
Photos:
Typhlomolge rathbuni
    Texas Blind Salamander
Palaemonias ganteri
    Kentucky Cave Shrimp

Clark, Brenda S. and Bryon K.
Oklahoma Cooperative Fish and Wildlife
Research Unit
404 Life Scioences West
Oklahoma State University
Stillwater, OK 74078
(405) 744-6342
Photos:
Plecotus townsendii ingens
    Ozark Big-Eared Bat

Clemmer, Glenn
Nevada Natural Heritage Program
201 S. Fall
Carson City, NV 89710
(702) 885-4370
Photos:
Eriogonum ovalifolium williamsiae
    Steamboat Buckwheat

Cochrane, Susan
California Nongame Heritage Program
Dept. of Fish & Game
1416 9th St., 12th Floor
Sacramento, CA 95814
(916) 322-2493
Photos:
Astragalus phoenix
    Ash Meadows Milk-Vetch

Centaurium namophilum
    Spring-Loving Centaury
Enceliopsis nudicaulis corrugata
    Ash Meadows Sunray

Collins, Joseph T. and Suzanne L.
1502 Medinah Circle
Lawrence, KS 66047
Photos:
Noturus placidus
    Neosho Madtom
Graptemys flavimaculata
    Yellow-Blotched Map Turtle
Plethodon nettingi
    Cheat Mountain Salamander

Cooper, John
Rt. 6
Box 549-C
Reidsville, NC 27320
(919) 342-2424
Illustration:
Palaemonias alabamae
    Alabama Cave Shrimp

Croy, Steve
George Washington National Forest
101 N. Main St.
Harrison Plaza
P.O. Box 233
Harrisonburg, VA 22801
(703) 433-2491
Photos:
Scirpus ancistrochaetus
    Northeastern Bulrush

Currie, Robert R.
U.S. Fish and Wildlife Service
100 Otis, Room 224
Asheville, NC 28801
(704) 259-0321
Photos:
Hexastylis naniflora
    Dwarf-Flowered Heartleaf
Hudsonia montana
    Mountain Golden Heather

Dawson, Jeffrey
Woodward-Clyde Consultants
Stanford Place 3, Suite 1000
4582 South Ulster Parkway
Denver, CO 80237
(303) 694-2770
Photos:
  Astragalus osterhoutii
    Osterhout Milk-Vetch

Dawson, Carol
Denver Botanic Gardens
909 York
Denver, CO 80206
(303) 331-4000
Photos:
  Penstemon penlandii
    Penland Beardtongue

DeLaney, Kris R.
Botanist, Environmental Research
Consultants,
2557 US 27 South
Sebring, FL 33870
(813) 385-7774
Specialty: Florida plants
Photos:
  Chionanthus pygmaeus
    Pygmy Fringe Tree
  Dicerandra frutescens
    Scrub Mint
  Liatris ohlingerae
    Scrub Blazing Star
  Ziziphus celata
    Florida Ziziphus

Delany, Michael F.
Florida Game and Fresh Water Fish
Commission
Wildlife Research Laboratory
4005 S. Main
Gainesville, FL 32601
(904) 376-6481
Photos:
  Ammodramus savannarum floridanus
    Florida Grasshopper Sparrow

DeLeon, John
Natural History Museum of Los Angeles
County
900 Exposition Blvd.
Los Angeles, CA 90007
(213) 744-3378
Photos:
  Euproserpinus euterpe
    Kern Primrose Sphinx Moth

Dennis, David M.
3363 Braumiller Rd.
Delaware, OH 43015
(614) 292-1371
Specialty: Reptiles and amphibians
Photos:
  Crotalus willardi obscurus
    New Mexican Ridgenose Rattlesnake
  Gopherus agassizii
    Desert Tortoise
  Graptemys oculifera
    Ringed Sawback Turtle
  Lepidochelys kempii
    Kemp's Ridley Sea Turtle
  Nerodia fasciata taeniata
    Atlantic Salt Marsh Snake
  Pseudemys rubriventris bangsii
    Plymouth Red-Bellied Turtle
  Ambystoma macrodactylum croceum
    Santa Cruz Long-Toed Salamander
  Peltophryne lemur
    Puerto Rican Crested Toad

Dimmitt, Sterling
Route 1
71 Village
Ormond Beach, FL 32074
(904) 677-7613
Photos:
  Rostrhamus sociabilis plumbeus
    Florida Snail Kite
  Orthalicus reses reses
    Stock Island Snail

Dobie, James
Dept. of Zoology and Wildlife Science
Auburn University
Auburn University, AL 36849-5414
(205) 844-4850
Photos:
  Pseudemys alabamensis
    Alabama Red-Bellied Turtle

Dodd, Jr., C. Kenneth
U.S. Fish and Wildlife Service
National Ecology Research Center
412 N.E. 16th, Room 250
Gainesville, FL 32601
(904) 372-2571
Photos:
  Anolis roosevelti
    Culebra Island Giant Anole
  Cyclura stegnegeri
    Mona Ground Iguana
  Eumeces egregius lividus
    Blue-Tailed Mole Skink
  Gopherus polyphemus
    Gopher Tortoise
  Neoseps reynoldsi
    Sand Skink
  Sphaerodactylus micropithecus
    Monito Gecko
  Sternotherus depressus
    Flattened Musk Turtle
  Uma inornata
    Coachella Valley Fringe-Toed Lizard
  Bufo houstonensis
    Houston Toad
  Phaeognathus hubrichti
    Red Hills Salamander
  Stygobromus hayi
    Hay's Spring Amphipod

Droege, Mary F.
Maryland Nature Conservancy
2 Wisconsin Circle, Suite 410
Chevy Chase, MD 20815
(301) 656-8673
Photos:
  Agalinis acuta
    Sandplain Gerardia
  Oxypolis canbyi
    Canby's Dropwort

Edwards, Robert J.
Dept. of Biology
University of Texas, Pan American
Edinburg, TX 78539
(512) 381-3537
Photos:
  Gambusia georgei
    San Marcos Gambusia

Elliott, Lang
Cornell Laboratory of Ornithology
159 Sapsucker Woods
Ithaca, NY 14850
(607) 254-2450
Photos:
  Campephilus principalis
    Ivory-Billed Woodpecker

Emmel, Thomas C.
Department of Zoology
Division of Lepidoptera Research
University of Florida
Gainesville, FL 32611
(904) 392-1137
Photos:
  Heraclides aristodemus ponceanus
    Schaus Swallowtail Butterfly

England, John L.
U.S. Fish and Wildlife Service
2068 Administration Bldg.
1745 W. 1700 S.
Salt Lake City, UT 84104
(801) 524-4430
Photos:
  Erigeron maguirei maguirei
    Maguire Daisy
  Glaucocarpum suffrutescens
    Toad-Flax Cress
  Primula maguirei
    Maguire Primrose
  Ranunculus acriformis aestivalis
    Autumn Buttercup
  Cynomys parvidens
    Utah Prairie Dog
  Chasmistes cujus
    Cui-ui

Etnier, David
Dept. of Zoology
University of Tennessee
Knoxville, TN 37996-0810
(615) 974-3107
Specialty: Eastern fishes
Photos:
  Etheostoma boschungi
    Slackwater Darter
  Noturus flavipinnis
    Yellowfin Madtom
  Percina antesella
    Amber Darter

Fleckenstein, John
Iowa Dept. of Natural Resources
Wallace State Office Building
Des Moines, IA 50319
(515) 281-5145
Photos:
   Discus macclintocki
     Iowa Pleistocene Snail

Florida Natural Areas Inventory
254 E. 6th
Tallahassee, FL 32303
(904) 224-0626
Photos:
   Felis concolor coryi
     Florida Panther

Forbes, Holly
Botanical Garden
Centennial
University of California, Berkeley
Berkeley, CA 94720
(415) 643-8040
Photos:
   Acanthomintha obovata duttonii
     San Mateo Thornmint
   Amsinckia grandiflora
     Large-Flowered Fiddleneck
   Arctostaphylos pungens ravenii
     Presidio Manzanita
   Eryngium constancei
     Loch Lomond Coyote Thistle
   Oenothera deltoides howellii
     Antioch Dunes Evening-Primrose

Foreman, Larry D.
Bureau of Land Management
California Desert District
Riverside, CA 92507
(714) 276-6402
Photos:
   Batrachoseps aridus
     Desert Slender Salamander

French, Thomas W.
Massachusetts of Fisheries and Wildlife
100 Cambridge
Boston, MA 02202
(617) 727-3151
Photos:
   Sarracenia oreophila
     Green Pitcher Plant
   Sorex longirostris fisheri
     Dismal Swamp Southeastern Shrew

Frest, Terry
Dept. of Geology and Paleontology
University of Washington
Seattle, WA 98195
(206) 543-6776
Photos:
   Discus macclintocki
     Iowa Pleistocene Snail

Friedman, Steve
Florida Natural Areas Inventory
254 East Sixth
Tallahassee, FL 32303
(904) 224-8207
Line drawing:
Polygonella basiramia
   Wireweed

Franklin, Ben
Utah Natural Heritage Program
1636 West North Temple, Suite 316
Salt Lake City, UT 84116-3193
(801) 538-7223
Photos:
   Lepidium barnebyanum
     Barneby Ridge-Cress

Gallo, Frank
P.O. Box 3391
New Haven, CT 06515
(203) 787-8028
(203) 562-4241 [home]
Photos:
   Balaena glacialis
     Right Whale
   Haliaeetus leucocephalus
     Bald Eagle
   Sterna dougallii dougallii
     Roseate Tern

Givens, Kerry
North Carolina Natural Heritage Program
Box 27687
Raleigh, NC 27611
(919) 733-7701
Photos:
  Isotria medeoloides
    Small Whorled Pogonia
  Lysimachia asperulaefolia
    Rough-Leaved Loosestrife

Goodyear, Numi C.
The Conservation Agency
97B Howland Ave.
Jamestown, RI 02835
(401) 423-0866
Photos:
  Neotoma floridana smalli
    Key Largo Woodrat
  Oryzomys palustris natator
    Silver Rice Rat
  Peromyscus gossypinus allapaticola
    Key Largo Cotton Mouse

Gould, William R.
Department of Biology
Montana State University
Bozeman, MT 59715
(406) 994-3491
Photos:
  Rhinichthys osculus thermalis
    Kendall Warm Springs Dace

Gustafson Robert J.
Natural History Museum
of Los Angeles County
900 Exposition Blvd.
Los Angeles, CA 90007
(213) 744-3378
Specialty: West Coast and Hawaiian plants
Photos:
  Abutilon eremitopetalum
    NONE
  Abutilon menziesii
    Ko'oloa'ula
  Alsinidendron trinerve
    NONE
  Chamaesyce celastoides var. *kaenana*
    Akoko
  Cordylanthus palmatus
    Palmate-Bracted Bird's-Beak
  Diella falcata
    NONE

Haplostachys haplostachya angustifolia
  Honohono
Isodendrion hosakae
  Aupaka
Kokia drynarioides
  Kokio
Malacothamnus clementinus
  San Clemente Island Bush-Mallow
Nitrophila mohavensis
  Amargosa Niterwort
Nototrichium humile
  Kulu'i
Pogogyne abramsii
  San Diego Mesa Mint
Remya kauaiensis
  Remya Kauaiensis
Remya mauiensis
  Maui Remya
Scaevola coriacea
  Dwarf Naupaka
Schiedea adamantis
  Diamond Head Schiedea
Sidalcea pedata
  Pedate Checker-Mallow

Haglund, Brent
Wisconsin Nature Conservancy
1045 E. Dayton, Room 209
Madison, WI 53703
(608) 251-8140
Photos:
  Lespedeza leptostachya
    Prairie Bush-Clover

Hammer, Roger L.
Castellow Hammock Nature Center
22301 SW 162 Avenue
Goulds, FL 33170
(305) 245-4321
Specialty: Florida plants
Photos:
  Amorpha crenulata
    Crenulate Lead-Plant
  Euphorbia deltoidea
    Deltoid Spurge
  Euphorbia garberi
    Garber's Spurge
  Galactia smallii
    Small's Milkpea
  Polygala smallii
    Tiny Polygala

Harris, Jessie M.
4401 W N.W.
Washington, D.C. 20007
(202) 338-9083
Specialty: Plants
Photos:
  Agalinis acuta
    Sandplain Gerardia
  Arabis serotina
    Shale Barren Rock-Cress
  Cirsium pitcheri
    Pitcher's Thistle
  Dalea foliosa
    Leafy Prairie Clover
  Echinacea tennesseensis
    Tennessee Purple Coneflower
  Geum radiatum
    Spreading Avens
  Helonias bullata
    Swamp Pink
  Isotria medeoloides
    Small Whorled Pogonia
  Pedicularis furbishiae
    Furbish Lousewort
  Rhododendron chapmanii
    Chapman's Rhododendron
  Silene polypetala
    Fringed Campion
  Solidago albopilosa
    White-Haired Goldenrod
  Solidago shortii
    Short's Goldenrod

Hatch, Michael D.
New Mexico Dept. of Fish and Game
Villagra Building
Santa Fe, NM 87503
(505) 827-7910
Photos:
  Notropis simus pecosensis
    Pecos Bluntnose Shiner

Hedges, S. Blair
Dept. of Biology
208 Mueller Lab
Pennsylvania State University
University Park, PA 16802
(814) 863-0278
Photos:
  Phaeognathus hubrichti
    Red Hills Salamander

Herbst, Derral
Hawaiian Botanical Society
Botany Dept.
University of Hawaii
3190 Maile Way
Honolulu, HI 96822
(808) 948-8369
Specialty: Hawaiian plants
Photos:
  Achyranthes rotundata
    Achyranthes
  Argyroxiphium sandwicense sandwicense
    Ahinahina
  Bidens cuneata
    Cuneate Bidens
  Euphorbia skottsbergii kalaeloana
    Ewa Plains Akoko
  Gardenia brighamii
    Na'u
  Gouania hillebrandii
    Hillebrand's Gouania
  Haplostachys haplostachya angustifolia
    Honohono
  Hibiscadelphus distans
    Kauai Hau Kuahiwi
  Kokia cookei
    Cooke's Kokio
  Kokia drynarioides
    Kokio
  Lipochaeta venosa
    Lipochaeta
  Mezoneuron kavaiense
    Uhiuhi
  Panicum carteri
    Carter's Panicgrass
  Santalum freycinetianum lanaiense
    Lanai Sandalwood
  Stenogyne angustifolia angustifolia
    Stenogyne
  Vicia menziesii
    Hawaiian Vetch

Herndon, Alan
Dept. of Botany
Louisiana State University
Baton Rouge, LA 70803
(504) 388-6579
Specialty: Florida plants
Photos:
  Amorpha crenulata
    Crenulate Lead-Plant
  Euphorbia deltoidea
    Deltoid Spurge

Euphorbia garberi
  Garber's Spurge
Galactia smallii
  Small's Milkpea
Polygala smallii
  Tiny Polygala

Hobdy, Robert
Hawaii Dept. of Land and Natural Resources
54 S. High St.
Wailuku, HI 96793
(808) 243-5352
Photos:
  Tetramolopium remyi
  NONE

Hoffman, John H.
1013 East Alta Vista
Tucson, AZ 85719
(602) 623-7380
Specialty: Southwestern U.S.
Photos:
  Felis yagouaroundi
  Jaguarundi
  Colinus virginianus ridgwayi
  Masked Bobwhite
  Gopherus agassizii
  Desert Tortoise

Holler, Nicholas R.
U.S. Fish and Wildlife Service
Alabama Cooperative Fish and Wildlife
Research Unit
331 Funchess Hall
Auburn University, AL 36849-5414
(205) 826-4796
Photos:
  Peromyscus polionotus allophrys
  Alabama Beach Mouse
  Peromyscus polionotus ammobates
  Choctawhatchee Beach Mouse
  Peromyscus polionotus trissyllepsis
  Perdido Key Beach Mouse

Holsinger, John
Dept. of Biological Sciences
Old Dominion University
Norfolk, VA 23529
(804) 683-3595
Photos:
  Antrolana lira
  Madison Cave Isopod

Houghton, William
Fairchild Tropical Garden
11935 Old Cutler Road
Miami, FL 33156
(305) 665-2844
Photos:
  Calyptronoma rivalis
  Palma de Manaca
  Harrisia portoricensis
  Higo Chumbo
  Ottoschulzia rhodoxylon
  Palo de Rosa
  Schoepfia arenaria
  Schoepfia Arenaria
  Stahlia monosperma
  Cobana Negra

Humphrey, Steve
Florida State Museum
University of Florida
Gainesvile, FL 32611
(904) 392-1721
Photos:
  Peromyscus polionotus niveiventris
  Southeastern Beach Mouse
  Peromyscus polionotus phasma
  Anastasia Island Beach Mouse

Jackson, Jerome A.
Dept. of Biological Sciences
Mississippi State University
Mississippi State, MS 39762
(601) 325-3120
Photos:
  Picoides borealis
  Red-Cockaded Woodpecker

Jacobs, Judy
USFWS
1825 Virginia St.
Annapolis, MD 21401
(301) 269-5448
Photos:
  Cicindela dorsalis dorsalis
  Northeastern Beach Tiger Beetle

James, Paul
Dept. of Zoology
Oklahoma State University
430 Life Sciences West
Stillwater, OK 74078
(405) 624-6342
Photos:
  Percina pantherina
    Leopard Darter

Johnson, F. D.
College of Forestry
University of Idaho
Moscow, ID 83843
(208) 885-6441
Photos:
  Mirabilis macfarlanei
    MacFarlane's Four O'Clock

Johnson, James E.
U.S. Fish and Wildlife Service Region 2
Division of Endangered Species
P.O. Box 1306
Albuquerque, NM 87103
(505) 766-3972
Specialty: Western fishes
Photos:
  Cyprinodon bovinus
    Leon Springs Pupfish
  Cyprinodon elegans
    Comanche Springs Pupfish
  Gambusia gaigai
    Big Bend Gambusia
  Gambusia nobilis
    Pecos Gambusia
  Gila ditaenia
    Sonora Chub
  Gila nigrescens
    Chihuahua Chub
  Gila purpurea
    Yaqui Chub
  Lepidomeda vittata
    Little Colorado Spinedace
  Poeciliopsis occidentalis occidentalis
    Gila Topminnow
  Poeciliopsis occidentalis sonoriensis
    Yaqui Topminnow

Keenlyne, Kent
Photos:
  Scaphirhynchus albus
    Pallid Sturgeon

Kepler, Cameron B.
U.S. Fish and Wildlife Service
Southeast Research Station
School of Forest Resources
University of Georgia
Athens, GA 30602
(404) 546-3215
Photos:
  Caprimulgus noctitherus
    Puerto Rican Nightjar

Kiff, Lloyd
Western Foundation for Vertebrate Zoology
1100 Glendon Ave.
Los Angeles, CA 90024
(213) 208-8003
Photos:
  Numenius borealis
    Eskimo Curlew

Knisley, C. Barry
Randolph-Macon College
Ashland, VA 23005
(804) 752-7254
Photos:
  Cicindela dorsalis dorsalis
    Northeastern Beach Tiger Beetle
  Cicindela puritana
    Puritan Tiger Beetle

Kral, Robert
c/o Cary Norquist
USFWS
Jackson Field Office
6578 Dogwood View Parkway, Suite A
Jackson, MS 39213
(601) 965-4900
Photos:
  Xyris tennesseenis
    Tennessee Yellow-Eyed Grass

Kuhn, Lee
1748 Cherokee
Sarasota, FL 34239
(813) 953-5831
Photos:
  Aphelocoma coerulescens coerulescens
    Florida Scrub Jay
  Falco peregrinus anatum
    American Peregrine Falcon
  Mycteria americana
    Wood Stork
  Polyborus plancus audubonii
    Audubon's Crested Caracara

Kurz, Don
Missouri Conservation Dept.
2901 W. Truman Blvd.
Jefferson City, MO 65109
(314) 751-4115 x202
Photos:
  Asclepias meadii
    Mead's Milkweed
  Boltania decurrens
    Decurrent False Aster
  Coryphantha minima
    Nellie Cory Cactus
  Echinocereus chisoensis chisoensis
    Chisos Mountain Hedgehog Cactus
  Echinocereus viridiflorus davisii
    Davis' Green Pitaya Cactus
  Lesquerella filiformis
    Missouri Bladder-Pod
  Trifolium stoloniferum
    Running Buffalo Clover

La Due, Noel
(916) 457-3393
Specialty: West Coast butterflies
Photos:
  Apodemia mormo langei
    Lange's Metalmark Butterfly
  Callophrys mossii bayensis
    San Bruno Elfin Butterfly
  Euphilotes enoptes smithi
    Smith's Blue Butterfly
  Euphydryas editha bayensis
    Bay Checkerspot Butterfly
  Icaricia icarioides missionensis
    Mission Blue Butterfly

LaBerteaux, Denise L.
P.O. Box 1021
Boulder City, NV 89005
(702) 293-7823
Photos:
  Pipilo fuscus eremophilus
    Inyo Brown Towhee

Ladd, Doug
Missouri Nature Conservancy
2800 S. Brentwood
St. Louis, MO 63144
(314) 968-1105
Photos:
  Geocarpon minimum
    Geocarpon

Lesquerella filiformis
  Missouri Bladder-Pod
Lindera melissifolia
  Pondberry

Larson, Jan K.
Natural Resources Office
Staff Civil Engineer (18N)
Naval Air Station, North Island (Bldg. 3)
San Diego, CA 92135-5018
(619) 545-1130
Specialty: San Clemente Island species
Photos:
  Castelleja grisea
    San Clemente Island
  Indian Paintbrush
    Delphinium kinkiense
  San Clemente Island Larkspur
    Lotus dendroideus traskiae
  San Clemente Island Broom
    Malacothamnus clementinus
  San Clemente Island Bush-Mallow
    Amphispiza belli clementeae
  San Clemente Island Sage Sparrow
    Lanius ludovicianus mearnsi
  San Clemente Island
    Loggerhead Shrike
  Xantusia riversiana
    Island Night Lizard

Lau, Joel
The Nature Conservancy of Hawaii
Photos:
  Cyanea marcrostegia var. *gibsonii*
    NONE

Lester, Gary
Louisiana Natural Heritage Program
P.O. Box 98000
Baton Rouge, LA 70898-9000
(504) 342-4602
(504) 765-2821
Photos:
  Margaritifera hembeli
    Louisiana Pearlshell

Liebman, David
981 S. Quail St.
Norfolk, VA 23513
(804) 8534-4722
Photos:
  Plethodon shenandoah
    Shenandoah Salamander

Lohoefener, Ren
USFWS
Jackson Field Office
6578 Dogwood View Parkway, Suite A
Jackson, MS 39213
(601) 965-4900
Photos:
  Graptemys flavimaculata
    Yellow-Blotched Map Turtle

Lorence, David
National Tropical Botanical Garden
P.O. Box 340
Lawai, HI 96765
(808) 332-7324
Photos:
  Cyanea undulata
    NONE
  Labordia lydgatei
    NONE
  Schiedea apokremnos
    Ma'oli'oli

Lunceford, Bruce
Bureau of Land Management
318 North First East
Kanab, Utah 84741
(801) 644-2672
Photos:
  Oxyloma haydeni ssp. *kanabensis*
    Kanab Ambersnail

MacGregor, John
102 Rest K Court
Nicholasville, KY 40356
(502) 564-5448
Specialty: Kentucky species
Photos:
  Solidago albopilosa
    White-Haired Goldenrod
  Solidago shortii
    Short's Goldenrod
  Myotis sodalis
    Indiana Bat
  Plecotus townsendii virginianus
    Virginia Big-Eared Bat
  Phoxinus cumberlandensis
    Blackside Dace
  Palaemonias ganteri
    Kentucky Cave Shrimp

Maltz, Alan
819 Peacock Plaza #620
Key West, FL 33040
(305) 745-2832
Photos:
  Felis concolor coryi
    Florida Panther
  Odocoileus virginianus clavium
    Florida Key Deer
  Sylvilagus palustris hefneri
    Lower Keys Rabbit
  Trichechus manatus
    West Indian Manatee
  Haliaeetus leucocephalus
    Bald Eagle
  Pelecanus occidentalis
    Brown Pelican
  Chelonias mydas
    Green Sea Turtle
  Crocodylus acutus
    American Crocodile

Martin, Richard
Louisiana Natural Heritage Program
P.O. Box 98000
Baton Rouge, LA 70898-9000
(504) 342-4602
(504) 765-2821
Photos:
  Graptemys oculifera
    Ringed Sawback Turtle

Mazzeo, Peter M.
U.S. National Arboretum
3501 New York NE
Washington, DC 20002
(202) 475-4841
Photos:
  Betula uber
    Virginia Round-Leaf Birch

McDonald, Charlie
U.S. Fish and Wildlife Service
3530 Pan American Highway, NE
Suite D
Albuquerque, NM 87107
(505) 883-7877
Photos:
  Cirsium vinaceum
    Sacramento Mountains Thistle
  Echinocereus fendleri kuenzleri
    Kuenzler Hedgehog

Erigeron rhizomatus
Zuni Fleabane
Thermosphaeroma thermophilum
Socorro Isopod

McKinstry, Ron
U.S. Fish and Wildlife Service
3616 W. Thomas, Suite 6
Phoenix, AZ 85109
(602) 261-4720
Photos:
Rallus longirostris yumanensis
Yuma Clapper Rail

McLaughlin, Steven P.
University of Arizona
Office of Arid Lands Studies
845 N. Park
Tucson, AZ 85711
(602) 621-7928
(602) 621-1955
Photos:
Amsonia kearneyana
Kearney's Blue-Star

McMahan, Linda R.
The Berry Botanical Garden
11505 SW Summerville
Portland, OR 97219
(503) 636-4112
Photos:
Agave arizonica
Arizona Agave
Dudleya traskiae
Santa Barbara Island Liveforever
Echinocereus triglochidialus arizonicus
Arizona Hedgehog Cactus
Eryngium cuneifolium
Snakeroot
Prunus geniculata
Scrub Plum

Melhop, Patricia
c/o Stephen W. Forsythe
USFWS
222 S. Houston, Suite A
Tulsa, Oklahoma 74127
(918) 581-7458
Photos:
Arkansia wheeleri
Ouachita Rock-Pocketbook

Meyer, Thomas A.
Wisconsin Natural Heritage Inventory
P.O. Box 7921
Madison, WI 53707
(608) 266-0394
Photos:
Aconitum noveboracense
Northern Wild Monkshood
Cirsium pitcheri
Pitcher's Thistle
Lespedeza leptostachya
Prairie Bush-Clover
Oxytropis campestris chartacea
Fassett's Locoweed

Michigan Natural Features Inventory
Stevens T. Mason Bldg.
P.O. Box 30028
Lansing, MI 48909
(517) 373-1552
Photos:
Mimulus glabratus var. *michiganensis*
Michigan Monkey-Flower

Middleton, Susan A. and
David Liittschwager
North American Endangered Species Project
California Academy of Sciences
Golden Gate Park
San Francisco, CA 94118
(415) 750-7356
Specialty: California species
Photos:
Centrostegia leptoceras
Slender-Horned Spineflower
Cordylanthus maritimus maritimus
Salt Marsh Bird's-Beak
Eriastrum densifolium sanctorum
Santa Ana River Woolly-Star
Opuntia treleasei
Bakersfield Cactus
Pogogyne abramsii
San Diego Mesa Mint
Sidalcea pedata
Pedate Checker-Mallow
Dipodomys ingens
Giant Kangaroo Rat
Vulpes macrotis mutica
San Joaquin Kit Fox
Falco peregrinus anatum
American Peregrine Falcon
Pelecanus occidentalis
Brown Pelican

Rallus longirostris obsoletus
  California Clapper Rail
Gambelia silus
  Blunt-Nosed Leopard Lizard
Gopherus agassizii
  Desert Tortoise
Thamnophis sirtalis tetrataenia
  San Francisco Garter Snake
Salmo aquabonita whitei
  Little Kern Golden Trout
Syncaris pacifica
  California Freshwater Shrimp

Mills, Glen
Texas Parks and Wildlife Dept.
4200 Smith School Rd.
Austin, TX 78744
(512) 389-4994
Photos:
Gambusia heterochir
  Clear Creek Gambusia

Missouri Botanical Garden
P.O. Box 299
St. Louis, MO 63166-0299
(314) 577-5100
Photos:
Spigelia gentianoides
  Gentian Pinkroot

Mitchell, Robert and Linda
Natural History Photography
2708 20th
Lubbock, TX 79410
(806) 797-1313
Specialty: Texas cave species
Photos:
Eschrichtius robustus
  Gray Whale
Felis pardalis
  Ocelot
Dermochelys coriacea
  Leatherback Sea Turtle
Nerodia harteri paucimaculata
  Concho Water Snake
Eurycea nana
  San Marcos Salamander
Typhlomolge rathbuni
  Texas Blind Salamander
Leptoneta myopica
  Tooth Cave Spider
Microcreagris texana
  Tooth Cave Pseudoscorpion

Rhadine persephone
  Tooth Cave Ground Beetle
Texamaurops reddelli
  Kretschmarr Cave Mold Beetle
Texella reddelli
  Bee Creek Cave Harvestman

Montgomery, Paul
4417 Garnett
Austin, TX 78745
(512) 443-9871
Specialty: Texas plants
Photos:
Abronia macrocarpa
  Large-Fruited Sand-Verbena
Ancistrocactus tobuschii
  Tobusch Fishhook Cactus
Callirhoe scabriuscula
  Texas Poppy-Mallow
Coryphantha minima
  Nellie Cory Cactus
Coryphantha ramillosa
  Bunched Cory Cactus
Coryphantha sneedii sneedii
  Sneed Pincushion Cactus
Cryptantha crassipes
  Terlingua Creek Cat's Eye
Echinocereus chisoensis chisoensis
  Chisos Mountain Hedgehog Cactus
Echinocereus lloydii
  Lloyd's Hedgehog Cactus
Echinocereus reichenbachii albertii
  Black Lace Cactus
Echinocereus viridiflorus davisii
  Davis' Green Pitaya Cactus
Frankenia johnstonii
  Johnston's Frankenia
Hedeoma apiculatum
  McKittrick Pennyroyal
Hoffmannseggia tenella
  Slender Rush-Pea
Hymenoxys texana
  Texas Bitterweed
Lesquerella pallida
  White Bladderpod
Manihot walkerae
  Walker's Manioc
Neolloydia mariposensis
  Lloyd's Mariposa Cactus
Phlox nivalis texensis
  Texas Trailing Phlox
Potamogeton clystocarpus
  Little Aguja Pondweed

Quercus hinckleyi
  Hinckley Oak
Spiranthes parksii
  Navasota Ladies'-Tresses
Styrax texana
  Texas Snowbells
Thymophylla tephroleuca
  Ashy Dogweed
Zizania texana
  Texas Wildrice

Moran, John
The Gainesville Sun
P.O. Drawer A
Gainesville, FL 32602
(904) 374-5027
Photos:
  Acipenser oxyrhynchus desotoi
    Gulf Sturgeon

Morgan, C. Allan
1642 N. Westridge
Tucson, AZ 85745
(602) 743-7862
Photos:
  Tumamoca macdougalii
    Tumamoc Globeberry
  Arctocephalus townsendi
    Guadalupe Fur Seal
  Balaena glacialis
    Right Whale
  Balaenoptera musculus
    Blue Whale
  Balaenoptera physalus
    Finback Whale
  Enhydra lutris nereis
    Southern Sea Otter
  Eschrichtius robustus
    Gray Whale
  Felis pardalis
    Ocelot
  Felis wiedi
    Margay
  Felis yagouaroundi
    Jaguarundi
  Leptonycteris sanborni
    Sanborn's Long-Nosed Bat
  Megaptera novaeangliae
    Humpback Whale
  Physeter catodon
    Sperm Whale
  Trichechus manatus
    West Indian Manatee

Ursus arctos horribilis
  Grizzly Bear
Colinus virginianus ridgwayi
  Masked Bobwhite
Falco peregrinus anatum
  American Perigrine Falcon
Grus americana
  Whooping Crane
Haliaeetus leucocephalus
  Bald Eagle
Mycteria americana
  Wood Stork
Pelecanus occidentalis
  Brown Pelican
Polyborus plancus audubonii
  Audubon's Crested Caracara
Tympanuchus cupido attwateri
  Attwater's Prairie Chicken
Chelonia mydas
  Green Sea Turtle
Dermochelys coriacea
  Leatherback Sea Turtle
Gopherus agassizii
  Desert Tortoise
Lepidochelys kempii
  Kemp's Ridley Sea Turtle
Lepidochelys olivacea
  Olive Ridley Sea Turtle
Bufo houstonensis
  Houston Toad
Cyprinidon macularius
  Desert Pupfish
Gila ditaenia
  Sonora Chub
Poeciliopsis occidentalis occidentalis
  Gila Topminnow
Ptychocheilus lucius
  Colorado Squawfish

Morgan, Sherry
315 S. Allen, Suite 322
State College, PA 16801
(814) 234-4090
Photos:
  Lindera melissifolia
    Pondberry

Morin, Nancy
Missouri botanical Garden
P.O. Box 299
St. Louis, MO 63166
(314) 577-5180
Photos:
  Campanula robinsiae
    Brooksville Bellflower

Morse, Larry
The Nature Conservancy
1815 N. Lynn
Arlington, VA 22209
(703) 841-5361
Photos:
  Torreya taxifolia
    Florida Torreya

Moseley, Richard E.
Ohio Dept. of Natural Resources
Building F, Fountain Square
Columbus, OH 43224
(614) 265-6452
Photos:
  Aconitum noveboracense
    Northern Wild Monkshood
  Hymenoxys acaulis glabra
    Lakeside Daisy
  Trifolium stoloniferum
    Running Buffalo Clover

Mull, William P.
P.O. Box 275
Volcano, Hawaii 96785
(808) 967-7352
Photos:
  Achatinella
    Oahu Tree Snails

Munsey, Larry D.
2530 Red Hill Ave
Santa Ana, CA 92705
(714) 250-5555
Photos:
  Ursus arctos horibilis
    Grizzly Bear

Murdock, Nora
USFWS
330 Ridgefield Court
Asheville, NC 28806
Photos:
  Cardamine micranthera
    Small-Anthered Bittercress
  Geum radiatum
    Spreading Avens
  Helianthus schweinitzii
    Schweinitz's Sunflower
  Hudsonia montana
    Mountain Golden Heather

Mutz, Kathryn M.
P.O. Box 819
Boulder, CO 80306
(303) 298-8719
(303) 443-0932 [home]
Photos:
  Ranunculus acriformis aestivalis
    Autumn Buttercup

Naumann, Tamara S.
(303) 441-3440
Photos:
  Astragalus humillimus
    Mancos Milk-Vetch
  Eriogonum pelinophilum
    Clay-Loving Wild Buckwheat
  Phacelia formosula
    North Park Phacelia

Nelson, John B.
South Carolina Heritage Trust Program
P.O. Box 167
Columbia, SC 29202
(803) 734-3886
Photos:
  Amphianthus pusillus
    Little Amphianthus
  Helonias bullata
    Swamp Pink
  Isotria medeoloides
    Small Whorled Pogonia
  Ptilimnium nodosum
    Harperella
  Ribes echinellum
    Miccosukee Gooseberry
  Sarracenia rubra jonesii
    Mountain Sweet Pitcher Plant
  Trillium persistens
    Persistent Trillium

New Mexico Bureau of Mines and Mineral Resources
Illustrations:
  Pyrgulopsis neomexicana
    Socorro Springsnail
  Tryonia alamosae
    Alamosa Springsnail

NOAA
National Marine Fisheries Service
Dept. of Commerce
1825 Connecticut Ave. NW
Washington, D.C. 20235
(202) 427-2333
Photos:
  Balaena glacialis
    Right Whale
  Balaena mysticetus
    Bowhead Whale
  Balaenoptera borealis
    Sei Whale
  Balaenoptera musculus
    Blue Whale
  Balaenoptera physalus
    Finback Whale
  Eschrichtius robustus
    Gray Whale
  Megaptera novaeangliae
    Humpback Whale
  Phocoena sinus
    Vaquita
  Physeter catodon
    Sperm Whale

Norman, Eliane M.
Dept. of Biology
Stetson University
De Land, FL 32720
(904) 734-4121 x235
Photos:
  Deeringothamnus pulchellus
    Beautiful Pawpaw
  Deeringothamnus rugelii
    Rugel's Pawpaw

Norquist, Cary
U.S. Fish and Wildlife Service
Jackson Mall Office Center
300 Woodrow Wilson, Suite 316
Jackson, MS 39213
(601) 965-4900
Photos:
  Marshallia mohrii
    Mohr's Barbara's-Buttons

Norton, Russell
P.O. Box 1070
New Haven, CT 06504
(203) 562-7800
Photos:
  Amblyopsis rosae
    Ozark Cavefish
  Antrolana lira
    Madison Cave Isopod

Nye, Peter
Wildlife Biologist (Unit
New York State Dept. of Environmental Conservation
Wildlife Resource Center
Delmar, NY 12054
Photos:
  Succinea chittenangoensis
    Chittenango Ovate Amber Snail

Obata, John
The Nature Conservancy of Hawaii
Photos:
  Abutilon sandwicense
    NONE
  Alsinidendron obovatum
    NONE
  Gouania meyenii
    NONE
  Hedyotis parvula
    NONE
  Hesperomannia arbuscula
    NONE
  Labordia lydgatei
    NONE
  Phyllostegia mollis
    NONE
  Silene perlmanii
    NONE
  Tetramolopium lobata var. *lepidotum*
    NONE

Olwell, Peggy
c/o Charles McDonald
USFWS
P.O. Box 1306
Albuquerque, NM 87103
(505) 766-3972
Photos:
  Argemone pleiacantha ssp. *pinnatisecta*
    Sacramento Prickly-Poppy

Opler, Paul
5100 Greenview
Fort Colins, CO 80525
(303) 226-2433
Specialty: Western butterflies
Photos:
    Apodemia mormo langei
        Lange's Metalmark Butterfly
    Boloria acrocnema
        Uncompahgre Fritillary Butterfly
    Euphydryas editha bayensis
        Bay Checkerspot Butterfly
    Hesperia leonardus montana
        Pawnee Montane Skipper Butterfly

Ordano, Jo-Ann
90 Parker #303
San Francisco, CA 94118
(415) 221-3171
Specialty: California plants
Photos:
    Arctostaphylos pungens ravenii
        Presidio Manzanita
    Cupressus abramsiana
        Santa Cruz Cypress
    Mahonia sonnei
        Truckee Barberry
    Oenothera deltoides howellii
        Antioch Dunes Evening-Primrose

Oregon Nature Conservancy
1205 NW 25th
Portland, OR 97210
(503) 229-5078
Photos:
    Catostomus warnerensis
        Warner Sucker
    Gila bicolor
        Hutton Spring Tui Chub
    Gila boraxobius
        Borax Lake Chub

Painter, Charles
New Mexico Game and Fish Dept.
Villagra Bldg.
Santa Fe, NM 87503
(505) 827-9901
Photos:
    Crotalus willardi obscurus
        New Mexican Ridgenose Rattlesnake

Parker, LuRay
Wyoming Game and Fish Dept.
5400 Bishop Blvd.
Cheyenne, WY 82006
(307) 777-5811
Photos:
    Bufo hemiophrys baxteri
        Wyoming Toad

Parnell, James F.
6451 Quail Run
Wilmington, NC 28409
(919) 395-3477
(919) 791-1365 [home]
Photos:
    Plecotus townsendii virginianus
        Virginia Big-Eared Bat
    Charadrius melodus
        Piping Plover
    Pelecanus occidentalis
        Brown Pelican
    Menidia extensa
        Waccamaw Silverside

Patrick, Thomas S.
Georgia Dept. of Natural Resources
Freshwater Wetlands and Heritage Inventory
Route 2, Box 119-D
Social Circle, Georgia 30279
(404) 557-2514
Photos:
    Amphianthus pusillus
        Little Amphianthus
    Isoetes tegetiformans
        Mat-Forming Quillwort
    Trillium reliquum
        Relict Trillium
    Acipenser brevirostrum
        Shortnose Sturgeon

Perlman, Steve
See USFWS Region 1
Photos:
    Chamaesyce kuwaleana
        NONE

Peters, Dana
USFWS
Pleasantville, NJ 08232
(609) 646-9310
Photos:
    Rhynchospora knieskernii
        Knieskern Beaked-Rush

Peterson, B."Moose"
P.O. Box 30694
Santa Barbara, CA 93130
(805) 569-3731
Specialty: California species
Photos:
Nitrophilia mohavensis
  Armagosa Niterwort
Caulanthus californicus
  California Jewelflower
Cordylanthus maritimus ssp. *maritimus*
  Salt Marsh Bird's Beak
Eremalche kernensis
  Kern Mallow
Opuntia treleasei
  Bakersfield Cactus
Lembertia congdonii
  San Joaquin Wooly-Threads
Dipodomys heermanni morroensis
  Morro Bay Kangaroo Rat
Dipodomys ingens
  Giant Kangaroo Rat
Dipodomys nitratoides exilis
  Fresno Kangaroo Rat
Dipodomys nitratoides nitratoides
  Tipton Kangaroo Rat
Dipodomys stephensi
  Stephens' Kangaroo Rat
Enhydra lutris nereis
  Southern Sea Otter
Reithrodontomys raviventris
  Salt Marsh Harvest Mouse
Vulpes macrotis mutica
  San Joaquin Kit Fox
Falco peregrinus anatum
  American Peregrine Falcon
Gymnogyps californianus
  California Condor
Haliaeetus leucocephalus
  Bald Eagle
Mycteria americana
  Wood Stork
Pelecanus occidentalis
  Brown Pelican
Rallus longirostris levipes
  Light-Footed Clapper Rail
Rallus longirostris obsoletus
  California Clapper Rail
Rallus longirostris yumanensis
  Yuma Clapper Rail
Sterna antillarum browni
  California Least Tern

Strix occidentalis caurina
  Northern Spotted Owl
Vireo belli pusillus
  Least Bell's Vireo
Gambelia silus
  Blunt-Nosed Leopard Lizard
Gopherus agassizii
  Desert Tortoise
Uma inornata
  Coachella Valley Fringe-Toed Lizard
Xantusia riversiana
  Island Night Lizard
Cyprinodon macularius
  Desert Pupfish
Cyprinodon radiosus
  Owens Pupfish
Gasterosteus aculeatus williamsoni
  Unarmored Threespine Stickleback
Salmo aquabonita whitei
  Little Kern Golden Trout

Phillips, Barbara G.
Museum of Northern Arizona
Route 4, Box 720
Flagstaff, AZ 86001
(602) 774-5211
Photos:
Cowania subintegra
  Arizona Cliffrose
Pediocactus peeblesianus peeblesianus
  Peebles Navajo Cactus

Phillips III, Arthur M.
Museum of Northern Arizona
Route 4, Box 720
Flagstaff, AZ 86001
(602) 774-5211
Photos:
Coryphantha robbinsorum
  Cochise Pincushion Cactus
Senecio franciscanus
  San Francisco Peaks Groundsel

Pierson, J. Malcolm
Alabama Power Company G.S.C. #8
P.O. Box 2641
Birmingham, AL 35291
(205) 664-6177
Photos:
Clematis socialis
  Alabama Leather Flower
Tulotoma magnifica
  Tulotoma Snail

Pinnell, Mildred
Atlanta Botanical Garden
P.O. Box 77246
Atlanta, GA 30357
(404) 876-5859
Photos:
  Silene polypetala
    Fringed Campion

Polhemus, Dan A.
Dept. of Entomology
National Museum of Natural History
Washington, DC 20560
(202) 382-1779
Photos:
  Ambrysus Amargosus
    Ash Meadow Naucorid

Poulson, Thomas L.
Dept. of Biological Sciences
University of Illinois at Chicago
Box 4348
Chicago, IL 60680
(312) 996-4537
Photos:
  Speoplatyrhinus poulsoni
    Alabama Cavefish

Poulson, Marv
3631 S. Carolyn
Salt Lake City, UT 84106
(801) 486-2131
Specialty: Western plants, especially cactii
Photos:
  Cycladenia humilis jonesii
    Jones Cycladenia
  Echinocereus engelmannii purpureus
    Purple-Spined Hedgehog Cactus
  Echinocereus triglochidialus arizonicus
    Arizona Hedgehog Cactus
  Echinocereus triglochidiotus inermis
    Spineless Hedgehog Cactus
  Pediocactus bradyi
    Brady Pincushion Cactus
  Pediocactus despainii
    San Rafael Cactus
  Pediocactus knowltonii
    Knowlton Cactus
  Pediocactus peeblesianus peeblesianus
    Peebles Navajo Cactus
  Pediocactus sileri
    Siler Pincushion Cactus
  Primula maguirei
    Maguire Primrose

Sclerocactus glaucus
  Uinta Basin Hookless Cactus
Sclerocactus mesae-verdae
  Mesa Verde Cactus
Sclerocactus wrightiae
  Wright Fishhook Cactus
Townsendia aprica
  Last Chance Townsendia

Powell, Robert L.
2795 Stanford Ave.
Boulder, CO 80303
(303) 494-9445
Photos:
  Lesquerella congesta
    Dudley bluffs bladderpod
  Physaria obcordata
    Dudley Bluffs Twinpod

Pratt, Douglas
4583 Downing
Baton Rouge, LA 70809
(504) 928-4297
Specialty: Hawaiian birds
Illustrations:
  Hemignathus lucidus hanapepe
    Kauai Nukupuu
  Hemignathus munroi
    Akiapolaau
  Hemignathus procerus
    Kauai Akialoa
  Loxioides bailleui
    Palila
  Loxops coccineus
    Akepa
  Melamprosops phaeosoma
    Poo-uli
  Myadestes lanaiensis rutha
    Molokai Thrush
  Myadestes myadestinus
    Large Kauai Thrush
  Myadestes palmeri
    Small Kauai Thrush
  Oreomystis mana
    Hawaii Creeper
  Palmeria dolei
    Crested Honeycreeper
  Paroreomyza flammea
    Molokai Creeper
  Pseudonestor xanthophys
    Maui Parrotbill
  Psittirostra psittacea
    Ou

Pritchard, Peter C. H.
Florida Audubon Society
401 S. Central
Oviedo, Florida 32765
(407) 365-6347
Specialty: Sea turtles
Photos:
  Chelonia mydas
    Green Sea Turtle
  Dermochelys coriacea
    Leatherback Sea Turtle
  Lepidochelys olivacea
    Olive Ridley Sea Turtle

Quinn, Meg
Arizona-Sonora Desert Museum
2021 N. Kinney Road
Tucson, AZ 85743
(602) 883-1380
Photos:
  Amsonia kearneyana
    Kearney's Blue-Star

Reveal, James
California Native Plant Society
909 12th, Suite 116
Sacramento, CA 95814
(916) 447-CNPS
Photos:
  Grindelia fraxinopratensis
    Ash Meadows Gumplant
  Mentzelia leucophylla
    Ash Meadows Blazing Star

Rilling, Ann
Utah Nature Conservancy
P.O. Box 11486
Salt Lake City, UT 84147
(801) 521-1034
Photos:
  Phacelia argillacea
    Clay Phacelia

Rinne, John N.
USDA Forest Service
Rocky Mountain Forest and Range
Experiment Station
Forest Science Lab
Arizona State University
Tempe, AZ 85287-1304
(602) 379-4365
Specialty: Western fishes
Photos:
  Crenichthys baileyi baileyi
    White River Springfish
  Gila elegans
    Bonytail Chub
  Gila robusta jordani
    Pahranagat Roundtail Chub
  Gila robusta seminuda
    Virgin River Chub
  Ictalurus pricei
    Yaqui Catfish
  Lepidomeda albivallis
    White River Spinedace
  Meda fulgida
    Spikedace
  Moapa coriacea
    Moapa Dace
  Notropis formosus
    Beautiful Shiner
  Plagopterus argentissimus
    Woundfin
  Salmo gilae
    Gila Trout
  Tiaroga cobitis
    Loach Minnow
  Xyrauchen texanus
    Razorback Sucker

Roberts, Rusty
Bureau of Land Management
P.O. Box 928
Meeker, CO 81641
(303) 878-3601
Photos:
  Lesquerella congesta
    Dudley bluffs bladderpod
  Physaria obcordata
    Dudley Bluffs Twinpod

Robinson, Andy
U.S. Fish and Wildlife Service
Eastside Federal Complex
911 N.S. 11th Avenue
Portland, OR 97232
(503) 231-6131
Photos:
  Arabis macdonaldiana
    McDonald's Rock-Cress
  Asimina tetramera
    Four-Petal Pawpaw
  Baptisia arachnifera
    Hairy Rattleweed
  Cereus eriophorus fragrans
    Fragrant Prickly-Apple
  Cereus robinii
    Key Tree Cactus
  Chrysopsis floridana
    Florida Golden Aster
  Dicerandra immaculata
    Lakela's Mint
  Eryngium cuneifolium
    Snakeroot
  Euphorbia deltoidea
    Deltoid Spurge
  Harperocallis flava
    Harper's Beauty
  Hudsonia montana
    Mountain Golden Heather
  Liatris helleri
    Heller's Blazing Star
  Lomatium bradshawii
    Bradshaw's Lomatium
  Lupinus aridorum
    Scrub Lupine
  Pityopsis ruthii
    Ruth's Golden Aster
  Rhododendron chapmanii
    Chapman's Rhododendron
  Sagittaria fasciculata
    Bunched Arrowhead
  Sarracenia oreophila
    Green Pitcher Plant
  Solidago spithamaea
    Blue Ridge Goldenrod
  Torreya taxifolia
    Florida Torreya
  Trillium persistens
    Persistent Trillium

Rohde, Fred
North Carolina Dept. of Marine Fisheries
7225 Wrightsville
Wilmington, NC 28403
(919) 256-4541
Photos:
  Acipenser brevirostrum
    Shortnose Sturgeon

Ross, Robert
Cayey University College
Antonio R. Barcelo Avenue
Cayey, PR 00636
Photos:
  Harrisia portoricensis
    Higo Chumbo

Roston, William
Box 623
Forsyth, MO 65653
(417) 546-2401
Specialty: Underwater Photos of live fish
Photos:
  Etheostoma nianguae
    Niangua Darter
  Etheostoma nuchale
    Watercress Darter
  Etheostoma okaloosae
    Okaloosa Darter
  Hybopsis monacha
    Spotfin Chub
  Percina pantherina
    Leopard Darter

Rue III, Leonard Lee
R.D. 3, Box 31
Blairstown, NJ 07825
(201) 362-6616
Photos:
  Canis lupus
    Gray Wolf
  Eumetopias jubatus
    Steller Sea-Lion
  Glaucomys sabrinus coloratus
    Carolina Northern Flying Squirrel
  Glaucomys sabrinus fuscus
    Virginia Northern Flying Squirrel
  Odocoileus virginianus clavium
    Florida Key Deer
  Rangifer tarandus caribou
    Woodland Caribou

Rutman, Susan
U.S. Fish and Wildlife Service
3616 W. Thomas, Suite 6
Phoenix, AZ 85019
(602) 379-4720
Photos:
Amsonia kearneyana
    Kearney's Blue-Star
Astragalus cremnophylax var. *cremnophylax*
    Sentry Milk-Vetch
Carex specuicola
    Navajo Sedge

Sada, Donald W.
2689 Highland
Bishop, CA 93514
(619) 873-8133
Photos:
Rhinichthys osculus nevadensis
    Ash Meadows Speckled Dace

Shallenberger, Robert
13267 SW Bull Mountain
Tigard, OR 97224
(503) 231-6214
Specialty: Hawaiian birds
Photos:
Vicia menziesii
    Hawaiian Vetch
Monachus schauinslandi
    Hawaiian Monk Seal
Acrocephalus familiaris kingi
    Nihoa Millerbird
Anas wyvilliana
    Hawaiian Duck
Buteo solitarius
    Hawaiian Hawk
Fulica americana alai
    Hawaiian Coot
Gallinula chloropus sandvicensis
    Hawaiian Common Moorhen
Himantopus mexicanus knudseni
    Hawaiian Stilt
Moho braccatus
    Kauai Oo
Nesochen sandvicensis
    Hawaiian Goose
Pterodroma phaeopygia sandwichensis
    Dark-Rumped Petrel
Puffinus auricularis newelli
    Newell's Townsend's Shearwater
Telespyza cantans
    Laysan Finch

Telespyza ultima
    Nihoa Finch

Shaw, Jonathan
Bok Tower Gardens
P.O. Box 3810
Lake Wales, FL 33853
(813) 676-1408
Specialty: Florida plants
Photos:
Asimina tetramera
    Four-Petal Pawpaw
Bonamia grandiflora
    Florida Bonamia
Chionanthus pygmaeus
    Pygmy Fringe Tree
Dicerandra cornutissima
    Longspurred Mint
Dicerandra frutescens
    Scrub Mint
Dicerandra immaculata
    Lakela's Mint
Eryngium cuneifolium
    Snakeroot
Hypericum cumulicola
    Highlands Scrub Hypericum
Lupinus aridorum
    Scrub Lupine
Paronychia chartacea
    Papery Whitlow-Wort
Prunus geniculata
    Scrub Plum
Rhododendron chapmanii
    Chapman's Rhododendron
Warea amplexifolia
    Wide-Leaf Warea
Warea carteri
    Carter's Mustard

Sjoberg, Jon C.
Nevada Dept. of Wildlife
1100 Valley Road
P.O. Box 10678
Reno, NV 89520-0022
(702) 688-1500
Photos:
Cyprinodon nevadensis pectoralis
    Warm Springs Pupfish
Lepidomeda mollispinis pratensis
    Big Spring Spinedace
Rhinichthys osculus nevadensis
    Ash Meadows Speckled Dace

Smith, Robert H.
2351 Hillside
Central Point, OR 97502
Photos:
 Salmo apache
  Apache Trout
 Salmo clarki henshawi
  Lahontan Cutthroat Trout
 Salmo clarki seleniris
  Paiute Cutthroat Trout

Smith, Norm
26 de San Ramon
Tucson, AZ 85710
(602) 621-1105
(602) 298-6645
Photos:
 Agave arizonica
  Arizona agave
 Tumamoca macdougalii
  Tumamoc Globeberry
 Tamiasciurus hudsonicus grahamensis
  Mount Graham Red Squirrel
 Branta canadensis leucopareia
  Aleutian Canada Goose
 Colinus virginianus ridgwayi
  Masked Bobwhite

Smith, Welby
Minnesota Natural Heritage Program
P.O. Box 7, DNR Bldg.
500 Lafayette
St. Paul, MN 55155
(612) 297-3733
(612) 646-6620 [home]
Photos:
 Erythronium propullans
  Minnesota Trout-Lily
 Planathera praeclara
  Western Prairie Fringed Orchid

Snyder, Noel F. R.
Arizona Game and Fish Dept.
P.O. Box 426
Portal, AZ 85632
(602) 558-2412
Photos:
 Rhynchopsitta pachyrhyncha
  Thick-Billed Parrot

Somers, Paul
Tennessee Dept. of Conservation
Ecological Services
701 Broadway
Nashville, TN 37219-5237
(615) 742-6549
Photos:
 Apios priceana
  Price's Potato-bean
 Arenia cumberlandensis
  Cumberland Sandwort
 Astragalus bibullatus
  Guthrie's Ground-Plum
 Conradina verticillata
  Cumberland Rosemary
 Dalea foliosa
  Leafy Prairie Clover
 Echinacea tennesseensis
  Tennessee Purple Coneflower
 Hedyotis purpurea var. *montana*
  Roan Mountain Bluet
 Pityopsis ruthii
  Ruth's Golden Aster
 Scutellaria montana
  Large-Flowered Skullcap

Sorrie, Bruce A.
150 Rumford #8
Mansfield, MA 02048
(617) 727-9194
Photos:
 Potentilla robbinsiana
  Robbins' Cinquefoil
 Scirpus ancistrochaetus
  Northeastern Bulrush
 Agelaius xanthomus
  Yellow-Shouldered Blackbird

Spreitzer, A. E.
Ohio State University Museum of Zoology
1813 N. High
Columbus, Ohio 43210
(614) 292-8560
Specialty: Mussels
Photos:
 Almost all federally listed
  freshwater mussels

Stihler, Craig W.
West Virginia Dept. of Natural Resources
Wildlife Resources Division
P.O. Box 67
Elkins, WV 26241
(304) 636-1767
Photos:
　Triodopsis platysayoides
　　Flat-Spired Three-Toothed Snail

Stiles, Robert
Biology Dept.
Samford University
Birmingham, AL 35229
(205) 870-2928
Photos:
　Notropis cahabae
　　Cahaba Shiner

Sutherland, Carol S.
228 Bethel Church
St. Clair, MO 63077
Photos:
　Lesquerella filiformis
　　Missouri Bladder-Pod
　Lindera melissifolia
　　Pondberry
　Falco peregrinus anatum
　　American Peregrine Falcon

Sweet, Samuel S.
Dept. of Biological Sciences
University of California, Santa Barbara
Santa Barbara, CA 93106
(805) 961-3730
Photos:
　Gambelia silus
　　Blunt-Nosed Leopard Lizard
　Ambystoma macrodactylum croceum
　　Santa Cruz Long-Toed Salamander
　Eurycea nana
　　San Marcos Salamander

Tandy, Gerald F.
c/o Ronald L. Garrett
U.S. Fish and Wildlife Service
1011 E. Tudor
Anchorage, AK 99503
(907) 786-3505
Photos:
　Polystichum aleuticum
　　Aleutian Shield Fern

Telfer, Thomas C.
Hawaii Dept. of Land & Natural Resources
Division of Forestry and Wildlife
P.O. Box 1671
Lihue, HI 96766
(808) 245-4433
Photos:
　Lasiurus cinereus semotus
　　Hawaiian Hoary Bat
　Monachus schauinslandi
　　Hawaiian Monk Seal
　Pterodroma phaeopygia sandwichensis
　　Dark-Rumped Petrel
　Puffinus auricularis newelli
　　Newell's Townsend's Shearwater
　Telespyza cantans
　　Laysan Finch
　Telespyza ultima
　　Nihoa Finch
　Chelonia mydas
　　Green Sea Turtle

Thompson, Bruce
Center for Wetland Resources
Coastal Fisheries Institute
Louisiana State University
(504) 388-6337
Photos:
　Percina jenkinsi
　　Conasauga Logperch

Thompson, Fred G.
Florida Museum of Natural History
University of Florida
Gainesville, FL 32611
(904) 392-1721
Photos:
　Orthalicus reses reses
　　Stock Island Snail

Troup, Randall
400 Knox
Anniston, AL 36201
(205) 236-1551
Photos:
　Sarracenia oreophila
　　Green Pitcher Plant
　Sarracenia rubra alabamensis
　　Alabama Canebrake Pitcher Plant

Tuhy, Joel
Utah Natural Heritage Program
3 Triad Center, Suite 400
Salt Lake City, UT 84180-1204
(801) 538-5521
Photos:
  Asclepias welshii
    Welsh's Milkweed
  Astragalus perianus
    Rydberg Milk-Vetch
  Echinocereus triglochidiotus inermis
    Spineless Hedgehog Cactus
  Glaucocarpum suffrutescens
    Toad-Flax Cress
  Lepidium barnebyanum
    Barneby Ridge-Cress

Tuttle, Merlin D.
Bat Conservation International
P.O. Box 162603
Austin, TX 78716
(512) 327-9721
Photos:
  Leptonycteris nivalis
    Mexican Long-Nosed Bat
  Leptonycteris sanborni
    Sanborn's Long-Nosed Bat
  Myotis grisescens
    Gray Bat
  Myotis sodalis
    Indiana Bat
  Plecotus townsendii ingens
    Ozark Big-Eared Bat
  Plecotus townsendii virginianus
    Virginia Big-Eared Bat

Tyus, Harold M.
U.S. Fish and Wildlife Service
1680 West Highway 40 #1210
Vernal, UT 84078
(801) 789-0354
Photos:
  Ptychocheilus lucius
    Colorado Squawfish

U.S. Fish and Wildlife Service Region 6
Division of Endangered Species
Larry R. Shanks, Chief
P.O. Box 25486
Denver Federal Center
Denver, CO 80225
(303) 236-7904
Photos:
  Mustela nigripes
    Black-Footed Ferret
  Sterna antillarum antillarum
    Least Tern
  Chasmistes liorus
    June Sucker
  Gila cypha
    Humpback Chub
  Salmo clarki stomias
    Greenback Cutthroat Trout
  Gila robusta seminuda
    Virgin River Chub
  Platanthera praeclara
    Western Prairie Fringed Orchid

U.S. Fish and Wildlife Service Region 7
Ronald Garrett, Coordinator
1011 East Tudor Road
Anchorage, AK 99503
(907) 786-3505
Photos:
  Falco peregrinus tundrius
    Arctic Peregrine Falcon

U.S. Fish and Wildlife Service Region 5
Paul Nickerson, Coordinator
One Gateway Center, Suite 700
Newton Corner, MA 02158
(617) 965-5100 x316
Photos:
  Iliamna corei
    Peter's Mountain Mallow
  Sciurus niger cinereus
    Delmarva Peninsula Fox Squirrel
  Pseudemys rubriventris bangsii
    Plymouth Red-Bellied Turtle
  Nicrophorus americanus
    American Burying Beetle
  Percina rex
    Roanoke Logperch
  Plethodon nettingi
    Cheat Mountain Salamander
  Plethodon shenandoah
    Shenandoah Salamander

U.S. Fish and Wildlife Service Region 2
Division of Endangered Species
James E. Johnson, Chief
P.O. Box 1306
Albuquerque, NM 87103
(505) 766-3972
Photos:
  Hedeoma todsenii
    Todsen's Pennyroyal
  Microtus mexicanus hualpaiensis
    Hualapai Vole
  Falco femoralis septentrionalis
    Northern Aplomado Falcon
  Argemone pleiacantha pinnatisecta
    Sacramento Prickly Poppy

U.S. Fish and Wildlife Service Region 3
Division of Endangered Species
James M. Engel, Chief
Federal Building, Fort Snelling
Twin Cities, MN 55111
(612) 725-3536
Photos:
  Platanthera leucophaea
    Eastern Prairie Fringed Orchid

U.S. Fish and Wildlife Service Region 4
Division of Endangered Species
Marshall P. Jones, Chief
Richard B. Russell Federal Building
75 Spring, SW, Suite 1276
Atlanta, GA 30303
(404) 331-3580
Photos:
  Phyllitis scolopendrium americana
    American Hart's-Tongue Fern
  Canis rufus
    Red Wolf
  Felis concolor coryi
    Florida Panther
  Trichechus manatus
    West Indian Manatee
  Ammodramus maritimus mirabilis
    Cape Sable Seaside Sparrow
  Grus canadensis pulla
    Mississippi Sandhill Crane
  Caretta caretta
    Loggerhead Sea Turtle
  Crocodylus acutus
    American Crocodile
  Eretmocheyls imbricata
    Hawksbill Sea Turtle
  Nerodia fasciata taeniata
    Atlantic Salt Marsh Snake

Etheostoma rubrum
  Bayou Darter
Hybopsis cahni
  Slender Chub
Cambarus zophonastes
  Cave Crayfish
Anguispira picta
  Painted Snake Coiled Forest Snail
Mesodon clarki nantahala
  Noonday Snail
Cardomine micranthera
  Small Anthered Bittercress
Cottus pygmaeus
  Pygmy Sculpin
Dicerandra christmanii
  Garrett's Mint
Hemistena lata
  Cracking Pearly Mussel
Obovaria retusa
  Ring Pink Mussel
Rhus michauxi
  Michaux's Sumac

U.S. Fish and Wildlife Service Region 1
Division of Endangered Species
Wayne S. White, Chief
Eastside Federal Complex
911 N.S. 11th Avenue
Portland, OR 97232
(503) 231-6150
Photos:
  Eriogonum gypsophilum
    Gypsum Wild Buckwheat
  Ivesia eremica
    Ash Meadows Ivesia
  Oenothera avita eurekensis
    Eureka Valley Evening-Primrose
  Stephanomeria malheurensis
    Malheur Wire Lettuce
  Swallenia alexandrae
    Eureka Valley Dunegrass
  Thelypodium stenopetalum
    Slender-Petaled Mustard
  Tuctoria mucronata
    Solano Grass
  Microtus californicus scirpensis
    Amargosa Vole
  Odocoileus virginianus leucurus
    Columbian White-Tailed Deer
  Anas laysanensis
    Laysan Duck
  Corvus hawaiiensis
    Hawaiian Crow

Gymnogyps californianus
  California Condor
Catostomus microps
  Modoc Sucker
Chasmistes brevirostris
  Shortnose Sucker
Chasmistes cujus
  Cui-ui
Crenichthys baileyi grandis
  Hiko White River Springfish
Cyprinodon nevadensis mionectes
  Ash Meadows Amargosa Pupfish
Deltistes luxatus
  Lost River Sucker
Empetrichthys latos latos
  Pahrump Killifish
Gila bicolor mohavensis
  Mohave Tui Chub
Gila bicolor snyderi
  Owens Tui Chub
Rhinichthys osculus
  Foskett Speckled Dace
Pacifastacus fortis
  Shasta Crayfish
Rhinichthys osculus lethoporus
  Independence Valley Speckled Dace
Rhinichthys osculus oligoporus
  Clover Valley Speckled Dace

U.S. Fish and Wildlife Service
Caribbean Field Office
P.O. Box 491
Boqueron, Puerto Rico 00622
(809) 851-7297
Photos:
  Banara vanderbiltii
    Palo de Ramon
  Buxus vahlii
    Vahl's Boxwood
  Cornutia obovata
    Palo de Nigua
  Crescentia portoricensis
    Higuero de Sierra
  Cyathea dryopteroides
    Elfin Tree Fern
  Daphnopsis hellerana
    Daphnopsis
  Goetzea elegans
    Beautiful Goetzea
  Ilex cookii
    Cook's Holly
  Peperomia wheeleri
    Wheeler's Peperomia

Solanum drymophilum
  Erubia
Trichilia triacantha
  Bariaco
Zanthoxylum thomassianum Thomas
  Prickly-Ash
Amazona vittata
  Puerto Rican Parrot
Columba inornata wetmorei
  Puerto Rican Plain Pigeon
Epicrates inornatus
  Puerto Rican Boa
Epicrates monensis monensis
  Mona Boa
Eleutherodactylus jasperi
  Golden Coqui

Vanderventer, Terry L.
1016 Andover St.
Clinton, MS 39056
(601) 924-1409
Photos:
  Graptemys flavimaculata
    Yellow-Blotched Map Turtle

Vinyard, Gary
Dept. of Biology
University of Nevada-Reno
Reno, Nevada 89557-0015
(702) 784-6188
Photos:
  Eremichthys acros
    Desert Dace
  Rhinichthys osculus oligoporus
    Clover Valley Speckled Dace
  Rhinichthys osculus lethoporus
    Independence Valley Speckled Dace

VIREO
Visual Resources for Ornithology
The Academy of Natural Sciences of
Philadelphia
19th & The Parkway
Philadelphia, PA 19103
(215) 299-1069
Photos:
  Anas laysanensis
    Laysan Duck
  Anas wyvilliana
    Hawaiian Duck
  Aphelocoma coerulescens coerulescens
    Florida Scrub Jay

Branta canadensis leucopareia
  Aleutian Canada Goose
Campephilus principalis
  Ivory-Billed Woodpecker
Charadrius melodus
  Piping Plover
Colinus virginianus ridgwayi
  Masked Bobwhite
Dendroica chrysoparis
  Golden-Cheeked Warbler
Dendroica kirtlandii
  Kirtland's Warbler
Falco peregrinus anatum
  American Peregrine Falcon
Grus americana
  Whooping Crane
Gymnogyps californianus
  California Condor
Haliaeetus leucocephalus
  Bald Eagle
Himantopus mexicanus knudseni
  Hawaiian Stilt
Mycteria americana
  Wood Stork
Nesochen sandvicensis
  Hawaiian Goose
Pelecanus occidentalis
  Brown Pelican
Picoides borealis
  Red-Cockaded Woodpecker
Pseudonestor xanthophys
  Maui Parrotbill
Rallus longirostris levipes
  Light-Footed Clapper Rail
Rhynchopsitta pachyrhyncha
  Thick-Billed Parrot
Rostrhamus sociabilis plumbeus
  Florida Snail Kite
Sterna antillarum antillarum
  Least Tern
Sterna dougallii dougallii
  Roseate Tern
Strix occidentalis caurina
  Northern Spotted Owl
Telespyza cantans
  Laysan Finch
Tympanuchus cupido attwateri
  Attwater's Prairie Chicken
Vermivora bachmanii
  Bachman's Warbler
Vireo atricapillus
  Black-Capped Vireo

Vogel, David
21600 Wilcox Rd.
Red Bluff, CA 96080
(916) 243-5831
Photos:
  Oncorhynchus tshawytscha
    Chinook Salmon

Wake, David B.
Museum of Vertebrate Zoology
University of California-Berkeley
Berkeley, CA 94708
(415) 642-3567
Photos:
  Batrachoseps aridus
    Desert Slender Salamander

Wallace, Rick
1321 Old County Rd.
Daphne, AL 36521
(205) 438-5690
Photos:
  Cottus pygmaeus
    Pygmy Sculpin

Webb, David H.
Tennessee Valley Authority
OSA 1B, Muscle Shoals, AL 35660-1010
(205) 386-3653
Photos:
  Lesquerella lyrata
    Lyrate Bladder-Pod

West, Larry
24 W. Barnes Rd.
Mason, MI 48854
(517) 676-1890
Photos:
  Neonympha mitchellii mitchellii
    Mitchell's Satyr Butterfly

White, Christopher
Ward, White & Associates
P.O. Box 6502
Annapolis, MD 21401
(301) 269-1591
Photos:
  Antrolana lira
    Madison Cave Isopod

Widener, Neil
P.O. Box 60821
Phoenix, AZ 85082
(602) 273-6017
Photos:
  Antilocapra americana sonoriensis
    Sonoran Pronghorn

Wieboldt, Thomas F.
Dept. of Biology
Virginia Polytechnic Institute & State
University
Blacksburg, VA 24061
(703) 231-5746
Photos:
  Arabis serotina
    Shale Barren Rock-Cress

Wiegand, R. Harrison
Maryland Natural Heritage Program
Tawes State Office Building, B-2
Annapolis, MD 21401
(301) 974-2870
Photos:
  Agalinis acuta
    Sandplain Gerardia
  Helonias bullata
    Swamp Pink
  Ptilimnium nodosum
    Harperella
  Sarracenia rubra alabamensis
    Alabama Canebrake Pitcher Plant

Wilburn, Jack
P.O. Box 9
Rescue, CA95672
(916) 989-4765
Photos:
  Rangifer tarandus caribou
    Woodland Caribou
  Ursus arctos horribilis
    Grizzly Bear
  Nesochen sandvicensis
    Hawaiian Goose
  Rallus longirostris obsoletus
    California Clapper Rail
  Rostrhamus sociabilis plumbeus
    Florida Snail Kite

Williams, Daniel F.
Dept. of Biological Sciences
California State University, Stanislaus
801 W. Monte Vista
Turlock, CA 95380
(209) 667-3485
Photos:
  Dipodomys nitratoides nitratoides
    Tipton Kangaroo Rat

Wilsmann, Leni
Michigan Natural Features Inventory
P.O. Box 30028
Lansing, MI 48909
(517) 373-1552
Photos:
  Iris lacustris
    Dwarf Lake Iris
  Solidago houghtonii
    Houghton's Goldenrod
  Dendroica kirtlandii
    Kirtland's Warbler

Wilson-Ramsey, Yevonn
Illustrations from *Manual of the Flowering*
Plants of Hawai'i
Published by the University of Hawaii Press
and the Bishop Museum Press, Honolulu
Illustrations:
  Centaurium sebaeoides
    NONE
  Cyanea pinnatifida
    Haha
  Cyanea superba
    Cyanea Superba
  Hedyotis st.-johnii
    Na Pali Beach Hedyotis
  Hesperomannia lydgatei
    NONE
  Lipochaeta lobata var. *leptophylla*
    NONE
  Lipochaeta tenuifolia
    Nehe
  Lobelia niihauensis
    NONE
  Phyllostegia glabra var. *lanaiensis*
    NONE
    Remya montgomeryi
  Remya montgomeryi
    Schiedea kaalae
    NONE

Tetramolopium filiforme
   NONE
Urera kaalae
   Opuhe

Woods, Charles A.
Florida Museum of Natural History
Museum Road, UF
Gainesville, FL 32611-2035
(904) 392-1721
Photos:
   Microtus pennsylvanicus dukecampbelli
      Florida Salt Marsh Vole

World Wildlife Fund
Sally A. Russell
Coordinator, Photo Library
1250 24th, NW
Washington, DC 20037
(202) 778-9531
Photos:
   Coryphantha sneedii leei
      Lee Pincushion Cactus
   Echinocactus horizonthalonius var nicholii
      Nichol's Turk's Head Cactus

Wunderlin, Richard P.
Dept. of Biology
University of South Florida
Tampa, FL 33620
(813) 974-2359
Photos:
   Justicia cooleyi
      Cooley's Water-Willow

Wyoming Game & Fish Dept.
5400 Bishop Blvd.
Cheyenne, WY 82006
(307) 777-7604
Photos:
   Mustela nigripes
      Black-Footed Ferret

Scientific Names Keyed to Locator Entry Numbers

A

Abronia macrocarpa, 1
Abutilon eremitopetalum, 2
Abutilon menziesii, 3
Abutilon sandwicense, 4
Acanthomintha obovata ssp. duttonii, 5
Achatinella sp., 619
Achyranthes rotundata, 6
Acipenser brevirostrum, 477
Acipenser oxyrhynchus desotoi, 478
Aconitum noveboracense, 7
Acrocephalus familiaris kingi, 368
Agalinis acuta, 8
Agave arizonica, 9
Agelaius xanthomus, 369
Alasmidonta heterodon, 567
Alsinidendron obovatum, 10
Alsinidendron trinerve, 11
Amazona vittata, 370
Amblyopsis rosae, 479
Ambrysus amargosus, 632
Ambystoma macrodactylum croceum, 466
Ammodramus maritimus mirabilis, 371
Ammodramus savannarum floridanus, 372
Amorpha crenulata, 12
Amphianthus pusillus, 13
Amphispiza belli clementeae, 373
Amsinckia grandiflora, 14
Amsonia kearneyana, 15
Anas laysanensis, 374
Anas wyvilliana, 375
Ancistrocactus tobuschii, 16
Anguispira picta, 620
Anolis roosevelti, 437
Antilocapra americana sonoriensis, 306
Antrolana lira, 609
Aphelocoma coerulescens coerulescens, 376
Apios priceana, 17
Apodemia mormo langei, 633
Arabis macdonaldiana, 18
Arabis serotina, 19
Arctocephalus townsendi, 307
Arctomecon humilis, 20
Arctostaphylos pungens var. ravenii, 21
Arenia cumberlandensis, 22
Argemone pleiacantha ssp. pinnatisecta, 23
Argyroxiphium sandwicense, 24
Aristida portoricensis, 25

Arkansia wheeleri, 568
Asclepias meadii, 26
Asclepias welshii, 27
Asimina tetramera, 28
Astragalus bibullatus, 29
Astragalus cremnophylax var. cremnophylax, 30
Astragalus humillimus, 31
Astragalus montii, 32
Astragalus osterhoutii, 33
Astragalus perianus, 34
Astragalus phoenix, 35
Astragalus robbinsii var. jesupi, 36

B

Balaena glacialis, 308
Balaena mysticetus, 309
Balaenoptera borealis, 310
Balaenoptera musculus, 311
Balaenoptera physalus, 312
Banara vanderbiltii, 37
Baptisia arachnifera, 38
Batrachoseps aridus, 467
Betula uber, 39
Bidens cuneata, 40
Bison bison athabascae, 313
Blennosperma bakeri, 41
Boloria acrocnema, 634
Boltania decurrens, 42
Bonamia grandiflora, 43
Branta canadensis leucopareia, 377
Bufo hemiophrys baxteri, 468
Bufo houstonensis, 469
Buteo solitarius, 378
Buxus vahlii, 44

C

Callirhoe scabriuscula, 45
Callophrys mossii bayensis, 635
Calyptronoma rivalis, 46
Cambarus zophonastes, 610
Camissonia benitensis, 47
Campanula robinsiae, 48
Campephilus principalis, 379
Canis lupus, 314
Canis rufus, 315
Caprimulgus noctitherus, 380

Common Names Keyed to Locator Entry Numbers

A
Achyranthes, 6
Agave
  Arizona, 9
Ahinahina, 24
Akepa, 402
Akialoa
  Kauai, 398
Akiapolaau, 397
Akoko, 59
Akoko
  Ewa Plains, 124
Alabama Beach Mouse, 349
Alabama Canebrake Pitcher Plant, 252
Alabama Cave Shrimp, 614
Alabama Cavefish, 564
Alabama Lamp Pearly Mussel, 589
Alabama Leather Flower, 65
Alabama Red-Bellied Turtle, 459
Alamosa Springsnail, 630
Aleutian Canada Goose, 377
Aleutian Shield Fern, 231
Amargosa Niterwort, 199
Armagosa Vole, 337
Amber Darter, 542
Ambersnail
  Kanab, 625
American Burying Beetle, 652
American Crocodile, 440
American Hart's-Tongue Fern, 221
American Peregrine Falcon, 389
Amphianthus
  Little, 13
Amphipod
  Hay's Spring, 616
Anastasia Island Beach Mouse, 353
Antioch Dunes Evening-Primrose, 202
Anole
  Culebra Island Giant, 437
Apache Trout, 557
Appalachian Monkeyface Pearly Mussel, 605
Arctic Peregrine Falcon, 388
Arizona Agave, 9
Arizona Cliffrose, 75
Arizona Hedgehog Cactus, 106
Arkansas Fatmucket, 587
Arrowhead
  Bunched, 246

Ash Meadows Amargosa Pupfish, 494
Ash Meadows Blazing Star, 193
Ash Meadows Gumplant, 135
Ash Meadows Ivesia, 163
Ash Meadows Milk-Vetch, 35
Ash Meadows Naucorid, 632
Ash Meadows Speckled Dace, 553
Ash Meadows Sunray, 109
Ashy Dogweed, 286
Aster
  Decurrent False, 42
  Florida Golden, 62
  Ruth's Golden, 225
Atlantic Salt Marsh Snake, 457
Attwater's Prairie Chicken, 433
Audubon's Crested Caracara, 417
Aupaka, 159
Autumn Buttercup, 238
Avens
  Spreading, 130

B
Bachman's Warbler, 434
Baker's Sticky Seed, 41
Bakersfield Cactus, 203
Bald Eagle, 395
Barbara's-Buttons
  Mohr's, 192
Barberry
  Truckee, 189
Bariaco, 289
Barneby Ridge-Cress, 171
Bat
  Gray, 342
  Hawaiian Hoary, 332
  Indiana, 343
  Mexican Long-Nosed, 333
  Ozark Big-Eared, 357
  Sanborn's Long-Nosed, 334
  Virginia Big-Eared, 356
Bay Checkerspot Butterfly, 642
Bayou Darter, 504
Beaked-Rush
  Knieskern, 244
Bear
  Grizzly, 365
Bear-Poppy
  Dwarf, 20

Cumulative Index
Volumes 1-3

A

A'a, 645
A'o, 683
Abies fraseri, 381
Abortopetalum eremitopetalum, 1181
Abortopetalum sandwicense, 1183
Abronia macrocarpa, 1
Abutilon cryptopetalum, 1181
Abutilon eremitopetalum, 1181
Abutilon menziesii, 3
Abutilon sandwicense, 1183
Acanthaceae (Acanthus), 240
Acanthomintha obovata ssp. *duttonii*, 5
Acanthus Family, 240
Accipitriidae (Eagles and Hawks), 584, 624, 694
Achatinella apexfulva, 1041
Achatinella bellula, 1041
Achatinella buddii, 1041
Achatinella bulimoides, 1041
Achatinella byronii, 1041
Achatinella concavospira, 1041
Achatinella curta, 1041
Achatinella decipiens, 1041
Achatinella fulgens, 1041
Achatinella fuscobasis, 1041
Achatinella juncea, 1041
Achatinella lehuiensis, 1041
Achatinella leucorraphe, 1041
Achatinella lila, 1041
Achatinella lorata, 1041
Achatinella mustelina, 1041
Achatinella papyracea, 1041
Achatinella pulcherrima, 1041
Achatinella pupukanioe, 1041
Achatinella sowerbyana, 1041
Achatinella spaldingi, 1041
Achatinella swiftii, 1041
Achatinella taeniolata, 1041
Achatinella thaanumi, 1041
Achatinella turgida, 1041
Achatinellidae (Hawaiian Tree Snails), 1041
Achyranthes rotundata, 7
Acipenser brevirostrum, 801
Acipenser oxyrhynchus desotoi, 1407
Acipenser oxyrhynchus, 801
Acipenseridae (Sturgeon), 801, 1407, 1433
Aconitum noveboracense, 9, 1047

Acrocephalus familiaris familiaria, 561
Acrocephalus familiaris kingi, 561
Actinonaias ligamentina, 1449
Ae'o, 634
Agalinis acuta, 11
Agavaceae (Agave), 13
Agave arizonica, 13
Agave Family, 13
Agelaius phoenicus, 563
Agelaius xanthomus xanthomus, 563
Agelaius xanthomus monensis, 563
Agelaius xanthomus, 563
Ahinahina, 35
Akepa
  Hawaii, 640
  Maui, 640
Akialoa
  Kauai, 632
Akiapolaau, 630
Akohekohe, 662
Akoko
  Ewa Plains, 184
Alabama Beach Mouse, 518
Alabama Canebrake Pitcher Plant, 353
Alabama Cave Shrimp, 1031
Alabama Cavefish, 950
Alabama Lamp Pearly Mussel, 989
Alabama Leather Flower, 95, 273
Alabama Red-Bellied Turtle, 768
Alae Ke'o Ke'o, 610
Alae'ula, 613
Alala, 599
Alamosa Springsnail, 1465
Alasmidonta heterodon, 1439
Aleutian Canada Goose, 581
Aleutian Shield Fern, 329
Alismataceae (Water-plantain), 347, 1340
Alligator
  American, 727
Alsinidendron obovatum, 1186
Alsinidendron trinerve, 1188
Alsophila dryopteroides, 120
Amaranth Family, 7
Amaranthaceae (Amaranth), 7, 1305
Amargosa Niterwort, 283, 933
Amargosa Pupfish
  Ash Meadows, 827, 933
Amargosa Vole, 494

Boxwood
  Vahl's, 67
Bradshaw's Lomatium, 261
Brady Pincushion Cactus, 299, 301, 363
Branta canadensis leucopareia, 581
Branta canadensis minima, 581
Branta sandvicensis, 656
Brassicaceae (Mustard), 25, 27, 176, 194, 248,
  250, 395, 417, 419, 1206, 1210, 1282, 1284, 1286,
  1318
Brazos Water Snake, 766
Broad-Bean
  Hawaiian wild, 415
Brooksville Bellflower, 73, 240
Broom
  San Clemente Island, 263
Brown Bear, 548
Brown Pelican
  California, 666
  eastern, 666
Brush-Footed Butterfly Family, 1075, 1097, 1469,
  1478
Buckthorn Family, 198, 425, 1253
Buckwheat
  clay-loving wild, 170
  gypsum wild, 166
  steamboat, 168
Buckwheat, 1071, 1073
Buckwheat Family, 81, 168, 170, 327
Buffalo Clover
  running, 405
Bufo americanus charlesmithi, 789
Bufo hemiophrys baxteri, 787
Bufo hemiophrys hemiophrys, 787
Bufo houstonensis, 789
Bufonidae (Toad), 787, 789, 795
Bulimulidae (Tree Snail), 1052
Bulrush
  barbed bristle, 1351
  northeastern, 1351
Bunched Arrowhead, 347
Bunched Cory Cactus, 106
Burke's Goldfields, 1275
Burying Beetle
  American, 1093
Bush-Clover
  prairie, 246
Bush-Mallow
  San Clemente Island, 271
Buteo solitarius, 584
Buttercup
  autumn, 341
Buttercup Family, 9, 95, 128, 341, 393

Butterfly
  bay checkerspot, 1075
  El Segundo blue, 1071
  giant swallowtail, 1081
  Lange's metalmark, 176, 287, 1063
  lotis blue, 1089
  mission blue, 1085
  Mitchell's satyr, 1478
  Oregon silverspot, 1097
  Palos Verdes blue, 1079
  Pawnee montane skipper, 1083
  San Bruno elfin, 1065
  Schaus swallowtail, 509, 1081
  Smith's blue, 1073
  Uncompahgre fritillary, 1469
Buxaceae (Boxwood), 67
Buxus vahlii, 67
Buzzard
  king, 675
  Mexican, 675

C

Cackling Canada Goose, 581
Cactaceae (Cactus), 23, 83, 85, 104, 106, 108, 110,
  112, 140, 142, 144, 146, 148, 150, 152, 154, 156,
  281, 299, 301, 303, 305, 307, 361, 363, 365,
  1255, 1308
Cactus
  Arizona hedgehog, 152
  Bakersfield, 1308
  black lace, 150
  Brady pincushion, 299, 301, 363
  bunched cory, 106
  Chisos Mountain hedgehog, 142
  Cochise pincushion, 108
  Davis' green pitaya, 156
  fragrant prickly-apple, 83
  Key tree, 85
  Knowlton, 301, 303
  Kuenzler hedgehog, 146
  Lee pincushion, 110
  Lloyd's hedgehog, 148
  Lloyd's mariposa, 281
  Mesa Verde, 363
  Nellie cory, 104
  Nichol's turk's head, 140
  Peebles Navajo, 301, 305
  purple-spined hedgehog, 144
  San Rafael, 301
  Siler pincushion, 299, 301, 307
  Sneed pincushion, 112
  spineless hedgehog, 154
  Tobusch fishhook, 23

flattened musk, 774
Green sea, 724
hawksbill sea, 743
Kemp's Ridley sea, 757
leatherback sea, 733
loggerhead sea, 721
olive Ridley sea, 760
Plymouth red-bellied, 770
ringed sawback, 755
yellow-blotched map, 1401
Twinpod
Dudley Bluffs, 1318
Tympanuchus cupido attwateri, 710
Typhlichthys subterraneus, 803
Typhlomolge rathbuni, 799

U

Ua'u, 681
Uhiuhi, 277
Uinta Basin Hookless Cactus, 361
Uma inornata, 778
Unarmored Threespine Stickleback, 863
Uncompahgre Fritillary Butterfly, 1469
Unio curtus, 1001
Unio heterodon, 1439
Unio penitus, 966
Unio powelli, 1449
Unionidae (Freshwater Mussel), 955, 958, 960,
962, 964, 966, 968, 970, 972, 974, 976, 978, 981,
983, 985, 987, 989, 993, 995, 997, 999, 1001,
1003, 1005, 1007, 1009, 1011, 1014, 1016, 1018,
1020, 1439, 1441, 1443, 1445, 1447, 1449, 1451,
1457
Urera kaalae, 1374
Ursidae (Bear), 548
Ursus arctos horribilis, 548
Urticaceae (Nettle), 1302, 1374
Utah Prairie Dog, 451
Utahia sileri, 307

V

Vahl's Boxwood, 67
Valley Elderberry Longhorn Beetle, 1067
Vancouver Island Marmot, 489
Vaquita, 523
Verbena
large-fruited sand, 1
Verbenaceae (Verbena), 102
Vermivora bachmanii, 712
Vespertilionidae (Bat), 483, 503, 506, 527, 530
Vetch
Ash Meadows milk, 51, 275

Hawaiian, 415
heliotrope milk, 45
Jesup's milk, 53
Osterhout milk, 47, 311
Rydberg milk, 49
Vicia menziesii, 415
Villosa trabalis, 1020
Viola adunca, 1097
Viola chamissoniana ssp. *chamissoniana*, 1376
Viola helenae, 1378
Viola helioscopia, 1376
Viola lanaiensis, 1380
Violaceae (Violet), 1271, 1376, 1378, 1380
Violet
western blue, 1097
Violet Family, 1271, 1376, 1378, 1380
Viperidae (Viper), 729
Vireo
black-capped, 714
least Bell's, 716
Vireo atricapillus, 714
Vireo belli arizonae, 716
Vireo belli pusillus, 716
Vireo bellii bellii, 716
Vireo bellii medius, 716
Vireonidae (Vireo), 714, 716
Virgin River Chub, 1411
Virginia Big-Eared Bat, 530
Virginia Fringed Mountain Snail, 1054
Virginia Northern Flying Squirrel, 480
Virginia Round-Leaf Birch, 59
Virginia Spiraea, 1364
Vittadinia chamissonis, 1370
Vittadinia remyi, 1372
Viviparidae (Live-bearing Snail), 1467
Vole
Amargosa, 494
California, 494
Florida salt marsh, 1387
Hualapai, 496
Vulpes macrotis mutica, 553
Vulpes velox velox, 556
Vulpes velox hebes, 556
Vulture, 621

W

Waccamaw Silverside, 899
Walker's Manioc, 1298
Wallflower
Contra Costa, 176, 287
Warbler
Bachman's, 712